VOYAGE
INTO
ASTRONOMY

In vain we scan from east to west,
The search for life is man's great quest.
Are we alone?
     Where are the rest?
We've barely come as far as Mars.
Who else is there among the stars?

               Fred M. Johnson

VOYAGE
INTO
ASTRONOMY

ITS RELEVANCE
AND
SIGNIFICANCE

FRED M. JOHNSON

California State University—Fullerton

KENDALL/HUNT PUBLISHING COMPANY

2460 Kerper Boulevard,
Dubuque, Iowa 52001

Cover photo: Man's first close-up view of the Martian
surface; panoramic landscape photo (NASA/JPL). Part
of Viking I is seen in foreground.

Printed in the United States of America

Contents

*Chapters marked with an asterisk are strictly X-rated. They may be read by mature adults only, consent of instructor is necessary.

Preface

This book is an attempt to present introductory astronomy and science by means of a new approach: Aside from the customary base of fundamental astronomy, it is far wider in its interdisciplinary approach and depth of coverage of selected topics than other astronomy books. The relevance of energy, chemical evolution and the origins of life should be part of everyone's college education. For the nonscience major, this course may be the only source for such knowledge. Observations and laboratory exercises are equally important in order to supplement the lecture and reading material. Separate laboratory manuals would have to be purchased for such an activity. This book not only includes such a manual, but has an added section of practical home exercises. The aim is to encourage direct student participation and to foster student creative endeavors.

The Technical Note Section encourages the gifted student to delve a little deeper into the material. The concepts and exercises are graded in order of difficulty, so as to provide something for everybody according to ability and interest.

Chapter 18 of this book deals with the history of astronomy and related scientific ideas, including old and new cosmology. This section could be considered a separate monograph. The subject matter of Chapter 18 can be presented as a separate minicourse.

Algebra is introduced very carefully in appropriate places. To teach science or astronomy without it, is like a restaurant removing sirloin steak from its menu for fear that its customers have no teeth. Over 2,000 students have been exposed to the material without a single case of indigestion. On the contrary, students relish the opportunity of being able to bite into something solid, *provided* it is properly seasoned and spicy. A recognized ingredient of successful student learning is continued stimulation of interesting and *relevant* material. "Gee Wizz," pretty-colored pictures are good, but not enough.

Professional astronomers recognize that their field has suddenly become more exciting. New discoveries are coming in faster now than can be fitted into our conventional framework. The excitement and challenges of a still wide open field of research should be conveyed to the reader. Physics was probably in a similar state of flux and excitement between 1900 and 1930. There are many frontiers in astronomy today: it is not a closed field—by a long shot.

I wish to express my gratitude to Dr. R. Rubin, Mr. E. Speyer, and Dr. J. Woodward for reading parts of the manuscript. The galley proofs were carefully read by Dr. R. Rubin, E. Speyer, Georgine R. Beaupre, and Susan D. Beran. I am most grateful to them for their enormous labor. I take full responsibility, of course, for any remaining errors. I wish to thank Tony Gonzalez for technical illustrations, Pam Mower for artwork, Jim T. Marshall for photography, John Ludin for cartoons, and Rose Silverstein for typing. Finally, I wish to express my gratitude to Professor Lloyd Motz of Columbia University for opening the world of astronomy to me.

Introduction

In the beginning. . . .

Every child is curious about his own origin. Man, throughout the ages, has consistently wondered and pondered, not only about his own beginnings, but about the origin of the universe as a whole and his unique place in the immensely vast scheme of things. The first chapter of the Bible is an excellent and highly significant example of what some men were thinking 3,000 years ago. Whereas the Bible is surely not intended as a text on Astronomy or Geophysics, it does attempt to put man's origin in an organized framework, sketching out finite steps prior to man's arrival. This is, in fact, an evolutionary concept. Some of the early Hebrews were indeed uniquely inspired cosmologists.

The general plan that we shall adopt in this book will be to travel through space and time. Our numerous space flights will take us from the center of the Solar System outward to the rim of the galaxy, and beyond. Our trips in time will take us back to man's early recorded history and trace his developing thought processes relating to Astronomy. One thing stands out: the steps forward were very sporadic and far between. Actually, as with all progress, it is marked by one, cautious, hesitant foot forward and then three steps backwards! Among the early Greek philosophers were, indeed, some precocious giants who had *some* correct ideas which, 1,500 years later, were rediscovered by others. Unfortunately, the forward march of accepted ideas does not come about on a solid front with all mankind sharing its advances equally. Rather, isolated forward thrusts were occasionally made which took a very long time to be shared with or accepted by most of mankind. To shake us out of our present day smugness, one has only to be reminded that in England, until recently, there existed a Flat Earth Society. The concept of a flat earth should surely have been eradicated long ago! The evidence for a round earth can be easily observed during lunar eclipses when the earth's shadow passes slowly across the moon. The implication of a round or spherically-shaped earth associated with this relatively simple event did not make a great impact on man in ancient times and is even today largely ignored. Whoever looks up today to watch the passage of the stars, planets, and the moon? Only a small fraction of the world's population. In fact, with present concerns about relevance, some might question: "Is Astronomy

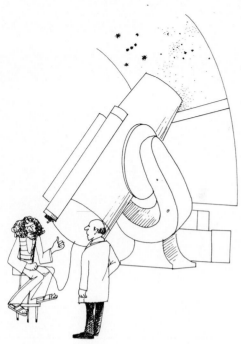

"The universe is sort of interesting, but is it relevent?"

relevant?" I say, only if it can provide the pathway which traces out the essential steps leading to man. This thread will guide us in our journey through space and time and ideas.

The question that is most often posed is, "Why, even now, is it so difficult to unravel the early origins of the Solar System and the steps leading to the evolution of life?" The answer is a rather sad one. Our lives are too short, far too short. To appreciate this concept, consider the ratio of an average human life of 70 years to 4 1/2 billion years (the presumed age of the Solar System):

$$\frac{70 \text{ years}}{4.5 \times 10^9 \text{ years}} = \frac{33 \text{ secs.}}{70 \text{ years}}$$

Hence, our *relative* age is like 33 seconds in relation to 70 years. Imagine a 33-second lifetime fly attempting to unravel the mysteries of human reproduction and propagation. It takes 1/3 of one's life to just get up to speed, hence, subtract 11 seconds. Then one sleeps away another 1/3 of one's life—subtract another 11 seconds. That leaves little time for the very few flies that might be inquisitive or adventuresome enough to ponder such mysteries. These few flies would see small people and big people—they would probably conclude that people originate from contracting clouds and that the big people are still shrinking to end up as little people and eventually die as Black Holes (the fanciful brainchild of some present-day scientists). Of course, at most, these few flies would spend but a fraction of a second or so of thinking time of their lives on the human reproduction mystery. They have, after all, jobs to do, food to gather, and more important matters to attend to. One or two of them might indeed see a human handshake, maybe a kiss, but would not live long enough to perceive the whole story. The nine-month human gestation period corresponds to 62,000 generations of 33-second flies, which is about the number of generations of man since the earliest fossil records of modern man's existence, recorded about three million years ago. By this analogy, we see why it is so incredibly difficult to unravel the origin of the Solar System. Four and one-half billion years before the advent of man is just too long relative to our lifetime. Hence, the apparent irony in man's scientific progress: the *origin* dilemma is on everyone's mind in varying degrees, but not tackled with the same determination as other technological challenges. Why is it low on the list of man's priorities?

A stickier question is: "How do we indeed know whether we have arrived at the *correct* answer?" Is it by the word of authority or by consensus of many? History teaches us that both approaches are tried and are equally fraught with uncertainties. The authority of the great Greek thinker, Aristotle, held sway for over 1,800 years until the time of Galileo. Lest we feel smug and overconfident, it may be interesting to note that in the year 1965 a chairman of an astronomical meeting took a vote of the attendees at that meeting in order to decide what chemical compounds comprise the vast expanses of interstellar dust. The choices were ice, "dirty ice," and graphite, or combinations of them. Nature was established by a democratic vote!! In the year 1600 Giordano Bruno was roasted for his advanced and deviant ideas about the Solar System and cosmology. That's not such a long time ago, and the memory of the more recent 1965 vote still hangs like a giant dust cloud on the mind of the only person who walked out on that meeting.

Chapter 1

PERSPECTIVE—MINI-TRIPS AROUND THE EARTH

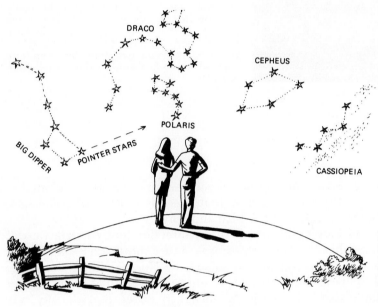

Figure 1.1. An evening under the stars. Note the well-known constellations: The Big Dipper, the two pointer stars, indicating the position of Polaris (and the NCP). Also on your right, the constellation Cassiopeia (The Chair). It is more easily recognized as a W.

An Evening Outing Under the Stars

We shall begin our journey into space and time on a small hilltop watching the sun go down and the majesty of the heavens appear into view. Myriads of stars begin to emerge above and all around us.

To paraphrase the ancient Chinese proverb: "A journey of a million light years requires taking the first step." It is this first step which everyone knows is the hardest. While watching the heavens, we may imagine that we are repeating a performance which has no doubt been enacted by many before us. There is a time to dream, there is a time to ponder.

Our mission will be to unravel what is really going on in space without sinking into the quagmire of imponderables, mysteries, and myths. We shall limit our first objectives to the earth's motion in space and to a better understanding of local distances in the solar system. It should also be apparent that the mysteries of the heavens are not to be solved in one evening, nor in a week—it had taken ancient men a lifetime of measurements and observations just to determine the seasons, the various positions of sunsets, and lunar motions. Can we do all that in one evening? Well, we have to start at a begin-

1

Figure 1.2. Photograph of circumstellar stars in the direction of the north celestial pole. Note that during this time exposure the stars seemed to rotate in circles around the north celestial pole (NCP). Polaris can be easily seen on this photograph. It is closest to the NCP. Note the many concentric circles each representing a star. By studying the length of the arcs, can you determine the exposure time of this photograph? (Photo by John Kerns.)

ning. Since the sun has already set and we are watching the stars, there is no doubt that there is motion of some sort. Some objects move. Which and why?

By looking in the northerly direction long enough, we will note that the stars *appear* to rotate counterclockwise around a single point in the sky called the North Celestial Pole (Fig. 1.2). If we look around us and see the earth as fixed, we can understand the ancients' mistaken belief that the sky was turning, and not the earth. Nor is the earth's roundness very apparent. Enough with hindsight—onward into the valley of facts, figures (heavenly, of course) and definitions. Is there a man or woman dismayed? Not yet? Good.

Figure 1.3 is a good representation of the way the sky appears from the point of view of a pair of observers on earth. The sky appears to rotate parallel to the earth's equator. If one uses the earth's reference frame, such as the equator and projects it all the way to the celestial sphere, he will have generated the celestial equator. That was easy—so far. Now observe Figure 1.4 (a view of the earth at a distance of about 40,000 miles). Note the earth's axis and the earth's equator. Of course, there is no stick through the center of the earth. There is just an imaginary axis of rotation about which the earth rotates once every 23 hours and 56 minutes (not 24 hours—this is our first surprise).

Next, we shall travel even further into space and examine the earth in relation to the sun. While the earth is spinning away on its axis, it is also busy travelling in an orbit around the sun. Technically, the earth revolves about the sun and rotates on its axis—both at the same time! (That's quite a feat, you must admit—like chewing gum and walking at the same time.) The plane in which the earth revolves is called the **plane of the ecliptic**. (See Fig. 1.5.)

2

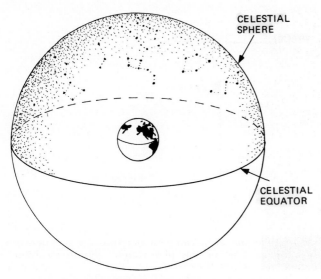

Figure 1.3. The celestial sphere as *seen* from the vantage point of an observer on earth.

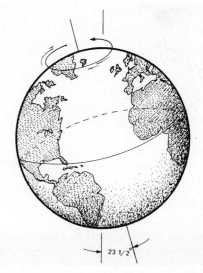

Figure 1.4. A view of the earth showing that its axis of rotation makes an angle of 23 1/2 degrees with respect to a perpendicular to the ecliptic plane. The earth rotates counterclockwise as seen by an observer looking down towards the North Pole.

We are now ready to tackle the basic questions of size and distances. How big is the earth? It is 8,000 miles in diameter. How big is the sun? It is 860,000 miles in diameter. How far is the earth from the sun? It is 93,000,000 miles distant (defined as one **astronomical unit**, abbreviated A.U.). It would take 108 suns placed end to end to span the distance of one A.U. How far is the next nearest star? It is four and one-half light years or about 30,000,000,000,000 miles. The light year is defined as the distance light travels in the course of a year. The sun is obviously not the only star; there are roughly a hundred billion stars in our galaxy of which our sun is but one.

We shall next embark on a quick trip which will take us clear out of our own galaxy. In order to obtain a better perspective, Figure 1.7 shows a schematic representation of our galaxy from two views. The galaxy is 100,000 light years across and about 10,000 light years thick. The sun is situated 30,000 light years from the center. (The sun is relegated to an off-axis position in the galaxy!)

Surrounding our galaxy are hundreds of globular clusters; each cluster comprising about 100,000 stars. There are billions of galaxies, most of them having comparable dimensions but in various stages of development. We shall come back to this topic in Chapter 16. We shall take many such voyages together. Our aim will be to prepare ourselves as

Earth
Diameter = 8,000 miles

Distance
Between = 93,000,000 miles

Sun
Diameter = 860,000 miles

Nearest
Star
30,000,000,000,000 miles =
4 1/2 light years

Galaxy
100,000 light years across
10,000 light years thick

Figure 1.5. This shows the earth spinning on its axis in a counterclockwise direction and revolving around the sun in the plane of the ecliptic, all in a counterclockwise direction. The moon and the rest of the solar system are not shown in this figure.

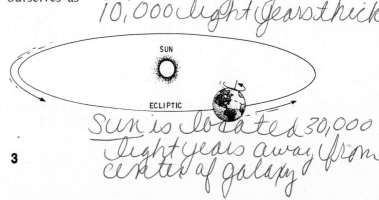

Sun is located 30,000
light years away from
center of galaxy

3

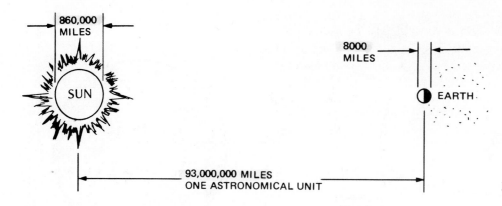

Figure 1.6.

much as possible before each trip and to stay alert for new discoveries enroute. It will be my pleasure to be your host and guide during these adventures into space and time.

After all this long-distance travelling, we shall attempt to find our way back. That won't be easy, since at this far distance the sun's light is insufficient to guide us back home.

Oops, we landed on the wrong planet. Mistakes can happen. Our spacecraft was built by the lowest bidder. We landed on a planet associated with the star Alpha Centauri.

We again look out into the sky in order to ascertain whether the constellations give us a clue. To our great surprise, all the constellations appear to look the same as before—all except one—Cassiopeia. There seems to be something extra in that constellation. We scratch our heads and of

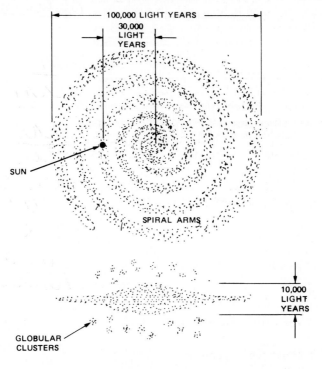

Figure 1.7. Two schematic views of our galaxy as seen face-on and edge-on.

4

course immediately realize that the extra star is none other than *our own* sun (Fig. 1.8). It would take us only four and one-half years, travelling at the speed of light, to traverse the distance back to our sun. In our minds it is easy to travel that fast or faster.

Now that you know what is going on with the earth's motion and our position in space, let's tackle briefly the problem the ancients had in solving this enigma.

Project Hindsight

Ancients saw the motions of the sky but had absolutely no idea of distance. They mistakenly thought the earth was fixed and the sky moving. That's an easy mistake. We are, after all, on an oversized merry-go-round. Those of you who remember being on such a ride also remember that everything outside seemed to be rotating in the opposite direction from your own motion on the merry-go-round. That's precisely the way we see the stars move from the point of view of the earth.

Again, we shall assume we are back with the ancients studying the stars for sheer entertainment and delight. Since there was no television then, we could easily project all kinds of figures (human or otherwise) among the stars, a sort of stellar, psychological, projective Rorschach test. This in turn might help us in identifying groupings. Frankly, the ancients had other reasons for studying the sky. If your life depends on seasons and the correct time for planting, for instance, you are more inclined to pay attention to the positions of these constellations! Besides, life was then, as it is still now, somewhat precarious and unpredictable. Hence, the universal

SUN

Figure 1.8. The constellation Cassiopeia as seen from the vantage point of Alpha Centauri. Note the additional star in this constellation. (The apparant brightness of the sun is slightly exaggerated in this figure: It would be about as bright as the other stars in the constellation.)

Figure 1.9. Andromeda.

Figure 1.10. Sagittarius.

In Greek mythology Andromeda was the daughter of Cepheus and Cassiopea. The latter boasted of being more beautiful than the Nereids. The enraged Poseidon sent a sea monster to ravage Cepheus' land, and only by sacrificing Andromeda to the monster could the disaster be averted. She was chained to a rock, awaiting her fate, when she was rescued by Perseus, who slew the monster. Having also slain his rival, Phineus, Perseus then married Andromeda.

It is apparent why such a fascinating story would captivate the imagination of the ancients and allow them to project such images conjured up in their minds to the constellations of the stars.

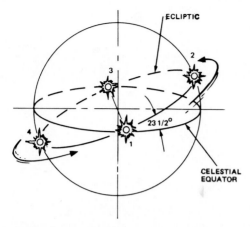

Figure 1.11. This shows the configurations from the point of view of an observer on earth. The sun appears to move on the ecliptic at position 1, vernal equinox; 2, summer solstice; 3, autumnal equinox; 4, winter solstice. With respect to an observer on earth, the sun appears to make an angle of 23 1/2 degrees in its orbit (ecliptic) with respect to the celestial equator.

Geocentric - earth fixed
Heliocentric - sun fixed
Retrograde Motion

longings to seek signs of future portents. Kings and generals would engage specialists in this field. Undoubtedly, astrology and astronomy became hopelessly entwined in the past, to the consternation of many present-day scientists who are aghast at the revival of astrology by the public. Most likely, however, if it were not for astrology, there would be no present-day astronomy.

After years of watching the sky, we would discover that there were 5 *wandering* stars (now affectionately called planets, the Greek word for wanderers). Of course, we would also be keeping track of the sun and the moon, which seemed generally to partake of the motion of the celestial sphere, but, in addition, had a counterclockwise motion of their own with respect to the celestial sphere. Over the course of a year, the sun would be found to trace out a path in the sky, called the **ecliptic,** which makes an angle of 23 1/2° with respect to the celestial equator (Fig. 1.11).

The moon is not too far removed from the ecliptic, but travels much faster, namely, about 13° per day in the sky eastwards with respect to the fixed stars. Since the moon subtends an angle of 1/2° in the sky, the moon's motion corresponds to about its own diameter eastwards every hour. The somewhat *rapid* motion of the moon on the celestial sphere plus its changing shape (phases of the moon) must have been very apparent to early civilizations. With present hindsight, it is easy to see what is really happening, even though it took thousands of years for men to finally come up with the correct picture. Let's concentrate on the earth.

There are at least two motions associated with the earth: its rotation about its axis, also known as **diurnal rotation,** and the revolution of the earth about the sun by about 1° per day.

In our mental picture, we shall have to switch back and forth many times between the way the sky appears to us and the way it really is. It is easy for us now to appreciate the difficulty of the ancients in unraveling the mystery of who revolves around whom. Is the earth fixed with the sun revolving about it (**geocentric theory**) or is the sun fixed with the earth revolving about the sun (**heliocentric theory**)?

If the earth revolves about the sun for say about 30 days, corresponding to 30°, then, by geometry, it would appear from the earth's perspective as if the sun had moved from position 1 to position 3 with respect to the stars in exactly the same 30° (Fig. 1.13). In fact, during a complete **sidereal year,** which is the time for the sun to complete one such cycle, both theories come up with *exactly* the same time. Of course, what confounded proponents of the old geocentric theory the most (as you probably suspected all along) were the five wandering planets since they, unlike the sun, did not always proceed in the same easterly direction, but would occasionally *reverse* their field of travel in the sky for a short while (**retrograde motion**) and then proceed on, undaunted and oblivious to the bafflement of earth's ancient astronomers.

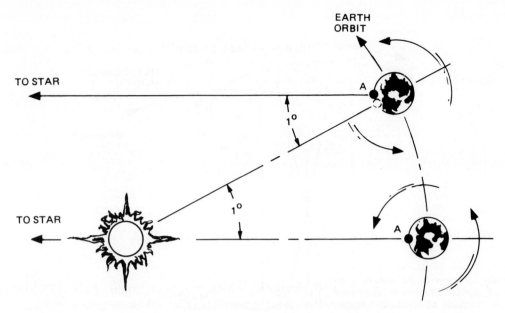

Figure 1.12. The difference between sidereal and solar day comes about as follows: Note position A on the earth as the earth rotates on its axis. During the course of 23 hours and 56 minutes, point A on the earth will have made one complete rotation with respect to a distant fixed reference point such as a star. It will have completed one sidereal day. Meanwhile, the earth has revolved in its orbit about the sun by one degree. Hence, point A on earth will have to rotate an additional one degree in order to line it back up again with the sun, thereby completing one solar day. The solar day is therefore four minutes longer than the sidereal day.

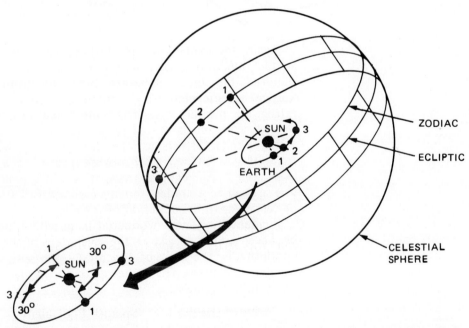

Figure 1.13. Observing the sun from the point of view of the earth and the actual motion of the earth about the sun. From the vantage point shown in the figure note that when the earth has revolved around the sun from positions 1, 2, and 3 the sun, as viewed from the earth, will have moved also to positions 1, 2, and 3 as projected onto the celestial sphere. If the angle the earth moves were 30 degrees, the sun would appear to move by the same angular measure of 30 degrees. The path traced out by the sun on the celestial sphere is defined as the ecliptic. The zones on either side of the ecliptic are divided arbitrarily by astrologers into the 12 familiar zones of the zodiac. Not shown are the constellations associated with each zodiac, because this is a course in astronomy, not astrology.

7

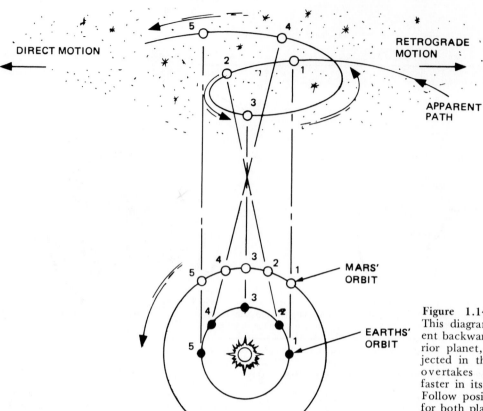

DIRECT MOTION

RETROGRADE MOTION

APPARENT PATH

MARS' ORBIT

EARTHS' ORBIT

Figure 1.14. Retrograde motion. This diagram illustrates the apparent backward movement of a superior planet, such as Mars, as projected in the sky when the earth overtakes it. (The earth moves faster in its orbit around the sun.) Follow positions 1, 2, 3, 4, and 5 for both planets. As the earth overtakes Mars, it appears for an observer on earth, as if Mars moves in a retrograde, that is backward motion.

Again, the explanation for this retrograde motion is a very simple one, but it gave serious concern to the ancients. It required the most elaborate types of motion, generally known as **epicycles**, to get them worked out. The actual retrograde motion arises from the apparent *projected* position of a planet as the earth overtakes it in orbit (see Fig. 1.14). Similar effects can be demonstrated with a passing train. If you sit in a slow moving local train which is being overtaken by an express train, it would appear to you that you are, all of a sudden, moving *backwards*. One cannot even be certain as to the *direction* of travel!

Incidentally, if you wondered from where the magic number seven comes to give us the seven days of the week, it was undoubtedly the sum of the moon, the sun, plus the five wandering planets. The names given to the days of the week verify this statement:

Days of the Week	Spanish Equivalent	Planets
Saturday	Sabado	(Saturn)
Sunday	Domingo	(Sun)
Monday	Lunes	(Moon)
Tuesday	Martes	(Mars)
Wednesday	Miercoles	(Mercury)
Thursday	Jueves	(Jupiter)
Friday	Viernes	(Venus)

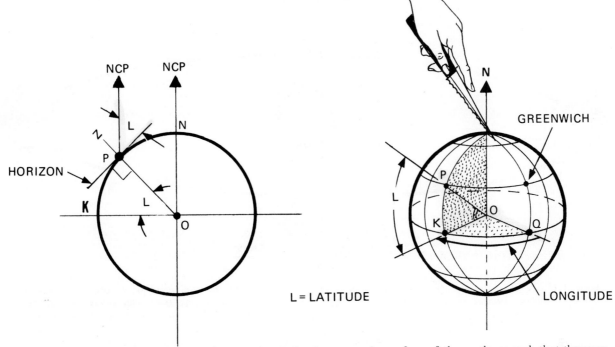

Figure 1.15. The earth and its coordinates. The circles drawn on the surface of the earth are such that they run either parallel to the equator or perpendicular to it. The perpendicular circle going through Greenwich specifies the zero point for measuring longitude. The longitude of point P is the angle QOK. The latitude is angle KOP. Also shown is the fact that the altitude of the north celestial pole is equal to observer's latitude (L). The zenith Z is a point directly overhead from the observer P, such that the line drawn from the center of the earth through P will be extended to Z.

A Look Around Us

Before our next venture into deep space, we shall look around us. What do we see? From a vantage point shown in Figure 1.5, the earth is seen spinning on its axis as it revolves around the sun in its yearly track. It takes roughly 365 1/4 days for the earth to make one complete revolution about the sun. During this time, a lot of changes take place on the earth, depending, of course, on your location on the earth.

One can divide the earth's surface by drawing circles parallel to the equator. The imaginary spin axis of the earth is exactly perpendicular to the plane of the equator. This axis emerges at the north and south poles and, when continued to infinity in either direction, is called the North Celestial or South Celestial Pole respectively.

The latitude is defined as the angle L subtended at the center of the earth between the equator and the location, P (e.g., the angle POK shown in Fig. 1.15). Thus, at the North Pole, the latitude is 90°. To complete the earth grid system, great circles passing from the North to the South Poles are a measure of longitude, with the fiduciary one passing through Greenwich, England, defined as measuring 0°.

As the earth is spinning, we note that its spin axis does not lie perpendicular to the plane of the ecliptic, but makes an angle of 23 1/2° with respect to the perpendicular (Fig. 1.16). The angle of 23 1/2 ° is important in determining the change of seasons as well as the variations in the hours of sunlight experienced during the course of the year.

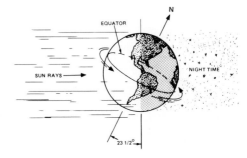

Figure 1.16.

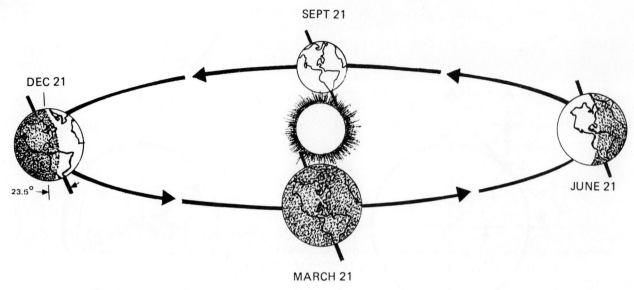

SEPT 21

DEC 21

23.5°

JUNE 21

MARCH 21

Figure 1.17. A view of the earth showing its position with respect to the sun in its yearly orbit. March 21st (vernal equinox); June 21st (summer solstice); September 21st (autumnal equinox); December 21st (winter solstice). The actual precise dates for these events may differ by one day, depending on the calendar. We shall stick to the 21st of each month for simplicity.

Another relevant factor, of course, is one's location on earth with respect to the latitude. Figure 1.17 shows the variations of the earth's positions at various times during the course of the year. If we start on March 21st (which is known as the **Vernal Equinox**) and follow through the position of the earth through the **Summer Solstice, Autumnal Equinox,** and **Winter Solstice,** one gets an idea of the variations of the amount of incident sunlight received on the earth during the course of the year. It is primarily the amount of sunlight or heat received per unit area, say per square foot or square mile per day, that determines the variations of seasons. Mountain ranges, proximity to oceans or icebergs, and clouds, of course, modify the weather, but the most important item is still the solar heat input.

Coordinate Systems

If you wish to visit a friend, it is important to know the street address. Similarly, if you wish to locate a celestial object, it can only be accomplished by means of a set of rules which everyone has agreed to in advance. Moreover, all people who agree to these rules must understand them and be able to reproduce them so that if you wanted to communicate with someone on the other side of the earth about a specific object in the sky, your set of coordinate numbers must make sense to this other person. Just as it takes two coordinates (house number and street name or number) to locate someone in the city, so it takes two coordinates, viz. latitude and longitude to locate an object on earth. There are two sets of coordinate systems in use that are most relevant. These are the **Horizon System** and the **Equator System.**

In the Horizon System (Fig. 1.18), astronomers use the following conventions: the point directly overhead is the **Zenith,** one then draws a great circle through the zenith and the **North Celestial Pole** ([NCP], which is the extension of the earth's axis from its North Pole). This will define the observer's **Celestial Meridian.** Where this meridian intersects the horizon, one has the **south** (S) and the **north point** (N). For measuring the position of an object in the Horizon System, we use **azimuth** and **altitude.** The azimuth is measured clockwise from the south point to the foot of the object's vertical circle. The altitude is measured from the foot of the horizon along the vertical circle to the star in question. Note that most astronomers measure azimuth from the south point, whereas navigators measure azimuth from the north point. As long as you will stay in the field of astronomy, this difference should not give you any problems. However, if you fly an airplane, you will be landing 180° in the wrong direction—which might be a more serious matter.

The Horizon System is very simple to use, except that if you look in the sky, the stars seem to move. How do we take care of this problem? Well, we could design another reference system based solely on the fact that the sky is rotating in a particular direction and along particular planes. It is obvious that the celestial equator is a natural plane which doesn't seem to change. We shall, therefore, take the celestial equator as a reference circle and measure angles along its circumference.

We take the corresponding south point from the Horizon System as the **sigma** (Σ) point (reference) on the Equator System and measure angles in a clockwise direction along the celestial equator. An angle measured in this manner is called the **hour angle.** Likewise, the angle measured along the hour

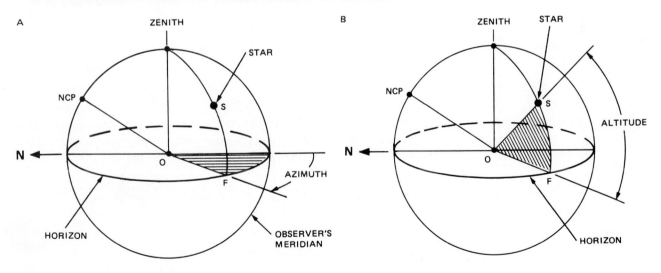

Figure 1.18. The horizon system. Note the azimuth is the angle measured from the south point along the horizon to the foot of the star's vertical circle, which passes through the zenith and the star's position S. Altitude is the angle measured along the vertical circle from the point F on the horizon to the star S.

11

circle from the celestial equator to the star is called **declination.** Thus, in order to locate an object, one draws a great circle from the celestial pole through the star's hour circle and lets it intersect the celestial equator. The point where it intersects is called the foot of the star's hour circle and is a very important **fiduciary mark.** The hour angle is then the angle measured from the sigma point (Σ) to the foot of the star's hour circle, the declination is measured from this foot of the star's hour circle to the star, so that again the two points will locate the object. Let's go through some simple examples:

Example 1. The hour angle of any star that crosses the observer's celestial meridian is zero.

Example 2. If the star is on the equator, its declination is zero.

Example 3. An object that is on the north celestial pole has a declination of 90°. In fact, the north celestial pole does not move at all.

This is a very easy to use coordinate system. It has only one problem; the hour angle of a star is constantly changing! The answer is to use a coordinate (or reference system) that is measured with respect to the **moving frame.** There is an important point in space which is determined by the sun's motion. The sun in its yearly motion in the sky describes a path: the ecliptic. As it moves along one degree a day, it will cross the celestial equator going from south to north on about March 21. That point in the sky is known as the **Vernal Equinox,** ♈, and it is used as a reference point to measure the coordinates of stars. Consider, for the time being, the Vernal Equinox (♈) as a primary fixed point on the celestial sphere. One now defines the angle measured from the Vernal Equinox to the foot of the star's hour circle, measured in a coun-

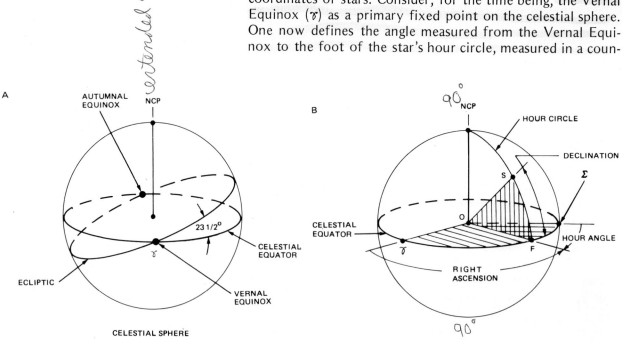

Figure 1.19. The equator system. Note the hour angle, right ascension, and declination. Also note that the hour angle of the vernal equinox is equal to the sidereal time. The vernal equinox is defined as the intersection on the celestial sphere of the sun's orbit on the ecliptic with the celestial equator, as the sun crosses from south to north. The angle that the ecliptic makes with the celestial equator is 23 1/2°.

terclockwise direction, as **right ascension** (RA). This angle is a fixed quantity for a star. Thus, the right ascension and the declination (δ) are coordinates that unambiguously determine the position of a star. You can write your friend on the other side of the world that you have located an object (be sure to mention its RA and δ) and be fairly certain that he could locate it as well. There is, of course, one other coordinate needed to find the star and that is the **hour angle** of the star; but at least your friend knows where the object is located with respect to the other stars.

Let us take another look at the Vernal Equinox. When the Vernal Equinox crosses the observer's celestial meridian, the sidereal time is zero. The hour angle of the Vernal Equinox is defined as sidereal time (divided into twenty-four hours so that one can actually use the sky to measure time; the Vernal Equinox ♈ being the fiduciary point). Another way to look at this is to think of the sky as a celestial clock with the observer's celestial meridian as the hour hand and the dial as the rotating sky. The sky has everything except the twenty-four hours marked out with luminous numbers! We have here a twenty-four hour sidereal clock which measures time very precisely. In fact, this was the primary method for the measurement of time until the advent of quartz oscillators and subsequently, the more precise atomic clocks which came into use about twenty years ago.

Synodic Period and Sidereal Period

In this chapter we also wish to define some of the terminology that is used by astronomers. Always keep in mind that every discipline defines its own units and terms. We will define only a few simple concepts.

First, **synodic** and **sidereal periods**. The sidereal period is the interval between successive transits of a planet or any object with respect to the stars. It is its true period for either rotation or revolution. The earth's sidereal period is its true period of rotation which is 23 hours and 56 minutes. The sidereal period for the moon is the time taken for the moon to move around the earth and come back again with respect to the same position in the sky. We assume that the stars do not move in the course of a year. Hence, the stars act as a fixed background. The sidereal period of the moon is 27 1/3 days.

The synodic period is the time interval in relationship to the sun (e.g., **the solar day**). It is defined as the mean time between, for example, successive high noons. Note that one has to line things up with the sun and that the solar day is four minutes longer than the sidereal day, because during the course of a day, the earth has revolved one degree around the sun as in Figure 1.12. After 23 hours and 56 minutes of earth rotation, we would line things up with the stars. During that time, the earth has moved one degree around the sun, so that we have to rotate the earth one degree's worth, or four minutes' worth of time, to line things up again with the sun.

13

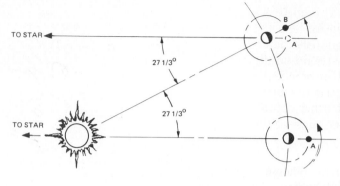

Figure 1.20. The difference between the sidereal lunar period and the synodic period comes about as follows: observe the moon in position A. It would take the moon 27 1/3 days to make one complete revolution around the earth. During this period, the earth has revolved around the sun by about 27 1/3 degrees. Consequently, the moon will have to revolve around the earth an additional 27 1/3 degrees to complete its synodic period corresponding to 29 1/2 days. As can be seen from this figure, the synodic period is the time from full moon to full moon (or time between equal phases of the moon, e.g., new moon to new moon).

Similar arguments pertain to the moon (Fig. 1.20). The moon's synodic period is the interval between successive equal phases of the moon, say between full moon and full moon. Note that after 27 1/2 days, the moon has made one complete revolution around the earth. During the course of 27 1/2 days, the earth-moon system has revolved about 27 1/2° around the sun. It would now be necessary for the moon to revolve another 27 1/2° or so in order to catch up again with the earth-sun line. In other words, the moon has to line up again so as to be seen as the full moon from the earth. Since the moon moves roughly 13° per day (27 1/2 divided by 13 is about 2), it would take another two days for the moon to line up, resulting in the synodic period of 29 1/2 days, two days longer than the sidereal period.

Foucault Pendulum

The Foucault Pendulum is an excellent device for demonstrating that the earth is turning and not the sky. It consists essentially of a heavy spherical ball suspended by a long steel wire. For a dramatic and vivid demonstration of its function, there is usually a small rod attached to the bottom of the ball and pieces of chalk are placed in a circular manner (Fig. 1.21). The principle behind this pendulum is a very simple one; it involves the following consideration: whenever a pendulum is set swinging in a certain plane, the plane of its swing does not change no matter what else is going on around it (as long as no one interferes with it). This can also be simply shown in the laboratory by suspending a string with a weight from a rotating platform. As you rotate the platform, the plane of the swing does not change (only the ball gets rotated). As the string or wire gets turned, the plane of the swing stays the same. As the earth is rotating below the Foucault Pendulum, one can demonstrate that it appears as if the plane of the swing is revolving in the opposite direction. Figure 1.22 shows the effect from the point of view of an observer performing the experiment at the North Pole. (Most scientists have more immediate problems to worry about at the North Pole.) It would take precisely 23 hours and 56 minutes for the earth to rotate once around below the Foucault Pendulum. It is a direct verification of the earth's rotation on its axis.

At latitudes other than the North Pole, the time for the Foucault Pendulum's plane to rotate on its axis is different from the earth's rotation because the earth does not rotate exactly below the pendulum at other latitudes. In fact, at the equator, the Foucault Pendulum's plane does not rotate at all (Fig. 1.22). At other latitudes, the equation which describes this rotation involves a geometric factor, involving the latitude (Tech. Note No. 3). Or in words, the period P is equal to 23 hours and 56 minutes divided by the sine of the latitude. Technical note number 3 gives values of the sin (latitude) as a function of latitude, e.g., for Los Angeles latitude of 34°, the sin 34° is 0.559. Thus

$$P = \frac{23 \text{ hours, } 56 \text{ minutes}}{\sin (\text{latitude } 34°)} = \frac{23 \text{ hours, } 56 \text{ minutes}}{.559}$$

$$P = 42 \text{ hours, } 49 \text{ minutes.}$$

The Foucault Pendulum is simple and elegant. It leaves no doubt regarding what is rotating about what.

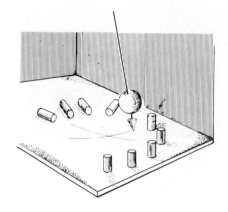

Figure 1.21. The Foucault Pendulum.

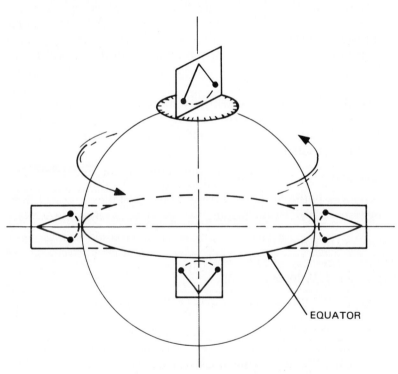

EQUATOR

Figure 1.22. The Foucault Pendulum suspended at the North Pole, indicating the rotation of the earth below the oscillating plane of the pendulum's swing. Note that similar experiments performed at the earth's equator: the plane of swing remains unchanged since the earth does not rotate below the pendulum at the equator.

Chapter 2

VOYAGE TO THE PLANETS—
BODE-TITIUS LAW

Before we take off on our solar system journey, it is advisable to study the distances involved in our forthcoming space trip. There is a very simple law discovered independently by Bode and Titius about 1772, for ascertaining the distances in **astronomical units**. The average distance from the sun to the earth (93 million miles) is defined as one astronomical unit, abbreviated A.U. (Fig. 1.6). To obtain Bode's Law: write down the numbers as shown in Table 2.1 starting with 0, 3, 6, 12, 24, 48, 96, etc. Add 4 to each one, then divide by 10. The numbers thus obtained represent the distances of the planets from the sun in astronomical units. Note for the earth the distance is exactly 1 A.U. The actual measured distances are also shown. Except for the planet Neptune, the agreement is exceedingly good. We will come back to the significance of this law in Chapter 18. It contains the *message* of how the planets are formed. Keep in mind that the distances are essentially doubled for successive planets as you travel outwards beyond Venus. To appreciate relative sizes and distances for our forthcoming trip, it is advisable to consult Figure 2.18.

To convert astronomical units to miles, multiply each astronomical unit by 93 million miles. Another measure of distances is the amount of time that light takes to travel. For light to travel from the sun to the earth it takes 8 1/2 min-

TABLE 2.1
The Bode-Titius Law of 1772
(Interpreted by F.M. Johnson 1972)

n	∞ Mercury	8 Venus	7 Earth	6 Mars	5 Asteroids	4 Jupiter	3 Saturn	2 Uranus	1b Neptune	1a Pluto
	0	3	6	12	24	48	96	192	—	384
Add 4	4	4	4	4	4	4	4	4	—	4
Divide by 10	0.4	0.7	1.0	1.6	2.8	5.2	10.0	19.6	—	38.8
Actual distance	0.387	0.723	1.0	1.523	(2.8)	5.202	9.540	19.18	30.0	39.44

$$d = 0.4 + (0.3)2^{8-n}$$ where n is an integer

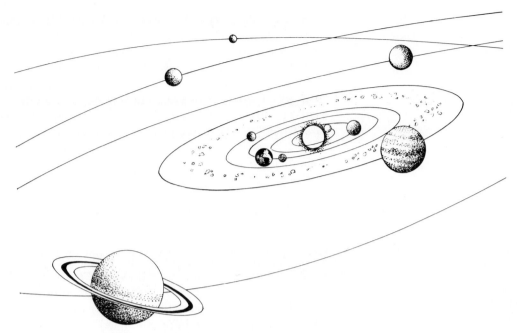

Figure 2.1. Scenic view of the solar system. This diagram is not to scale. It illustrates that the planets lie approximately in the same plane and also revolve about the sun in the same direction.

utes. Thus, a trip to Saturn of ten astronomical units would be roughly a billion miles; or if we were to travel at the speed of light it would take 85 minutes. The round trip would be twice that. If we were to receive a message from the earth at Saturn and expect to answer it, these round trip times have to be taken seriously into account. It would be a long wait between messages if you were to conduct a normal conversation.

Let us begin our trip with the sun (Fig. 2.2), ruler of all the planets. The surface temperature of the sun is 6,000°C. The sun rules by virtue of its powerful gravitational attrac-

Surface Temp. of Sun 6,000°C

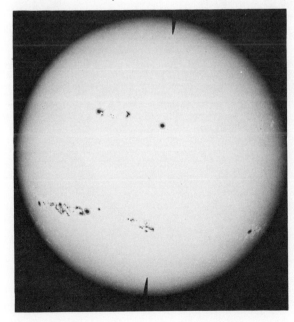

Figure 2.2. The sun, ruler of the solar system. It prevents its planetary offsprings from escaping into deep space by its powerful gravitational attraction. Provider of plentiful energy. (Sunlight is the real manna from heaven.) The sun keeps a firm grip on its own energy production, thus assuring uniform output. Energy is supplied free to all the planets without wires, pollution, fuss, or contracts.

17

tion and the energy it radiates to each of the objects that revolve around it (most of its energy is lost to space). Naturally, the closer we get to the sun, the hotter it would get, and the more energy we would receive by the familiar inverse square law relationship (Tech. Note No. 4). We receive about a hundred watts per square foot at the surface of the earth. Halfway towards the sun, this would be four times as great and when we are three-quarters of the way to the sun, we would receive sixteen times as much energy per unit area than at the earth.

Our first stop-over in the outward bound trip from the sun is the planet Mercury. We note that Mercury is very similar in its outward appearance to the moon, neglecting their size difference. Unless one were familiar with the details of the craters, a comparison of pictures of the moon and Mercury, at a distance of ten feet to an untrained observer, would result in the conclusion that they look extremely alike (Figs. 2.3 and 2.4). The origin of these craters on both planets is of great interest and fascination. Some features on Mercury are undoubtedly volcanic in origin. There are also scarps and rifts which suggest that there might have been tectonic or geologic activity in Mercury's distant past.

Next, we proceed to Venus. These are some of the features that stand out concerning that planet. It is almost the same

Figure 2.3. The moon.

Figure 2.4. Planet Mercury. A glimpse of Mercury's surface first seen by man via the Mariner spacecraft. (NASA/JPL)

size as the earth, Venus is only 4% less in diameter. Its mass is 20% less than that of the earth. Its surface gravity is similar, its escape velocity (minimum velocity needed to escape a planet's gravitational pull) is consequently similar to that of the earth. But wherein lies the difference? The most obvious feature of the planet Venus is the fact that it has a very thick atmosphere surrounding its surface. It is so thick that we cannot see the surface, because visible light will not penetrate its atmosphere. As a consequence of this atmosphere, heat is trapped by the **greenhouse effect** on Venus, and its surface temperature is in excess of 400°C. It is far too hot to sustain life on its surface. Its rotation period was unknown until a decade ago. When radar reflection measurements were sent out from the earth, they were able to pick up sufficient details from the surface of Venus to obtain an accurate measurement of the rotation period. To our great surprise, this rotation period turned out to be 243.1 days. This means that Venus essentially ceases to rotate. Its rotation period is so slow compared to that of the earth, that one wonders what mechanism was at work to slow it down so drastically. It also rotates in the opposite direction to the earth's! It is not *locked in* by tidal forces of the sun as the moon is locked in by the earth.

The plane of Venus' equator lies almost in the plane of its orbit, very similarly to another planet: Jupiter. Recent pictures taken by the Mariner spacecraft flying by Venus, showed turbulence and rather rapid variations in the outer layers of Venus' atmosphere (Fig. 2.5). The assumption that

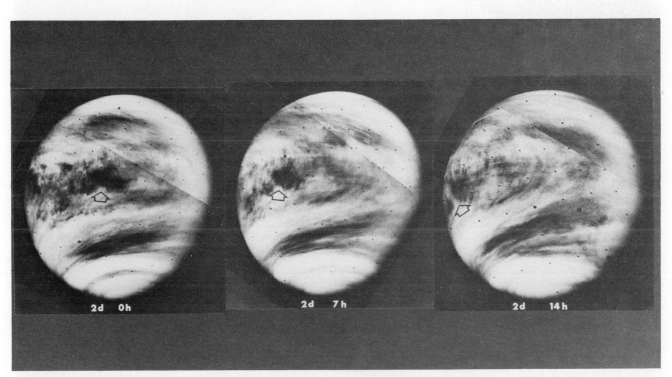

Figure 2.5. The atmosphere of Venus showing rapid rotation in its outer layers. This was a surprising result since Venus' surface rotation is extremely slow (243.1 days). Mariner photograph (NASA/JPL).

is generally made, because Venus is now too hot and cannot support life, is to ignore it and land on Mars instead. What one should not assume is that Venus would have been this way all the time in its past. Since its temperature was certainly hotter than the earth's in the very beginning, 4 1/2 billion years ago, life could have developed there more rapidly, assuming that it had initial conditions that were similar to earth. Venus should be explored more thoroughly, even though the technical problems of temperature and high atmospheric pressure have to be overcome. The Russians have attempted a number of landings on Venus with limited success. The measurements of 2 satellites that they landed confirmed the high temperature and high atmospheric pressure on Venus. We should make a stronger effort in our space program to land probes on Venus to see whether or not life had developed in the past on that planet.

With this speculation fresh in our minds, we shall make a quick pass at the earth at a distance of about 240,000 miles, roughly the distance to the moon, and see what the earth looks like (Fig. 2.6). As we pass by the earth at that distance, we can very well wonder whether there is life on that planet. There is no evidence at that distance of *any* life, certainly not of intelligent life (unless we listen to the electromagnetic noise that emanates from there).

Figure 2.6. The earth. (NASA/JPL)

Next we proceed on to Mars. We note that Mars has features in common with the moon and Mercury—the craters. On the other hand, there are features which are distinctly different and some which remind us a little bit of the earth. There are northern and southern polar caps. The inclination of Mars' equator is 24° with respect to a perpendicular to the plane of its orbit. It is only a half of a degree different from that of the earth. Its period of rotation is very similar to that of the earth; it rotates at a period of 24 hours and 37 minutes, whereas the earth's is 23 hours and 56 minutes. However, its radius is about half that of the earth, its mass about 10% of the earth's mass. These two factors combine to give a much smaller **escape velocity** (Chap. 5); about half that of the earth. Consequently, its present atmosphere is vastly different from earth's. Since it is further away from the sun, the amount of energy it receives is correspondingly less, by a factor of $(1.52)^2$, roughly 2.2 less, or 45 watts per square foot on the surface of Mars. This factor, plus a very tenuous atmosphere, provides a mean temperature near the equator of Mars roughly 20°C less than that of the earth. Consequently, the ability for life to get started and develop on Mars is diminished relative to earth, but it is not impossible.

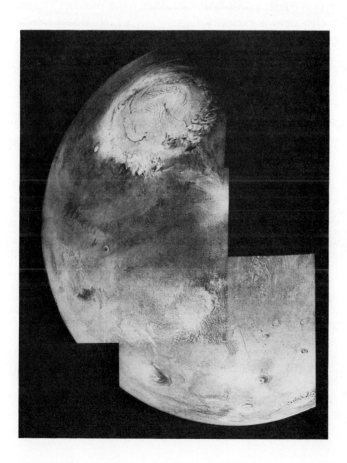

Figure 2.7. The northern hemisphere of Mars—from the polar cap to a few degrees south of the equator—is seen in this mosaic of three photos taken by the Mariner 9 spacecraft on August 7, 1972. The north polar ice cap is shrinking during the late Martian spring and the area shows complex sedimentary systems. Fractured terrains partially flooded by volcanic extrusions are visible in the center of the disk. In the bottom photo are the huge Martian volcanoes and the west end of the great equatorial canyon (lower right). The volcanic mountain Nix Olympia (lower left) is 500 kilometers (310 miles) across at the base and stands higher than any feature on earth. When Mariner 9 went into Mars orbit, only Nix Olympia and the three aligned volcanoes to the right protruded above a planet-wide dust storm. When the dust settled, clouds of water or dry ice crystals continued to obscure the area north of the 50th parallel until recent months. The northern hemisphere now appears free of atmospheric obscuration. The three photos, among 7,273 obtained by Mariner 9, were taken 84 seconds apart from an average range of 13,700 kilometers (8,500 miles). They have been computer-enhanced by the Jet Propulsion Laboratory's image processing team (JPL/NASA).

Mars has a very spectacular volcano called Nix Olympia (renamed Olympus Mons), larger than anything we have on earth (Fig. 2.8). It has a "Grand Canyon" which is four times as deep and four times as wide as the famous Grand Canyon in Arizona (Fig. 2.9). So far, we have not been able to unravel the mystery of why every few years or so a yellow cloud seems to completely surround the planet Mars. During the beginning of one of the Mariner picture-taking missions, a severe dust storm enveloped Mars for about two months, until finally it cleared enough to allow pictures to be taken.

There is one peculiar facet about the satellites of Mars which is worth mentioning, not because it has any relevance to life, but because it is an interesting clue as to how discoveries are sometimes predicted long before they occur. There are two satellites of Mars called **Deimos** and **Phobos** which are very small in size (Fig. 2.10). They were not discovered until 1877. However, a hundred and fifty years before their discovery, the English writer, Jonathan Swift, talks about the satellites of Mars, their periods of revolution around the planet, and their distances. The surprising thing is that he was fairly accurate in his predictions. How did he have such insights a hundred and fifty years before the discovery of these satellites? It's a minor mystery that should baffle the scientific sleuths among the readers. This mystery will puzzle us as we are passing through the Asteroid Belt, 2.8 astronomical units from the earth.

The **Asteroid Belt** consists of a rather wide band of stones and meteorites and a variety of material, which floats over a considerable distance span (perhaps 0.4 A.U.) 2.8 A.U. is just its mean distance, between Mars and Jupiter (Fig. 2.1). How did these asteroids get there? Some of the objects in this Asteroid Belt are larger than a hundred miles across; in fact, the largest hundred or so of these objects are being tracked and recorded on a systematic basis. Since they are light and

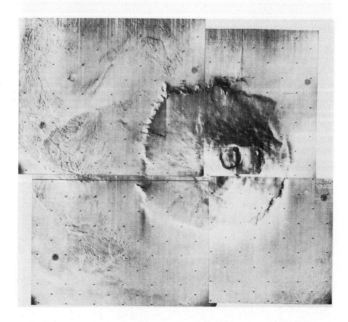

Figure 2.8. One of the largest known volcanoes in the solar system—Nix Olympia (renamed Olympus Mons) on Mars. This volcano is 500 km at its base and about 30 km high. The caldera or summit is about 70 km in diameter. The absence of impact craters on the slope of this volcano suggests a recent age for its origin. Mariner 9 photograph (NASA/JPL).

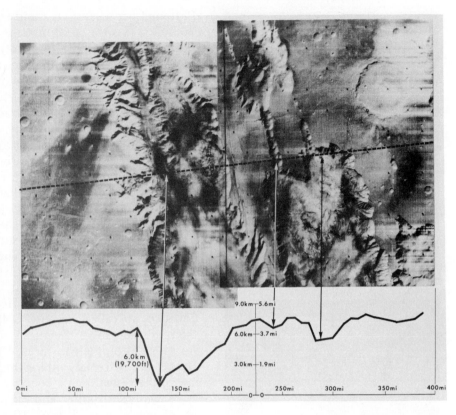

Figure 2.9. This photograph of the Tithonius Lacus region on Mars was taken by the Mariner 9 spacecraft revealing a canyon nearly four times as deep as the Grand Canyon in Arizona when the pictures were compared with pressure measurements taken by the ultraviolet spectrometer experiment aboard the spacecraft. The white arrow at left points to the Martian canyon estimated to be 19,700 feet (6 kilometers) deep. Earth's Grand Canyon is 5,500 feet (1.6 kilometers). 75 miles (120 kilometers), the Grand Canyon is 13 miles (21 kilometers) wide. The jagged line at bottom represents pressure measurements, taken by the ultraviolet instrument, which are translated through the picture is the instrument's scan path across the surface. The vast chasms and branching canyons represent a landfrom evolution apparently unique to Mars. (NASA/JPL)

easily perturbed by other planets, they have provided an interesting exercise as to the way gravity works in the Solar System.

If we successfully negotiate this Asteroid Belt without getting belted by one, we shall come to the largest of the planets, the majestic Jupiter (Fig. 2.11). We will notice that it is

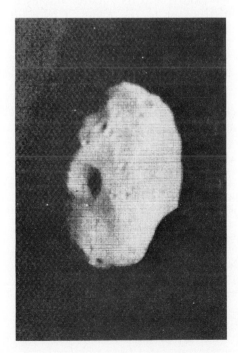

Figure 2.10. Close-up view of Mars satellite Phobos. The size of this tiny satellite is 21 km high and about 25 km long. Note crater in this picture, which is about 6.8 km across. This picture taken by the Mariner 9 orbiter was one of the major surprises of the mission (NASA/JPL).

Figure 2.11. Photograph of Jupiter taken by Pioneer spacecraft at a distance of 3.5 million km from the planet. Note the giant Red Spot on its surface, which is particularly conspicuous in blue light (NASA/JPL).

flattened because of its rapid rotation. It rotates in less than 10 hours. It is the most massive and the largest of the planets, being 317 times more massive than the earth and roughly 11 times larger. It is an impressive sight.

We can only see the surface of the planet's atmosphere. We cannot see the actual solid surface of Jupiter, if indeed there is one. The gravitational attraction of Jupiter is enormous because of its mass; certainly enough to prevent all gasses from escaping. There is a great amount of motion in the atmosphere and a lot of turbulence. Its magnetic field is much larger than that of the earth. Microwave radiation is being radiated in some peculiar manner and is governed by Jupiter's satellite Io. Four of Jupiter's satellites (Fig. 2.12) are large enough to be comparable to some of the smaller planets in the Solar System, such as Mercury and our moon. By studying the satellites of Jupiter, we see a miniature solar system, having a total of 14 satellites.

Four of the five innermost are the largest. They are the famous Galilean satellites (Io, Europa, Ganymede, and Callisto), so called because Galileo was the first to observe them. Presumably, they also have an atmosphere or some frozen gases on their surfaces. The spacings of the satellites of Jupiter are extremely interesting. They obey a Bode's type of law of their own.

As we leave Jupiter and make our way to the most scenic of all our planets, Saturn, 10 astronomical units away from the sun, we observe a most majestic sight: Saturn's rings (Fig. 2.13). It is the only one of our planets which has a ring structure. As we get closer, we notice that those rings are not a solid sheet but are composed of individual particles of varying sizes and shapes. They may be rocks but more probably are composed of ice or frozen hydrocarbon compounds that are individually circulating around Saturn. Saturn, too, has a rotation period close to ten hours, and its equator makes an angle of 26° and 44′ with respect to the plane of its orbit

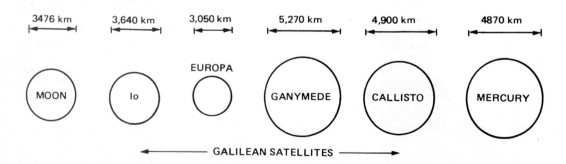

Figure 2.12. The sizes of the Galilean satellites compared with the moon and Mercury.

(only a few degrees different from that of the earth). It is rotating so fast that it is also noticeably flattened on the north and south poles like Jupiter. Its surface features remind us a little of Jupiter's. Saturn is slightly smaller than Jupiter. Its radius is 9 1/2 times larger and its mass 95 times heavier than that of the earth. In spite of its similarities to Jupiter, the most conspicuous of the differences is the fact that Saturn has the unique ring structure. Again, let us ask the critical key questions: Where does the "ring" really come from? How and why did Saturn develop such a structure? What is its significance? What is the story that it is telling us, particularly if the material it contains is made of ice and perhaps hydrocarbons? These are questions which still need answers.

Our next planet will be a short stop-over on Uranus whose mass is 14 1/2 times heavier than the earth's, but whose rotational period is also similar to that of Saturn, only slightly longer, 10 hours and 49 minutes. The inclination of its spin axis is peculiarly aligned. It is approximately in the plane of the ecliptic.

We should also mention the fact that Saturn, Uranus, and Neptune each has its own satellite system, but not as spectacular as that of Jupiter. Satellite spacings occur in a systematic way—almost Bode's law-type regularities.

Neptune, being the last major-size planet that we visit, has a mass that exceeds that of Uranus, 17 times heavier than that of the earth, but its radius is almost equal to that of Uranus. Its rotation period is slightly longer, about 15 hours. Its equator is inclined 28° 48' with respect to its orbit.

Note now as we are comparing these planets, that four of them (the earth, Mars, Saturn, and Neptune) have rotational axis inclinations that are within a few degrees equal to each other. Jupiter and Venus however have spin axes that are perpendicular to their orbital plane. What caused this peculiar series of alignments? The reason why the motions, the spacings, and the inclinations are of primary interest is that certain quantities and angles should remain the same for all time, if our physical laws, such as conservation of angular momentum, are to hold. Certainly, the angle that the spin axis makes with respect to the ecliptic must be one of the

Figure 2.13. The majestic planet Saturn with its remarkable ring system. Photo taken with the 100-inch telescope (Hale Observatories).

properties that should have stayed the same for billions of years. Consequently, in our preliminary travels, while trying to unravel the origin mystery, these are some of the clues that we have to pay a lot of attention to, even though we do not know all of the answers—yet.

Last, but not least, the furthest out of our planets, Pluto, is 40 astronomical units away (Fig. 2.14). Pluto is an anomaly because somehow it does not fit into the sequence of the other major planets. Its smaller size and mass make little sense. Methane ice was identified recently on its surface. Its rotation period is 6 days, 9 hours. As a matter of fact, since its discovery in 1930, Pluto has not even made one complete revolution around the sun! It has barely moved about one-fifth of the way since 1930. Pluto is one of the many mysteries of our solar system yet to be solved. If its radius and mass, which are not known with precision, have any significance, then its average density is much higher than any of the major planets that lie beyond the range of the Asteroid Belt.

We should extend our trip to somewhat beyond what is considered the extremities of the solar system because there are objects beyond Pluto which are of interest. We encountered some of these objects on the way out. There are billions of them at distances from hundreds to thousands of times further out than Pluto. These are the **comets**. Some of them occasionally decide to pay a visit to the vicinity of the sun, increasing their speed as they approach the sun, rounding it, and returning from whence they came. A picture of a typical cometary spectacular photographed recently is shown in Figure 2.15. Note the long tail that follows the head of the comet. The tail consists of two portions: one presumed to be dust, the other gas. The chemical constituents in the tail have been spectroscopically identified to consist of C_2, C_3, CN, CH, H_2O^+, and other small chemical radicals. (See Chapter 6. Spectroscopic techniques will be more fully discussed in Chapter 11.) These other smaller radicals must be disintegration products of larger molecules that have been broken up,

PLUTO

Figure 2.14. 200-inch photograph of the planet Pluto (Hale Observatories).

26

Figure 2.15. Comet Kohoutek (1973f). 48-inch Schmidt Telescope photograph taken January 12, 1974 (Hale Observatories).

perhaps by the solar wind, as the comet approaches the sun. There is a hydrogen cloud two or three times larger than the diameter of the sun which surrounds the comet. This is peculiar, since the velocity of escape for hydrogen should be such that the free hydrogen should have long been evaporated from the comet. There must obviously be a continuous process which generates hydrogen from within the comet head. Presumably, a comet head also contains elements under high pressure which are frozen in and become heated as the comets approach the warmth of the sun's rays, or is the water molecule dissociated into hydrogen and oxygen by the solar wind? (The solar wind consists mainly of charged particle ejections into space [Chap. 8].) The comets, perhaps, hold one of the keys to the origin of life. Since they contain water and very likely organic compounds, and because of the large number of them associated with the solar system, the role that they play must be such that they cannot be ignored.

On the outward trip, we noticed that there are swarms of comets in the vicinity of Jupiter's orbit. A few of them have such elongated orbits that they intercept a number of planetary orbits. One spectacular comet which reappears roughly every 70 years is Halley's Comet. It was known to the ancients at least as far back as 2,500 years ago. Its last spectacular appearance was in 1910. The next expected visit of Halley's Comet is in 1986. The tail of this comet is long enough to intercept the earth's atmosphere, as it sweeps across the sky.

For those who wish to prepare for the return of Halley's Comet, Table 2.2 gives the appropriate date, as well as all the previous observed ones, that some of you may have missed!

Two documents are supplied from our first interplanetary space flight. These are Table 2.3 and Table 2.4, which are a complete inventory of all the planets, their satellites and some of their properties. These compilations are an invaluable aid for further study and to refresh our recollections of places that we visited.

Now let us return to the earth quickly to resume our quest by studying some of the laws of nature, including historical developments, to give us a perspective for subsequent journeys into the past as well as into the future.

Historical Footnotes

Deimos and Phobos

Here is the solution to the mystery of Jonathan Swift's vision of two satellites going around Mars as described in his Gulliver's Travels in 1726. It appears that Swift had read the works of Kepler, who had, in 1610, predicted that Mars should have two satellites. Swift had also learned of Kepler's laws, which he had incorporated in his stories. It is, therefore, Kepler, as we suspected all along, who was the great visionary.

Another famous writer, Voltaire, mentions the two Martian satellites in his *Micromegas,* published in 1750. Apparently Voltaire had read *Gulliver's Travels.* It is interesting to see how a long series of speculations can be traced back to its source.

When were these elusive satellites actually discovered? On the nights of August 11 and August 17, 1877, Asoph Hall spotted them while observing from the U.S. Naval Observatory in Washington, D.C.

Why did Hall name these satellites Phobos (fear) and Deimes (panic)? Hall had read Homer's *Iliad* where the sons of Mars, Phobos, and Deimos are summoned to yoke his steeds.

Now that we finally had a close-up look of these satellites (Fig. 2.10), our next puzzle is: How did Mars capture these satellites and when? Nobody knows. Even Homer in his wildest dreams could not have imagined the exciting history of all the objects in the solar system!!

The Bode-Titius Law of 1772

In 1766, Johannes D. Titius, professor of mathematics at Wittenberg discovered a rather simple mathematical relationship predicting the distances of the planets from the sun. The same relationship was published by Johann E. Bode, director of the Berlin Observatory, in a popular astronomy book in 1772. The two Johanns presumably discovered these relationships independently (?). Titius priority claim is found in a footnote of a book which he had translated. Instead of calling it the Bode-Titius law, one should perhaps call it the (Johann)^2 law.

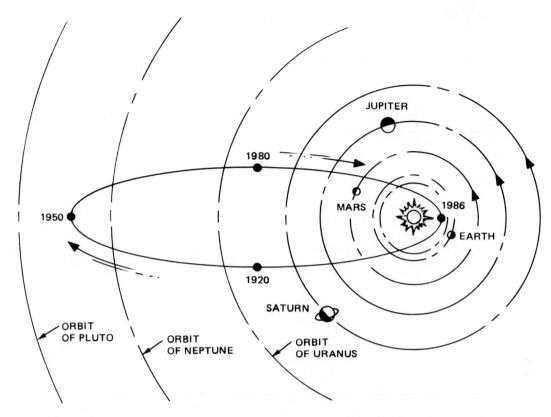

Figure 2.16. This shows the orbit of Halley's Comet. Note that the comet goes in a clockwise direction, contrary to the other planets in the solar system. Also note that the extreme position (aphelion) occurs between the orbits of Neptune and Pluto. Halley's Comet will make its reappearance on schedule by 1986.

TABLE 2.2
Returns to Perihelion of Halley's Comet
(Cowell and Crommelin)

240	(B.C.)	May 15?	912	(A.D.)	July 19
163	(B.C.)	May 20?	989	(A.D.)	Sept. 2
87	(B.C.)	Aug. 15	1066	(A.D.)	Mar. 25
12	(B.C.)	Oct. 8	1145	(A.D.)	April 19
66	(A.D.)	Jan. 26	1222	(A.D.)	Sept. 10
141	(A.D.)	Mar. 25	1301	(A.D.)	Oct. 23
218	(A.D.)	April 6	1378	(A.D.)	Nov. 8
295	(A.D.)	April 7	1456	(A.D.)	June 2
374	(A.D.)	Feb. 13	1531	(A.D.)	Aug. 25
451	(A.D.)	July 3	1607	(A.D.)	Oct. 26
530	(A.D.)	Nov. 15	1682	(A.D.)	Sept. 14
607	(A.D.)	Mar. 26	1759	(A.D.)	Mar. 12
684	(A.D.)	Nov. 26	1835	(A.D.)	Nov. 15
760	(A.D.)	June 10	1910	(A.D.)	April 19
837	(A.D.)	Feb. 25	1986	(A.D.)	Feb. ?

TABLE 2.3
Solar System Planets

Planet	Semimajor Axis of Orbit	Sidereal Period	Eccentricity e	Inclination of Equator to Orbit		Sidereal Rotation Period (Equatorial)				Radius (Equator)	Mass
	AU	Tropical Years		°		d	h	m	s	km	10^{27} gm
Mercury	0.387099	0.24085	0.205628	~0		58.6				2,425	0.331
Venus	0.723332	0.61521	0.006787	3		243.1	retrograde			6,070	4.870
Earth	1.000000	1.00004	0.016722	23	27		23	56	04.1	6,378	5.976
Mars	1.523691	1.88089	0.093377	23	59		24	37	22.6	3,395	0.642
Jupiter	5.202803	11.86223	0.04845	3	05		9	50	30*	71,300	1899.3
Saturn	9.53884	29.4577	0.05565	26	44		10	14		61,100	568.6
Uranus	19.1819	84.0139	0.04724	97	55		10	49		24,500	86.89
Neptune	30.0578	164.793	0.00858	28	48		15	48		25,100	102.97
Pluto	39.44	247.7	0.250			6	9			3,200	1.0

*Jupiter $9^h 55^m 29^s.37$ radio

TABLE 2.4
The Satellites

Planet	Satellite	Mean Distance from Planet	Sidereal Period	Orbit Incl.	Orbit Eccentricity	Radius
		10^3 km	days	°		km
Earth	Moon	384	27.321661	23	0.055	1,738
Mars	1 Phobos	9	0.318910	1	0.021	~20
	2 Deimos	23	1.262441	2	0.003	~8
Jupiter	1 Io	422	1.769138	0	0.000	1,820
	2 Europa	671	3.551181	1	0.000	1,525
	3 Ganymede	1,070	7.154553	0	0.001	2,635
	4 Callisto	1,883	16.689018	0	0.007	2,450
	5	181	0.418178	0	0.003	80
	6	11,476	250.566	28	0.158	50
	7	11,737	259.65	26	0.207	12
	8	23,500	739	147R	0.40	10
	9	23,600	758	156R	0.275	9
	10	11,700	259.22	29	0.12	8
	11	22,600	692	163R	0.207	9
	12	21,200	630	147R	0.169	8
	13	11,010	239.2	26.7	0.147	8
	14					
Saturn	1 Mimas	186	0.942422	2	0.020	270
	2 Enceladus	238	1.370218	0	0.004	300
	3 Tethys	295	1.887802	1	0.000	500
	4 Dione	377	2.736916	0	0.002	480
	5 Rhea	527	4.417503	0	0.001	650
	6 Titan	1,222	15.945449	0	0.029	2,440
	7 Hyperion	1,483	21.276657	1	0.104	220
	8 Iapetus	3,560	79.33084	15	0.028	550
	9 Phoebe	12,950	550.33	150R	0.163	120
	10 Janus	159	0.7490	0	0.0	150
Uranus	1 Aeriel	192	2.52038	0	0.003	350
	2 Umbriel	267	4.14418	0	0.004	250
	3 Titania	438	8.70588	0	0.002	500
	4 Oberon	586	13.46326	0	0.001	450
	5 Miranda	130	1.414	0	0.00	120
Neptune	1 Triton	355	5.87654	160R	0.00	1,900
	2 Nereid	5,562	359.88	28	0.75	120

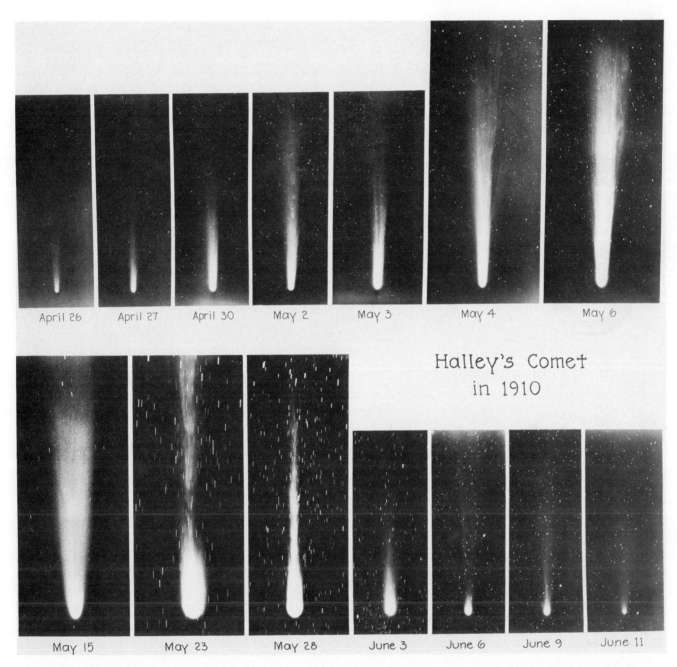

April 26 April 27 April 30 May 2 May 3 May 4 May 6

Halley's Comet
in 1910

May 15 May 23 May 28 June 3 June 6 June 9 June 11

Figure 2.17. Halley's Comet. Fourteen different views of the comet taken between April 26 and June 11, 1910 (Hale Observatories).

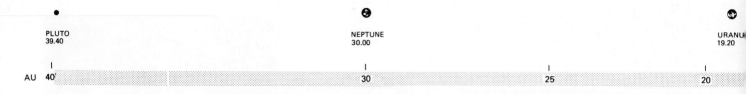

PLUTO
39.40

NEPTUNE
30.00

URANU
19.20

AU 40   30   25   20

FIGURE

ASTEROIDS

JUPITER

AU   5   4   3

FIGURE

Figure 2.18. This drawing is to exhibit the relative sizes of the planets and the sun
to scale, as well as the relative distances—but not both.

To obtain some idea of the relative sizes and distances *together*, take the sun as a 2.2-inch diameter sphere, then if
we let the planets be drawn to scale, as in the top figure, the earth would be about 20 feet from the sun and Pluto
790 feet. Most of the space in the universe, even close to the solar system is really empty.

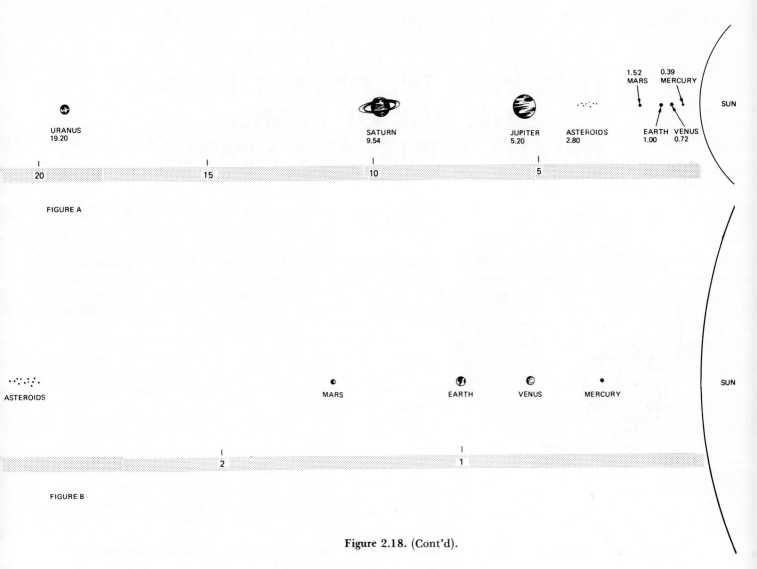

Figure 2.18. (Cont'd).

33

Chapter 3

TRIPS INTO THE DISTANT PAST— THE AGE OF BRAHE, GALILEO, KEPLER, AND NEWTON

Figure 3.1. The earth.

The purpose of this trip is to provide us with a historical perspective in time and to provide us with the proper setting for our later studies. We may be forced to reexamine our present theories many times over in different contexts. A closer study of the evolution of scientific ideas and the manner in which some wrong turns have been taken in the past teaches us to be more critical of the accepted cosmological ideas not based on experiment but rather on conjecture and plausible hypotheses. The history of science teaches us that theories have to be continually tested and reassessed, updated if necessary, sometimes completely overthrown and supplanted by newer theories. It is a never-ending evolutionary process in search of truth.

Man, who is now in apparent command of the earth's resources, after having made his appearance about three million years ago, is certainly not the earliest of the species that was aware of its environment and dependent on the "forces" of nature. One has only to examine the trees, for instance. They tell the seasons by measuring the length of periods of darkness. Birds, in travelling long distances navigate, in part, from a knowledge of the constellations in the night sky and the position of the sun in the day sky. All living systems have built-in clocks, biological clocks, the mystery of which scientists are only now beginning to probe and partially comprehend. Thus, the change in the daily **light-dark cycle, the circadian rhythm,** the monthly cycle and the yearly cycle resulting from the earth's rotation and revolution around the sun as well as the position of the moon in its orbit around the earth, have made their imprints on "living" matter on the earth.

Is astronomy relevant? Our lives are very much dependent on the motions of the so-called heavenly bodies, the radiation of the sun, and even the motion of the moon.

Biological evolution is well enough established so that it need not be argued here. Evolution is not restricted to biology but relates to all of matter in the universe. It should not be surprising that the species of man, which is very much dependent on the environment as all living things are, should have observed in detail the motions of the heavenly bodies.

One finds that virtually every major civilization in the past had developed some knowledge of astronomy. Special classes of people, priests, and scholars for example, were dedicated to a mixture of religion, mysticism, and astrology as well. The general population was likewise involved to some degree, because their lives depended on the change of the seasons and the cycles of nature. A typical example would be the flooding of the Nile, which was observed to occur yearly as soon as the star, Sirius, was visible over the horizon. If you get flooded out of your home a couple of times and have to scamper for your life, you are more likely to pay attention to the stars in the sky. That is relevant astronomy.

As early as 4000 B.C., the Chinese were known to have developed some elements of astronomy. Perhaps they were the earliest astronomers. They were known to predict solar and lunar eclipses. There are records dating from the third century B.C., where it was noted that the court astronomers Hi and Ho were put to death for neglecting to predict a solar eclipse which occurred while they were attending a garden party. (It may be presumed that subsequent court astronomers were more attentive to their work.) The Chinese also kept accurate records of comets, and included Halley's Comet of 467 B.C. in their ancient records. They also observed and recorded a so-called "guest" star, which we now know as a **supernova** (Crab Nebula).

Stonehenge

One of the surprises in this century was the interpretation of the famous **Stonehenge** structure, its significance, astro-

Figure 3.2. Stonehenge.

nomical uses, and the general knowledge of the people that constructed it. Prior to this time, the artifacts that were found at Stonehenge were typical for that period. They were pottery, stone axes, hammers and drills, antlers and shoulder bones for digging and clearing the land; indications of a people with a primitive culture. Stonehenge showed, however, that although these people were illiterate, they were sophisticated observers of the heavens. There are over 300 such structures in England, consisting of megolythic sites, as if each structure were a modern-day place of assembly or a church. These structures served purposes other than as observation sites. They were, no doubt, places of assembly and places where the lunar and solar calendar could be recorded. The earliest period of Stonehenge falls in the 2350 to 1900 B.C. era. Later periods extended to 1700 and then to 1350 B.C. The last period corresponded to the transportation of the large Sarsen stones from Marlborough Down and their erection at Stonehenge.

There are enough stones and remaining holes and features at the site to allow a fairly complete reconstruction of the ancient celestial phenomena. Since the objects under study (sun and moon) can still be seen today, it allows a fairly complete verification of the astronomical observations made at this site. They indicate that the lunar studies were fairly extensive and sophisticated. The measurements were taken mainly of lunar settings, sunrises, and sun settings.

The **Sarsen circle** represented 29.5 days of the lunar synodic month. A double circle or spiral of holes represented the 59 days of two lunar months. Also, the 19-year cycle, or the 18.61 year nodal cycle was represented by 19 blue stones inside the Trilithon "horseshoe." Such an arrangement would serve as an enduring calendar. By moving a staff or indicator one stone each day along the outer circle, the person in charge could keep tally with the lunar month. He would always know the number of days since the last full moon or the days before the next one was due. The same principle would apply to the 59 holes or stones. The 19 stone horseshoe served as a yearly device indicating the direction of the midwinter full moonrise, and the year it would appear over or near the Heel stone. There is some indication these people had even attempted to possibly define periods of eclipses.

There is no doubt that the astronomical activities at this site were interwoven with possible religious rituals; perhaps some forms of fertility cult. However, during each of the three periods of the monument, the development of lunar considerations played a very major part. Stonehenge is, indeed, a monument that has outlasted time: a monument to a civilization that was more advanced than we had given them credit for being.

The Greeks

Astronomy flourished in ancient Mesopotamian civilizations as well. The Babylonians left us a rather rich record of astronomy. They were responsible for a good calendar which utilized the lunar months. Their view of the universe is also interesting.

We shall not spend any time on the mythology of the ancient world, but refer interested readers to other sources.

The ancient Greeks left a very prominent mark in the field of astronomy. Instead of an exhaustive historical perspective, we shall merely mention some of the highlights in keeping with the theme of this book.

Among the greats of ancient Greece was Aristotle, who established the **Lyceum** about 344 B.C. One of his interesting beliefs was that all the celestial bodies were made from the fifth element, which he called **quintessence**.

Another Greek from the Alexandrian School, whose contribution was not adequately recognized, was Aristarchus (300-250 B.C.). He had already proposed the heliocentric theory: that is, the sun is central, and the earth and the planets revolve around it in circular orbits. The sphere consisting of stars was thought to be at a much larger distance from the earth; so far away that it was impossible to observe their apparent motions. It is incredible that this highly accurate analysis of the universe proposed in the third century, B.C. was essentially ignored by scholars until the fifteenth century A.D.

Eratosthenes (276-194 B.C.) was the head of the Alexandrian Museum. He was the first person to measure the circumference of the earth to a precision of better than ten percent—an amazing accomplishment at that time. He used a rather ingenious method. Eratosthenes noticed that during a certain time of the year at high noon, the Obelisk at Alexandria cast a shadow of seven and one-half degrees, while at the same time at another location, in the town of Syene, Egypt, a known distance away, no shadow at all was cast.

From the geometric construction shown in Figure 3.3, it was easy now to deduce the radius of the earth, because you have a triangle with an apex angle of seven and one-half degrees. The precision depended both on the angular measurements as well as the measurement of the distance between the two cities. That was an impressive result, especially when we consider that the earth was thought to be flat and not round by many until just a few hundred years ago.

Finally, Ptolemy, who lived in Alexandria at about 150 A.D., codified astronomy in his famous book the *Almagest,* which included ideas that came down from other Greek scholars. To account for the motions of the planets, a rather complicated scheme involving spheres moving on spheres (**epicycles**) was devised. At first it was only a device to explain the motion, but later it became accepted as the real truth. It was not until the 1500s that the erroneous concept that the earth was the center of the solar system was overthrown by Copernicus and Galileo.

Nicholaus Copernicus (1473-1543) published his famous book, *On the Revolution of the Celestial Bodies,* in the year 1543, shortly before his death. In it he described the helio-

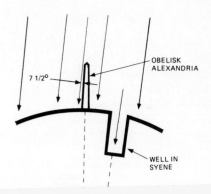

192. 27 meter
≈ 600 Olympic ft

1 meter = 3.280833 ft
630.80576 feet

$\frac{360}{50} = 7.\frac{1}{5}° = 7.2°$
vs $7.14°$

Fig...
Era...
ear...
No...
obe... corresponds to the angle subtended at the center of the earth (the obelisk cast a giant shadow or a shadow of the giant).

Nicholaus Copernicus.

centric theory. He fell into disfavor with the Church as a result of his findings. However, he was sufficiently circumspect to avoid the fate of **Giordano Bruno.**

Bruno (1548-1600), an eminent philosopher and lecturer on the Copernican theory, proclaimed that the universe is infinite and came to contain stars like the sun with orbiting planets that might possibly be inhabited. Bruno was charged with heresy by the Inquisition, and was tortured and burned at the stake in the year 1600.

Galileo Galilei (1564-1642) left an indelible imprint on the history of Physics and Astronomy. Born in Pisa in 1564, he became a teacher at the universities of Pisa and Padua. The theory of the planets according to Ptolemy and Aristotle, which he covered in his lectures, did not seem convincing to him. He began to follow the Copernican system. His star rose simultaneously with that of the sighting of the supernova in the year 1604. Public lectures by him on this event received a great deal of attention.

So did his construction of a telescope in 1609. The telescope design was an improved version of a similar one belonging to the Count Maurice in Flanders. Galileo had, no doubt, rediscovered the optical principles of the telescope and designed and built one for his own use.

The telescope was first installed in the highest belfry in Venice to spy out distant ships, to the great delight and astonishment of the distinguished senators and gentlemen of that fair city. History does not tell us what further terrestrial use this telescope was put to, for Galileo soon applied his now famous "cannon" to the study of heavenly objects.

In March of 1610, he published his first spectacular discoveries under the title *Sidereus Nuncius* or *Astronomical Announcement.* Of all of Galileo's works, this was the one which created the greatest sensation and excited the greatest curiosity in the entire scientific world at that time. In it he described observations of the moon, the stars in the Milky Way, and the four satellites of Jupiter. Galileo described his discovery of stars in the constellation Orion, which cannot be seen by the unaided eye, probably in the region of the belt and sword of Orion. Next, he described the Pleiades. The Milky Way revealed a myriad of stars which, without the telescope, merely resembled a large luminous cloud.

Galileo clearly demonstrated a principle which was to be repeated in astronomy many times subsequently: *Whenever a new scientific tool is discovered which can be successfully applied to the study of the heavens, new discoveries invariably result.* Galileo's telescope was the first of many such instruments. In the hands of a competent and imaginative scientist, such inventions invariably brought light to the dark and cloudy curtain of ignorance.

The discovery of the four innermost satellites and their motion about Jupiter convinced Galileo that the earth was not the central object in the solar system.

Next Galileo discovered the phases of Venus, as the planet revolves about the sun. This was the "clincher" for Galileo in

Figure 3.4. Galileo Galilei.

Figure 3.5. Galileo's telescope.

his quest for the proof of the heliocentric theory. He announced his discovery in the form of an anagram: *Cynthiae figures aemulatur mater amorum* (Venus imitates the aspects of the moon).

Why was it so important for Galileo to see the phases of Venus, and how did this convince him of the correctness of the heliocentric theory? (Exercise 19)

It is interesting that Galileo, in the latter part of his life, subsequent to his conviction at the hands of the Inquisition (Fig. 3.6), spent a great deal of time on physics. He also worked on practical problems related to the use of his discoveries for purposes of navigation: the determinations of longitude and latitude. His idea was to use the revolutions of the satellites of Jupiter as a means for accomplishing this. He was, however, unfamiliar with the difficulties of taking observations on a rolling ship, yet his findings showed a great deal of ingenuity.

During the last few years of his life, Galileo became blind. Nevertheless, he carried on an active life through his disciples. It is fascinating to study his projections for the future. They involved suggestions for better time-keeping devices and for better telescopes. He dictated this in a paper entitled *Astronomical Operation*, in which he revealed a great deal of vision and foresight. He suggested that the micrometer and auxiliary instruments would bring positional astronomy to great accuracy and physical astronomy to its beginning and development. He was right on all counts. He even suggested that meridian stars could be seen in daylight with more powerful telescopes.

It is sad that such a giant was treated as shabbily as he was by the power structure in Rome.

Figure 3.6. Inquisition scene by Robert-Fleury in the Louvre, Paris (Yerkes photo).

Figure 3.7. Tycho Brahe (Yerkes Observatory).

Coming out of the Dark Ages

Tycho Brahe (1546-1601) stands out as the last of the naked-eye observers. His work in tracking the planets to a high precision, particularly Mars, played a very important role, as we shall see. Tycho Brahe had built an observatory with the financial support of the King of Denmark on the small island of Hveen near Copenhagen, where he accumulated a very large amount of astronomical data.

It seemed that one of the early lucky breaks for Tycho Brahe was the fact that a supernova occured in November of 1572, in the constellation Casseopeia. It was as bright as Venus at its very brightest. Brahe studied this very carefully and noticed the changes in its luminosity.

In 1577 Brahe observed a brilliant comet and established the fact that it could not belong, as was generally believed, to our atmosphere, but that it revolved around the sun at a greater distance than Venus.

Brahe did not accept the Copernicum system, perhaps for religious reasons. He compromised somewhat by having the sun and the moon revolve around the earth while Mercury, Venus, Mars, Jupiter, and Saturn revolved around the sun. This was known as the Tychonic system.

Brahe possessed a large celestial globe on which he marked the positions of the stars according to his observations. His star catalogue included 777 stars. His precise measurements allowed him to correct Ptolemy's value for the precession of the equinoxes.

Tycho Brahe was a character of the first degree. His life style was more befitting a courtier than that of an astronomer. He drank avidly, and this proved later to be his undoing. One quarrel with another man led to a duel, the result of which was the loss of his nose. A metal substitute was fabricated for him, but it certainly must have detracted from his looks. Consequently, he married a commoner rather than someone from high station.

His observatory on the Island of Hveen was, by far, superior to any up to that era. He received ample funds from the king. The Danish aristocracy however, did not take too well to him, and upon the death of his benefactor, he was compelled to leave the island of Hveen.

His next patron was Emperor Rudolph the Second of Bohemia, a great patron of the sciences. Brahe settled in Bohemia in 1599 in the Castle of Benatek, about 20 miles from Prague, where he set up shop again.

This was a great boon to astronomy, since there he met young **Johann Kepler**, who, as it turned out, was best qualified to solve the riddle of planetary motions. However, the two men did not hit it off too well. Kepler was not able to obtain any of the precious data that Tycho Brahe had so laboriously accumulated until just prior to Brahe's death.

Brahe died as a result of overindulgence and strict court protocol. According to the custom of Emperor Rudolph's court, no one was permitted to leave the dinner table until the host himself led the way. Brahe, having drunk to excess and being unable to leave, suffered through the evening until eventually his bladder burst. He died within a few days, in November of 1601, but not before he had passed his data on to Kepler.

Planetary Orbits

Johannes Kepler (1571-1630)

Kepler's life and career are fascinating to study. It was indeed a fortunate happenstance for science that Kepler came into possession of Tycho Brahe's very precise measurements on the orbit of Mars. Through the persistent efforts of Kepler's imaginative and creative mind, this data became the foundation of his **three laws of planetary motion.** (These were published between 1609 and 1618.)

They are as follows:

Law I *Each planet moves in an elliptical orbit with the sun situated at one of the two foci.*

Law II *A line drawn from the sun to the planet sweeps out equal areas in equal times.* This very significant law is equivalent to the conservation of angular momentum. (Laboratory Exercise 6)

Law III *The square of the sidereal period (P) of orbital revolution around the sun is proportional to the cube of the mean distance (a) of the planets.* This law is equivalent to the *conservation of energy* for each of the planets.

$$\frac{P^2}{a^3} = \text{constant}$$

A few comments are in order now about the laws and their significance. Law I is a significant departure and advance from Copernicus, who had proposed that the sun is at the center and that the planets move in circular orbits about the sun. Kepler discovered that they travel in *elliptic* orbits, of which a circle is a special case (Fig. 3.9) (Tech. Note No. 5).

Figure 3.8. Johannes Kepler.

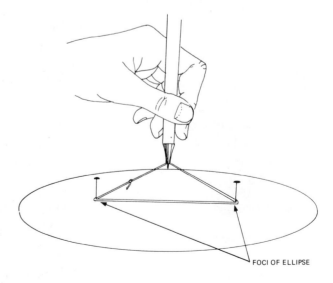

Figure 3.9. The construction of an elipse using pencil and string. The pins corresponding to the position of the foci. The sun would be at the position of only one of these foci.

FOCI OF ELLIPSE

41

To repeat, the *first* law implies that the sun is *not* at the center of the ellipse. In the case of the earth's orbit, it is closest to the sun during the winter season in the northern hemisphere. Hence, the northern hemisphere has slightly milder winters than the southern hemisphere.

An implication of the *second* law is that when a planet is closer to the sun, it moves faster. The speed of the planet changes during the course of its orbit. Most of us are ordinarily unaware of the earth's motion in its track around the sun. The effect is much more dramatic, however, for objects whose elliptic paths are far more elongated than those of the planets. Some long period comets have elliptic orbits that are indeed enormously elongated. They move extremely slowly when they are far away from the sun, but increase their speed as they are "rounding" the sun, then slow down again as they move away. Just like a pendulum, which changes its speed as it lobs back and forth, so the planets change their speed as they revolve around the sun. They continually exchange some of their potential energy for kinetic energy and vice versa. A pendulum at its furthest extreme has maximum potential energy and minimum kinetic energy. At its lowest point of the swing while moving the fastest, it has maximum kinetic energy. That midpoint of the pendulum's swing would correspond to the closest proximity (called perihelion) to the sun of a typical comet or planet. Maximum kinetic energy implies that they are moving the fastest.

Here are some comments on the *third law:* the square of the sidereal period is proportional to the cube of the mean distance. Let's take Mars for an example. If we take the proportionality constant as unity, and measure distances in astronomical units (A.U.) and sidereal periods (P) in years, then since the mean distance for Mars is 1.52 years, the period would be the square root of $(1.52)^3$ which is equal to:

$$P = \sqrt{(1.52)^3} = 1.87 \qquad \text{(exact value is 1.88089 as given in Table 2.3)}$$

See Exercise No. 7.

Sir Isaac Newton (1642-1727)

We are now ready to study the work of one of the greatest scientific minds that ever lived, Sir Isaac Newton (Fig. 3.10).

Newton was born on Christmas day in the small village of Woolsthorpe in England. He entered Trinity College of Cambridge University at the age of 18. His mathematics teacher, Professor I. Barrow, was so impressed with Newton that he later resigned his Lucasisn Professorship to give it to his superior star pupil. The university closed down because of the bubonic plague in 1665, which necessitated Newton's return home to Woolsthorpe. It was during this quiet period that Newton made his great discoveries.

Among his many other accomplishments, he invented and built the first **reflecting telescope**, whose optical design principles, with minor modifications, is used even on the largest of telescopes such as the 200″ at Mt. Palomar.

Figure 3.10. Sir Isaac Newton.

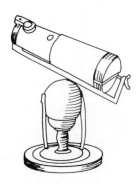

Figure 3.11. Isaac Newton's reflecting telescope.

Newton's accomplishments were recognized during his lifetime. He was knighted by Good Queen Anne in 1705; he was elected to Parliament and was appointed Warden of the Mint.

It fell upon Newton to quantify the laws of motion, the laws of gravity, and more or less tie everything together. In order to accomplish this, Newton had to invent calculus, discover the laws of gravity and the laws of motion. It is alleged that he did all of this while still in his twenties, although his celebrated book, the *Principia*, was not published until 1687.

Newton's accomplishments included the task of organizing and essentially laying the groundwork for *classical* physics. We shall restrict ourselves here to his contribution to the field of mechanics and the dynamics of motion. First, let us state his laws of motion, which were based in part on the work of Galileo.

Newton's **first law**: A body will remain at rest or will move in a straight line in uniform motion unless external forces are acting upon it.

Newton's **second law**: *If a body is acted upon by a force, it will accelerate in the direction of the applied force.* The force and the acceleration that result are related by the simple expression that the force is equal to the mass times the acceleration produced.

$$F = Ma$$

Actually, Newton phrased it a little differently: "The applied force is equal to the time rate of change of the momentum of the body."

Newton's **third law**: *If a body is subjected to a force, there is an equal and opposite force counteracting it; that is, to every action there is an equal and opposite reaction.*

Finally, the **law of gravity** is postulated as follows:

If there are two masses M_1 and M_2 separated by a distance d, then the force of attraction between them is directly proportional to the product of their masses and inversely propor-

Figure 3.12. The launching of Saturn V rocket demonstrates the principle of Newton's third law. To every action there is an equal and opposite reaction.

FIGURE A

FIGURE B

tional to the square of the distance between them. Expressed algebraically, it will look like this:

$$F = \frac{G M_1 \times M_2}{d^2}$$

where G is the gravitational constant; a constant to all matter in the universe.

The constant $G = 6.67 \times 10^{-8}$ (In c.g.s. units, mass is in grams, distances are measured in cm, and time in seconds. See Tech. Note No. 6.)

A few examples are necessary at this point to indicate how these laws apply, and how one can use these laws, for instance, to differentiate between mass and weight. Mass is an *intrinsic property of a body which does not change.* The mass of a body is the same whether it is on the earth or on the moon or on Jupiter or anywhere else in the universe. The weight of an object is defined as a force which depends on the acceleration that it received, such that on the earth the weight of an object is its mass times the acceleration of gravity. Since the acceleration of gravity on the moon is one-sixth that of the earth, the weight of the object is one-sixth on the moon of what it would be on earth. On Mars, it would be different again. Note that we could write F = mg = weight, where g is acceleration of gravity.

One of the problems Newton had in quantifying his theory was the fact that in the law of gravity, every little piece of matter is attracted by every other little piece of matter. If you have two spheres attracting each other, you have to add up the attractions from every little point from each of the spheres. That is a complicated problem. To solve it, Newton had to invent calculus. The solution that he discovered was that one can place the total mass of the sphere at its center (Fig. 3.13), which simplifies the problem enormously, because instead of now dealing with bulk masses, one has reduced the problem to point masses (provided one is dealing with spherical objects). Since solar system objects are usually spherical, it becomes rather simple now to calculate the acceleration on the earth's surface. We replace the whole mass of the earth, at the center of the earth. We can now use the radius of the earth as the distance between the attracting objects, namely mass m on the earth's surface, and the mass M, that of the earth itself, placed hypothetically at the center. If we do this, we discover a very simple relationship for the acceleration of gravity.

The acceleration of gravity g =

$$\frac{G \times \text{(the mass of the planet)}}{\text{(radius of the planet)}^2}$$

From this you can immediately see that the acceleration of gravity depends on the mass of the planet and on its radius.

Using these laws, it was now possible for Newton to calculate precisely the orbits of the planets. In particular, he was

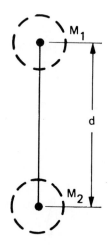

Figure 3.13.

able to derive Kepler's third law and show that Kepler was not quite correct.

Kepler's third law should precisely be:

$$\frac{P^2}{a^3} = \frac{4\pi^2}{G(M+m)}$$

where a = mean distance between M and m, M = mass of sun, m = mass of planet.

Note that the denominator now has the sum of the sun's mass (M) plus that of the planet. It is not a constant, because the mass of each planet changes as we go from one planet to the next. The constant in Kepler's third law is not truly a constant, but approximately so. Since the sun's mass is overwhelmingly larger than any of the planets masses, except for Jupiter (whose mass in one-thousandth that of the sun), the effect is no greater than one-tenth of 1%. This is so small that Kepler could not have discovered it.

Some Simple but Important Laws of Physics

These laws surprisingly apply to many situations in our daily lives and to your utter amazement, they even apply to the planets. Hence our interest. Let's discuss the simplest one first.

Conservation of Linear Momentum

Imagine experimenting on a billiard table and letting ball A hit another billiard ball B head-on. Notice that the previously stationary ball B now moves with the same speed as ball A, and that ball A came to rest where B used to be. This experiment works well if you do not put any extra "English" or spin on ball A. A simple toy shown in Figure 3.14 will perform the same demonstration. The momentum of an object is the product of its mass times its velocity (v):

$$\text{linear momentum} = m \times v$$

In any situation where no outside forces are at play other than simple, perfectly elastic impacts between interacting bodies, the linear momentum of the system has to be preserved—no matter what!

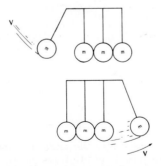

Figure 3.14. Conservation of linear momentum. A simple experimental demonstration involving the suspension of steel balls. When one such ball hits the others with a speed v, the last ball will move out with the same speed as the incoming ball.

After many exhausting and futile efforts to try to prove this law erroneous, you might be ready to see a conceptual demonstration of this law in a car pile-up situation. You may be unlucky enough to witness a real demonstration of the law on the freeway, since they occur occasionally during rush hour whenever a series of cars are stopped and when an inattentive driver plows into the back of such a car line-up. Should all the parked cars be of equal mass, all bumpers at the same height, and none having applied their brakes, then the front car will move rather suddenly with the same velocity as the car that plowed into the mass (or mess) of the rear car (Fig. 3.15).

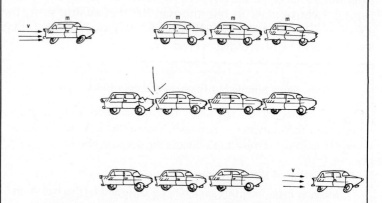

Figure 3.15. This shows another demonstration of the principle of conservation of linear momentum, using a set of cars on the freeway, each of equal mass, but no brakes set, and being hit from behind by another car. This demonstration is not recommended for beginners.

The Conservation of Angular Momentum

Angular momentum is the product of mass, velocity, and distance, as shown in Figure 3.16. For circular motion:

$$\text{Angular momentum} = m \times v \times r$$

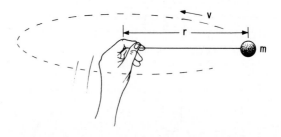

Figure 3.16. This shows the angular momentum of mass (m) revolving in an orbit, radius (r), and speed (v). Note the force that has to be applied by the hand to maintain the mass in its orbit.

Once an object is completely isolated, with no forces or outside torques acting on it, its angular momentum is preserved forever.

We can illustrate this by a simple demonstration. A person is placed on a rotating table as shown in Figure 3.17. A mass, m, is put in each outstretched hand. Then we shall set him gently spinning. He is now left all to himself on the turntable. If he decides to place the masses close to his chest, note the dramatic effect on his speed, v. This is a direct consequence of the conservation principle.

$$m \times v \times r = \text{constant}$$

i.e., it must remain unchanged. Thus, by decreasing r, the only choice the system has is to increase v in the *same* proportion. If he halved r, his speed would double. If he decreased r by a factor of 5, his speed would increase by a factor of 5.

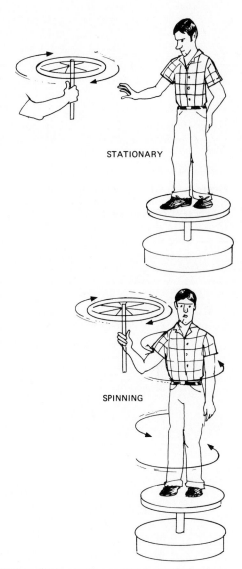

STATIONARY

SPINNING

Figure 3.18. A demonstration of the conservation of angular momentum. The experimenter has no angular momentum to begin with. When handed a spinning bicycle wheel, he has to commence spinning in order to compensate for the angular momentum that he had received, such that the total angular momentum would still remain zero as it was before. Consequently, the experimenter will move in the opposite direction to the rotation of the spinning wheel. By flipping the bicycle wheel in the opposite direction, a very effective demonstration can be achieved.

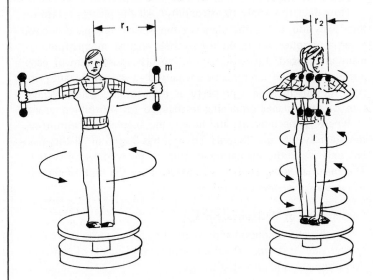

Figure 3.17. Demonstration of conservation of angular momentum.

There is another vivid demonstration of the law demonstrated in Figure 3.18. A student stands on the motionless turntable (i.e., the total angular momentum of the system is zero, absolutely zero). Now an assistant will hand him a spinning bicycle wheel which has a substantial angular momentum. Note what happens to the motion of the student as he takes hold of the spinning wheel.

Q. Why does he spin in the opposite direction to the wheel?

Q. What do you expect to happen if the spin direction of the bicycle wheel is reversed, or if it is rotated through 90°?

Hint: Angular momentum has *direction* associated with it. Such an additional property is called a **vector** quantity. Thus, to cancel out angular momentum, one has to match not only magnitude but also place the vector in opposite directions. The usual convention is to point the angular momentum vector in the same direction as the corresponding direction of penetra-

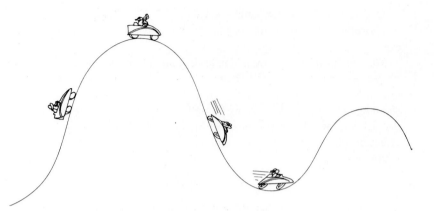

Figure 3.19. Attempted demonstration of conservation of kinetic and potential energy at Disneyland.

tion of a right- or left-handed screw. For example, two oppositely spinning wheels of equal angular momentum would cancel out exactly.

How does this apply to astronomy? All the planets rotate on their axes and, unless the planets either shrink or expand or have external torques acting on them, their angular momentums remain unchanged. Likewise, *orbital* angular momentum of each planet around the sun remains unchanged—a very important principle indeed. Imagine a property as the orbital angular momentum of each planet remaining unchanged for 4.6 billion years!

Where is the bulk of, and how is the angular momentum of, the solar system distributed? The sun has 99.9% of all the mass but only 2% of the angular momentum of the whole solar system. The major planets, Jupiter and Saturn have the bulk of the observable angular momentum.

Conservation of Mechanical Energy

Recall your childhood and the thrilling experiences on a rollercoaster ride: it demonstrated the important principle of conservation of kinetic and potential energy.

First, your car gets pulled up, increasing its potential energy, work is done against gravity. At the peak of the initial climb, the car and everybody in it has maximum potential energy and minimum kinetic energy.

$$E_k = [1/2\, mv^2] \qquad \text{(kinetic energy)}$$

Note: (Kinetic energy is equal to $1/2\, mv^2$, where m is the mass and v is the velocity.) Now comes the fun part, down it goes and everyone screams and panics, since, at the bottom of the ride all the potential energy is converted to kinetic energy (that's why the speed is so enormous). The car then climbs up to the next peak, exchanging kinetic energy for potential energy. Now, if there were no friction, the peaks could all be of equal heights and the ride, in principle, would go on forever. It would demonstrate the law of mechanical conservation of energy. Because of friction, successive peaks are constructed successively lower.

This elegant physical principle applies equally to the planets which, in their inimical way, are completely cognizant of this law, as was discovered by Newton and is implied in Kepler's third law. There is no friction, though, in space; hence, the law applies precisely and forever.

DID YOU HAVE FUN-FUN ON THE ROLLER COASTER BILLY?

I THINK THE BEST PART WAS WHEN THE POTENTIAL ENERGY WAS AT A MAXIMUM, POP!

Figure 3.20. The Calendar. A dramatic change in 1582.

The Calendar

The following subject matter is a slight digression from our main theme, which is cosmic evolution, leading to the evolution of man. This digression can be justified on the basis that our lives are very much regulated by a calendar which, although man-made, is based on the motions of the earth and recurrent cycles.

The daily motion of the sun, an obvious division for time, is recognized even by plants. As a matter of fact, all living systems, including man, contain sophisticated biological clocks which are geared to the diurnal cycle which is the earth's rotation with respect to the sun.

Some species are also aware of the moon cycle, namely the grunions who procreate on certain beaches during a new or full moon at high tide. Half of the human species presumably carries vestiges of an early entrained lunar period known as the menstrual cycle of 29±5 days. Another example of a biological clock are the trees, which can determine the yearly cycle. Everyone knows that one can tell the age of a tree by counting tree rings, since tree growth occurs during specified times in the year. Trees have the ability to measure the length of nighttime. That is how they determine the seasons. Birds migrate with the change of seasons, and so do fish. Salmon return to their points of origin after a certain number of years. Perhaps salmon are able to measure larger intervals than a year? Man's ability to measure time is not as astounding if we look at the overall system of living entities that share the planet earth with us.

The lunar cycle provides a natural division for time. It is not surprising, therefore, to find that early civilizations, such as the Babylonians and the ancient Hebrews, did use the calendar based on the lunar synodic period. Our "months" are descendants of this early division. We already pointed out that the week is based on the magic number seven. The month apparently was the next stage in the development of the calendar. The synodic period for the moon, which is 29 1/3 days from new moon to new moon, is a very natural division of time.

From a historical point of view, the calendar throws some light on how early civilizations viewed the universe. Our present calendar has some aspects which can easily be traced to ancient civilizations that existed four thousand years ago. Early civilizations (as well as modern ones) were interested in the growing seasons, since planting and harvesting are critical for survival. The lunar cycle is not quite adequate for this purpose. It does not take into account the position of the earth's orbit with respect to the sun. Hence, a combination lunisolar calendar was introduced about three thousand years ago. This calendar has survived to the present day in the form of the Hebrew calendar. The Mohammedan calendar, on the other hand, is an absolute lunar system in which every month follows the moon closely, thus preserving the more ancient custom. In the early days of the Hebrews, two witnesses or observers were necessary to provide the information of the first sighting of the new moon to the priests of the Supreme Court in Jerusalem, who would then challenge the witnesses to test their credibility. Once the priests were satisfied that these witnesses had indeed seen the new moon, announcements via night fires and later by messengers would be made throughout the land that a new month had occurred. This practice, as well as the intercalations of extra months, was in use from 516 B.C. to 70 A.D. Religious festivals were strongly correlated with certain months of the year, allowing control to be vested with the priests. Only much later (ca. fourth century A.D.) was this system codified and put down on paper, making it independent from determination by a single group of individuals. The problem that arises when a calendar is fixed by one or more individuals is the fact that one has to communicate this information to a large number of people in the country. The weak link is the reliance on messengers. It allows false signals, false information and a lot of uncertainties (to say nothing of short tempers) to be introduced. An obvious advance was the codification, simple enough to be deciphered by learned scholars and specialists in the field. A complication associated with the lunisolar calendar was the fact that the number of lunar months in a year do not come out exactly as integers in 365 1/4 days. Consequently, an additional month had to be intercalated so that, on the average, a tropical year could be approximated. Some of these complications were removed by the Julian calendar.

The Julian Calendar

In 45 B.C., Julius Caesar introduced a calendar which is essentially the calendar we are using today. Twelve months were introduced. The days associated with each month were fixed so as to be independent of the lunar cycle. The month of July was named after Julius Caesar. He assigned it an extra day, and this day was taken away from February. That is why February, which originally had 30 days, was diminished to 29. The Roman emperor, Augustus, not to be outdone by Caesar, subsequently renamed another month August, and also gave it an extra day. Thus, another day was robbed from February, which was then left with 28 days. The **leap year** was introduced by Julius Caesar, which added an extra day to the month of February every four years, provided that the year is divisible by four. This extra day was introduced by Julius Caesar to account for the extra 1/4 day beyond 365.

The Gregorian Calendar

The Julian Calendar year is 11 minutes and 14 seconds too long with respect to the seasonal year, the tropical year. Consequently, it falls out of phase by approximately one day every 128 years. The reason being is that the tropical year is not 365 days and 6 hours but 365 days, 5 hours, 48 minutes, and 46 seconds. What effect does 11 minutes error per year have among friends? Not very much. But if you wait fifteen centuries, it adds up to about ten days. If you wait long enough then, the Easter season would eventually occur in the wintertime.

By the year 1582, Pope Gregory XIII noticed the seriousness of the situation and revised the calendar, which now bears his name, the **Gregorian Calendar.** October 5 of the year 1582 was changed to October 15 by an edict of the Pope. The calendar was accepted by Catholic countries and later on by Protestant countries as well. However, there was a considerable time lag between 1582 and the time this calendar was introduced in some countries. Russia adopted this calendar only in the twentieth century! Consequently, Christmas, as celebrated by the Eastern Orthodox Church, falls on a different day than Christmas as celebrated by the Roman Catholics in the western countries.

The main difference between the Julian and the Gregorian Calendar is the assignment of leap years. To account for the 11 minutes and 14 seconds by which the Julian Calendar is too long, Pope Gregory decided to omit three leap years in 400 years. Consequently, century years are only leap years if they are divisible by 400. The year 1600 was a leap year but not the years 1700, 1800, nor 1900. The year 2000 will be a leap year again. Other than the century years, the assignment of leap years is identical in the Julian and Gregorian Calendars.

Other Calendars

A: **The Chinese Calendar.** The ancient Chinese used three different calendars. The first one was a lunar calendar made up of 12 lunar months of 29 or 30 days each. Their solar calendar consisted of 24 sections of 15 days each. They had a third type of calendar which was used mainly for dating historical events. The Chinese started computing time from the reign of the Yellow Emperor, Huang Ti (1627 B.C.). The first calendar, according to Chinese legend, was commissioned by an emperor named Yao.

The problem with the lunar calendar lies in the fact that even by alternating successive months of 29 or 30 days each, at the end of the year one has only used up 354 instead of 365 1/4 days. Over a period of 19 years, this discrepancy adds up to 209 days altogether, which can be divided into six months of 30 days and one of 29 days. Using this device, it is possible to equalize the lunar-solar year by inserting additional months during the course of the year. (A similar calendar is still in use today, as the Hebrew calendar.)

Attempts were made by Jesuit missionaries, in 1582, to introduce the Gregorian calendar into China, without much success. It was not until 1912, when China became a republic, that the Gregorian calendar was officially adopted.

Aztec Calendar

The Aztec Calendar in the Western Hemisphere is also worthy of note. It has 360 days in the year. The extra five days were taken care of in characteristic style by designating them as holidays. There is ample evidence that ancient civilizations in the middle Americas had an advanced state of knowledge in the field of astronomy. They left us observatories but few written records. (They presumably used the proverb: "Do right and fear no man, don't write and fear no astronomical controversy.")

The Julian Day

It should not be surprising to find that astronomers, having struggled with the various calendars for so long, decided to establish one of their own, the Julian Calendar. It is completely independent of months and years. It considers days only by establishing a running number, the Julian Day. This seems to be necessary if one wants to compare events that are periodic in nature. It is a more scientific method of keeping track of time. The only problem astronomers had was similar to the dilemma of other civilizations; namely, they had to start some time for the day zero.

Astronomers decided to pick January 1, 4713 B.C. as the Julian Day zero. Presumably, no written records prior to that date are in existence. These early Julian days were of interest for checking on eclipses, which, in turn, were used to check on present gravitational theories. Why 4713 B.C.? I do not know. It is remarkably close, however, to the year zero in the Hebrew calendar, which uses 3760 B.C. as a starting date.

TABLE 3.1
Julian Dates

Date (noon)	Year	Julian Day
January 1	4713 B.C.	0
January 1	1 B.C. = 0 A.D.	1,721,058
January 1	1 A.D.	1,721,424
January 1	1770 A.D.	2,367,551
January 1 (Gregorian)	1770 A.D.	2,367,540
March 1 (Gregorian)	1770 A.D.	2,367,599
March 1	1970 A.D.	2,440,647
March 1	1980 A.D.	2,444,300
March 1	1990 A.D.	2,444,952
March 1	2000 A.D.	2,451,605

Chapter 4

LUNATIC EFFECTS—
PRECESSION, TIDES, BIOCLOCKS

Precession of the Equinoxes

In our earlier discussions concerning the earth's revolution about the sun, we had assumed that the earth's spin axis always points in the same direction in space. Actually, this is not quite accurate. The axis precesses slowly as shown in Figure 4.1.

If one draws a line perpendicular to the plane of the ecliptic, then the spin axis describes a cone in the heaven as it slowly precesses in the clockwise direction. Note that the angle of 23 1/2° does not change in the course of time—only the direction of the earth's spin axis with respect to the background stars. It takes 26,000 years for the spin axis to complete one **precessional rotation**. Hence, the shift per year is only fifty seconds (50″) of an arc. Whereas the general public is even today oblivious of this *happening*, the Greek astronomer, Hipparchus, about 150 B.C. had discovered this precession by comparing specific stars along the Zodiac with sketches made 150 years before his time. The effect of the precession is to shift westward the intersection of the ecliptic with the celestial equator which is the vernal equinox (♈) (Fig. 4.2). Hipparchus noted a two-degree shift—a most remarkable observation.

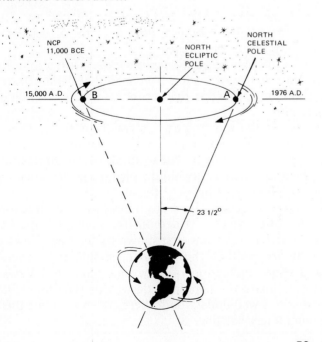

Figure 4.1. The precession of the earth's axis resulting in the precession of the equinoxes. Note that the earth's axis describes a cone in the heaven. The center point of the cone being the north ecliptic pole. It takes 26,000 years for this motion of the earth's axis to complete one circle in the sky, whose semiangle is 23 1/2 degrees.

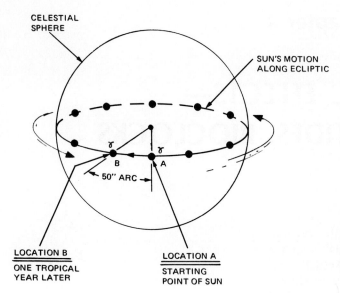

CELESTIAL
SPHERE

SUN'S MOTION
ALONG ECLIPTIC

50" ARC

LOCATION B
ONE TROPICAL
YEAR LATER

LOCATION A
STARTING
POINT OF SUN

Figure 4.2. From the point of view of an observer on earth. The sun moves on the ecliptic as shown. A tropical year is the interval of time between successive transits of the vernal equinox. Starting at location A, the sun moves along the ecliptic, but because of the precession of the equinoxes, the vernal equinox during the course of a year would have moved from A to B. When the sun returns to the vernal equinox at position B, the vernal equinox has moved to meet it. Therefore, the tropical year will be shorter by 20 minutes or (50 seconds of arc) than the sidereal year.

Shown in Figure 4.1 is the present location of the spin axis, pointing close to the so-called North Star Polaris. In 13,000 years, the spin axis will not point to A but to B, so that Polaris will no longer have the dubious honor of being misnamed the North Star. 13,000 years in the future, it will be close to the star **Vega**; if you look back in time, 13,000 years ago Vega was probably revered as the North Star.

Superimposed on the precession is a ripple called **nutation** which makes the spin axis wiggle a little in an 18.6 year cycle. The many successively smaller motions of the earth's axis, all superimposed on each other, remind one of flies having smaller flies having smaller flies ad infinitum. Today's accurate astronomical detection equipment is able to keep track of these many varied earth motions.

What causes the precession? It is the torque exerted by the sun and the moon on the earth's bulge trying to straighten up the earth's axis. Neither the sun nor the moon succeed in straightening up the axis, i.e., changing the 23 1/2° to zero. The torque, or turning moment, does have the effect, however, of causing the axis to precess.

The precession can be easily demonstrated with a spinning top. I am sure that most readers have seen that demonstrated in early childhood, without the awareness of the cosmological implications.

In the case of the top, the earth's gravity is trying to pull the top down, as shown in Figure 4.4, so that the torque will cause it to precess as shown. The example demonstrates that celestial phenomena are really child's play once they are comprehended by the practitioners of the art.

Finally, does precession have any relevance to cosmic evolution or evolution of life? It demonstrates an application of the laws of mechanics as was first shown by Sir Isaac Newton and thereby exemplifies the elegance, simplicity, universitality, and wide application of Newton's (Nature's) Laws—never underestimate the happiness derived by scientists when a phenomenon is well-understood, there are enough out there that are completely baffling.

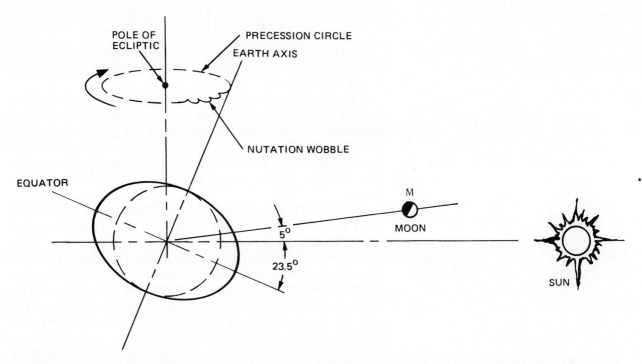

Figure 4.3. The sun and the moon pull on the bulge of earth's equator in an attempt to straighten up the earth's crooked (23 1/2°) inclination. This results in the precession of the earth's axis as shown around the pole of the ecliptic. The additional smaller nutations are caused by the moon's motion around the earth.

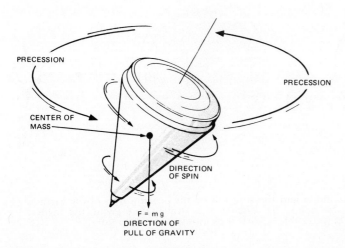

Figure 4.4. The precession of a spinning top (gyro). Note the earth's gravitational pull at the center of mass, exerting a torque, in an attempt to tip the gyro downwards. This torque results in a precession in the direction shown.

Tides
The Rise and Fall of the Oceans

If ever a subject is relevant to life on earth, it is the tides. How do they come about? Tides are caused by both the moon and the sun.

Isaac Newton was the first to provide an explanation for the periodic ocean tides. They are caused by the differential gravitational effects of the moon and the sun (Exercise No. 14). Specifically, tides arise because of the *difference* in the gravitational force between points at various distances across the diameter of the earth facing the attracting object: the moon.

Let us start with fundamentals. Consider, for simplicity, three points along the earth's diameter: one at the center of the earth; one facing the moon, and one furthest away from the moon on the other side of the earth. The point closest to the moon experiences the greatest gravitational attraction, the point furthest removed, on the other side of the earth, the least. We now consider the *relative* attractive forces at the extreme points compared to the center point. This is done by subtracting the attraction to the center of the earth from each of the extreme positions. The point away has a *net force away* from the center, and the point closest to the moon has a *net force towards* the moon, when measured relative to the mass at the center.

The ocean waters of the earth are acted upon in this manner and cause the observed tides as shown in Figure 4.5.

As a result of the earth's rotation, the earth spins beneath the tides, thus causing an observer on the earth to see two high tides and two low tides each day. (Actually every 24 hours and 50 minutes due to the moon moving around the earth.)

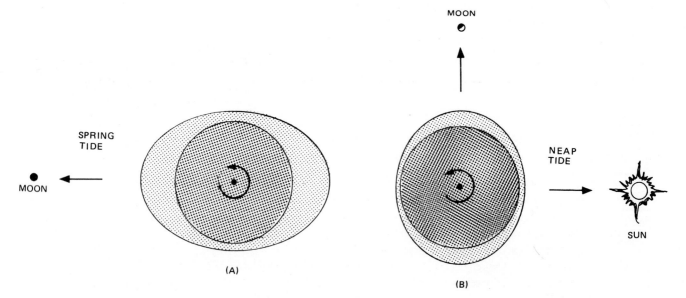

Figure 4.5. A schematic diagram illustrating how the moon and the sun pull on the ocean waters of the earth as the earth rotates. *Position A:* Both the sun and the moon are aligned in a straight line giving the highest tides-**spring tides.** *Position B:* the moon in first quarter (or in third quarter) resulting in the **neap tides.**

The time between two high tides is 24 hours and 50 minutes, not 24 hours. The reason for the extra 50 minutes is a direct verification that the moon is the principle object which causes the waters of the ocean to be pulled out. (Laboratory Exercise No. 3 provides discussion of the 24 hour, 50 minute lunar tidal cycle.)

Experimental verification of the time differences between tides is readily available. Examples are shown in Figures 4.6 and 4.7. A close examination of these figures does indeed verify that the time between any two high tides is 24 hours and 50 minutes. (Or, the interval between any two successive peaks is 12 hours and 25 minutes.) A closer look also shows that the heights of the tide differ quite dramatically during the course of a month. This is related to the fact that both the sun *and* the moon cause the tides of the ocean waters. The moon's effect, however, is twice as great as that of the sun. Consequently, as the moon traverses its monthly cycle around the earth, the position of the moon and the sun changes relative to the earth. The strongest gravitational effect occurs at new moon or at full moon when both the sun and the moon act together in a straight line to cause the maximum differential tidal pulling effect on the ocean waters. The resulting high tides are known as **spring tides**. During first-quarter or third-quarter moon, the sun and moon work slightly against each other, causing the smallest difference between high and low tide. These are called **neap tides** (Fig. 4.5).

The earth's rotation is slowing down, *partly* due to friction resulting from lunar tidal action. Because of conservation of angular momentum, the moon must therefore take up some of the angular momentum, since the *total angular momentum* of the earth-moon system must remain unchanged. The moon's period of revolution about the earth is postulated by some astronomers to have been shorter in earlier epochs.

(If this discussion is not too clear, start rereading it from the beginning of the chapter.)

Summary of Tides

1. The interval between any two high tides (or two low tides) is clearly 24 hours and 50 minutes, strongly implicating the moon as the main influence.
2. The heights of the tides vary, being greatest near new or full moon, thus confirming the sun's secondary influence.
3. The actual difference between high and low tide varies with geographical location, shape of coastline and inlet bay geometry. Note the significant difference in the tide height between Seattle (12 feet at full moon) and Anchorage (34 feet) (Figs. 4.7 and 4.8).

   For the Los Angeles data shown in Figure 4.6, the time when the moon crosses the observer's meridian is indicated by a solid circle.

START REREADING AGAIN! THIS IS THE FIFTH TIME NOW.

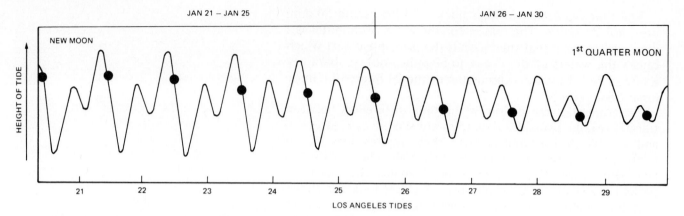

Figure 4.6. This is the tidal amplitude curve at Los Angeles. The position when the moon was on the meridian is indicated on the diagram. Note the change in position of maximum tide with respect to the phase of the moon during the course of a few days.

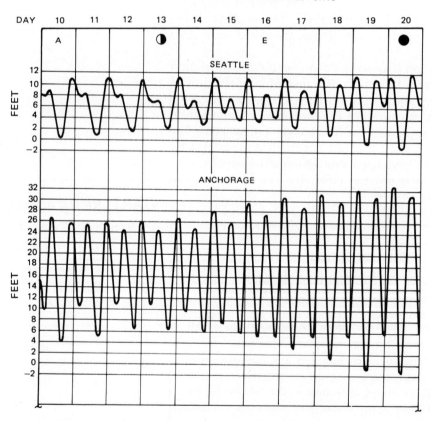

Figure 4.7. Tidal tide curves for two United States ports. Notice the variation in amplitude during the course of ten days, resulting from different phases of the moon. Also note that the amplitude of the tides is far greater at Anchorage than they are at Seattle.

4. The time of maximum tide does not occur when the moon is directly overhead. Since the earth rotates too rapidly for the ocean waters to adjust themselves completely, a type of forced oscillation (**resonance effects**) is set up in the ocean, forcing large areas of the ocean to move in unison. This, theoretically at least, accounts for part of the time lag. If you study the actual observations in Figure 4.6 carefully, you will note that the time lag between high tide and the time the moon is on the meridian varies during the course of the month.

Let us not forget the relevance of life. There are quite a number of species of fish and other ocean-living organisms that perform their breeding function during periods of high tide, e.g., the grunions, which effectively make use of the ability to be washed up high on the beach to give them some advantage in their biological activities. This certainly is relevant to life.

Since the moon exerts a tidal force on the earth, does the earth allow this to happen to it without retaliation? Remember Newton's third law? In fact, the earth exerts an appreciable tidal force on the moon. By virtue of the earth's tidal effect, the moon is completely *locked in,* so that it always faces in the same direction toward the earth. The period of rotation of the moon on its axis is equal to its period of revolution around the earth. The same differential tidal effect that is exerted on the ocean waters is also exerted on rocks.

See Exercise No. 20.

Figure 4.8. High and low tide at Anchorage, Alaska (a difference of 34 feet). (Dept. of Commerce.)

Biological Clocks and the Moon

There is a great fascination in studying living systems and relating their activities with the movement of the moon and sun with respect to the earth. For example, fiddler crabs live their lives in close harmony with the tides. Experiments performed on these crabs by removing them from their native habitat proved that in addition to the circadian (24 hour) cycle, the crabs also maintained a **tidal clock** of 12 hours, 25 minutes.

The possession of these internal clocks may give some advantage in the competitive world of survival. There are cases where the advantage of the internal clock is not so obvious. These include lunar cycles of fresh water and terrestrial organisms which have physiological relics of no adaptive value to their present-day practitioners'. Half the human species during its active reproductive life span possesses an ancient relic close to either the lunar synodic period of 29 1/2 days or the sidereal period of 27 1/3 days. This intrinsic period in humans, if left untampered, shows a host of variations from one individual to another and even during the year for the same individual.

Homo sapiens, however, have only been around for less than 2-3 million years. It might perhaps be more fruitful for biological sleuths to seek evidence of tidal clocks in some of the lower species and even in some plants.

Giovanni Abrami, while at the University of Padua, Italy in December of 1971, wrote a paper on lunar phases and plant growth. In his findings, he presents seven herbaceous species and correlates how each, and the group as a whole, follow certain lunar rhythms. "The stem growth of the seven species has revealed rhythmic components of 29.5-, 14.7-, 7.3-day periods. The first two components of 29.5, and 14.7 days, which are the most evident, appear to be best correlated with the phases of the new and full moon. This fact suggests that some unknown periodic environmental change is directly or indirectly connected with the position of the moon. The other two shorter components in growth, 9.7 and 7.5 days, may be endogenous rhythms that are expressive of the overall physiology of stem development of each species."

Frank Brown and Carol Chow chose the water uptake in pinto beans as a simple process to ascertain responses to natural atmospheric and laboratory related variations. Their research on lunar-correlated variations in water uptake by bean seeds showed a similarity to Abrami's finding in that they also show a quarterly lunar rhythm. In their summary, they stated that the "rate of water uptake by bean seeds during the initial four hours displays a significant quarterly lunar variation. Under what appears to be minimally disturbed environmental conditions relative to environmental electromagnetic fields, maximum rates tend to occur close to new and full moons and the moon's quarters."

One phenomenon that may affect biological systems in

rhythms associated with the moon is cycles of precipitation. Data received on precipitation activity over the United States from 1900-1949 was correlated with the moon. According to some scientists, precipitation activity over broad areas appears to be closely associated with the monthly lunar/solar cycle. "There is a marked tendency for extreme precipitation in North America to be recorded near the middle of the first and third weeks of the synodical month, especially on the third and fifth days after the configurations of both new and full moon. The second and fourth quarters of the lunation cycle are correspondingly deficient in heavy precipitation, the low point falling about three days previous to the date of an alignment of the earth-moon-sun system. There is a demonstrable persistence of this lunar/solar effect in United States weather records throughout the history of official meteorological observation." This is matched by similar effects in the southern hemisphere as suggested by Adderly and Bowen in New Zealand. At a time and place where droughts are occurring, however, such alleged correlations seem somewhat unimpressive.

A study of 501,000 live births was compiled for New York City for the period 1961-1963. The period constituted thirty-seven synodic lunar months. "When these births were plotted on the synodic lunar cycle, it was found that the half cycle with the highest birth rate (number of births per day) began the day after the one on which the first quarter occurred; thus the half of the lunar month with the lowest birth rate began the day after last quarter day." Walter Menaker, M.D. suggests a future report on a period of at least a decade should be done. He feels that the thirty-seven months should be considered as a preliminary report.

An interesting phenomenon under contention is the theory of lunar influence on human emotional disturbance. The people proposing such an occurrence are Arnold L. Lieber, M.D. and Carolyn R. Sherin, Ph.D. The opposing side, Alex D. Pokorny, M.D. and Joseph Jachimczyk, M.D., found no significant relationship. The subject may be described as the **lunatic phenomenon.**

Lieber and Sherin acquired homicide data for Dade County, Florida, for a fifteen-year period. "Homicides in Dade County, plotted for lunar intervals, showed an apparent lunar periodicity. The homicides peaked at full moon and showed a trough leading up to new moon, followed by a secondary peak just after new moon. These homicides showed statistically significant groupings around full moon and new moon. The number of cases occurring within the 24 hours before and after a full moon over the 15-year period was significantly greater than the expected values." Their report also found a similar periodicity for homicides occurring over a 13-year period in Cuyahoga, Ohio.

In contrast, Pokorny and Jachimczyk studied 2,494 homicides in Harris County, Texas over a 14-year period. They were "unable to confirm, with an independent sample, the findings of Lieber and Sherin that homicides peak at full moon and that they are related to the lunar cycle when it is divided in 30 equal intervals."

Obviously there is need of more studies to be performed before either side can be considered conclusive.

In any event, this subject of lunar, solar interactions, and internal clocks needs a great deal more study. It is certainly relevant for life—particularly if it is safer to stay indoors during full moon.

Chapter 5

THE GREAT ESCAPE: ATMOSPHERES. MISSIONS POSSIBLE: MARS, VENUS, AND MERCURY

Escape Velocities

In order to make a clean getaway for the many trips that we are embarking on in this book, we have to be familiar with the laws that govern such activities. These laws of nature cannot be ignored, circumvented or repealed—we have to study them seriously.

Who was the first scientist to analyze space flight? None other than Sir Isaac Newton. Using the laws of physics which he discovered, he deduced that the **escape velocity** (V) is related to the **mass** (M) of a planet and its **radius** (R) by the following equation:

$$V = \sqrt{\frac{2G \cdot M}{R}}$$

The equation that gives the condition for a satellite (of mass m) to remain in orbit can also be derived, it is $V = \sqrt{\frac{G \cdot M}{R}}$. To derive this equation, the equality between the **centriputal force** and the **gravitational attraction** was used. The centriputal force is given by $m \frac{V^2}{R}$. If we equate this to the gravitation attraction $\frac{GM \cdot m}{R^2}$, we obtain the necessary condition for mass m to remain moving with velocity (v) in circular orbit of radius R. This "poor man's derivation" is quite adequate as long as the satellite mass is small compared to the object around which it travels. This holds true for anything that we are capable of launching around the earth. In the event we have competing objects of comparable masses (M ≈ m), the equation has to be modified. In a case where the two cannot decide who goes around whom, they do, in fact, move around their common center of mass (Barycenter).

$$V_{orbital} = \sqrt{\frac{G(M + m)}{R}}$$

$$V_{escape} = \sqrt{\frac{2G(M + m)}{R}}$$

With these two equations, we can perform some analysis. Notice that the difference between the escape velocity and that of the velocity necessary to remain in the circular orbit

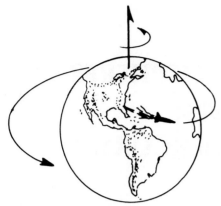

Figure 5.1. The launching and achievement of orbital velocity from Cape Kennedy.

in only $\sqrt{2}$. To remind those of you who were watching the spectacular Apollo missions, it required a velocity of roughly 17,500 mph for the rocket moving parallel to the earth's surface to remain in orbit.

Another interesting point is that satellites are launched in the direction of the earth's rotation, because the earth's surface has an orbital velocity of about a thousand miles an hour. We get a free ride of roughly $\frac{1}{17.5}$ or six percent of the velocity that ordinarily would be necessary to achieve injection velocity. If you recall the Apollo flights, you will also remember that the astronauts orbited the earth a few times before they launched themselves towards the moon by firing their retrorocket. By increasing their speed greater than $\sqrt{2}$, they escaped the earth. By using the equations for the escape velocities and substituting values of mass and radius for the moon and the earth, we calculate that the escape velocity from the earth is seven miles per second. It takes only one and one-half miles per second to escape from the moon. Consequently, a much smaller engine sufficed to launch the spacecraft from the moon.

Does the escape velocity depend on the mass (m) of the object? Is it seven miles per second for a million pound

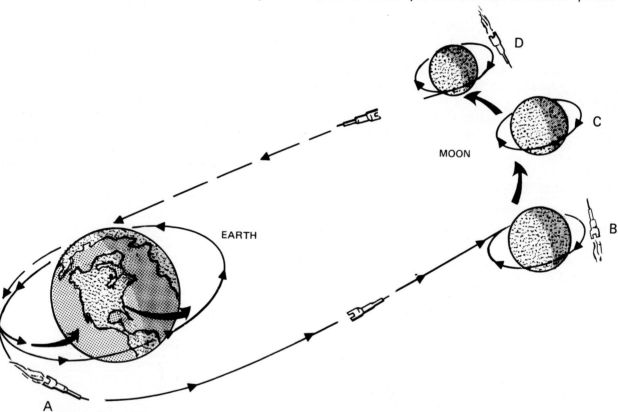

Figure 5.2. This is a schematic diagram indicating the different steps involved in the lunar landing of the Apollo program. Launch from Cape Kennedy; staging events and the achievement of orbit upon reaching orbital velocity of about 17,500 miles per hour. Then, at position A, the firing of the third stage rocket in order to achieve escape velocity-speed at $\sqrt{2}$ times greater. Orbital insertion is achieved around the moon at position B when the rocket is fired so as to slow down its speed in order to achieve orbital velocity around the moon. Meantime, the moon revolves around the earth and the astronauts proceed in their landing on the moon from orbit using the LEM. Upon redocking, precious lunar cargo plus men are transferred back to the main spacecraft. LEM is jettisoned. The rocket is fired for the last time at position D, to break out of the moon's gravitational field and return back to earth.

rocket, a one pound rocket, or for a one ounce bullet? Actually, the escape velocity is the same for all of these objects, since V_{escape} does not involve the mass of the object (provided $[m < M]$ the object mass m is small compared to the mass of the earth). If the escape velocity is the same for all of these objects, how about for an extremely light object like an atom or a molecule? Here, too, the escape velocity is seven miles per second. This is one of the crucial problems regarding conditions necessary for life. The retention of an atmosphere by a planet is critically dependent on the mass of the planet and its radius. It also depends on the atmospheric temperature and *types* of gases it contains.

Gases

By studying gases in an enclosed room and observing individual atoms as they bounce around inside the room, one discovers that they have a range of velocities until they bounce into each other and go randomly in other directions. The study of the motions of gases is an old one, dating well into the nineteenth century. It was discovered that the average velocity of atoms or molecules in a gas is given by $v = \sqrt{\dfrac{3kT}{m}}$, where T is the temperature in degrees Kelvin and k is a constant (**Boltzmann's constant**). Molecules have a whole range of velocities, as shown in Figure 5.3. Such a distribution curve is very similar to the distribution of, say, speeds of cars on highways or the distributions for the ages of people. All these distribution curves would have somewhat different shapes, but that is not really our main concern. We are interested in the average and in the high velocity tail end. If there are enough gas molecules whose velocities exceed the average by a very large multiplication factor, these molecules will have a far better chance to escape. To insure that the planet retains an atmosphere, one would have to put on some safety factors. The safety factor has to be great enough so

Figure 5.3. The speed distribution of hydrogen and of oxygen molecules. Note the following important points for each gas: Their mean speed and (6x mean speed). Next, note the velocity of escape from the earth and from the moon. Hence, hydrogen can escape the earth, but not oxygen. Both can escape the moon.

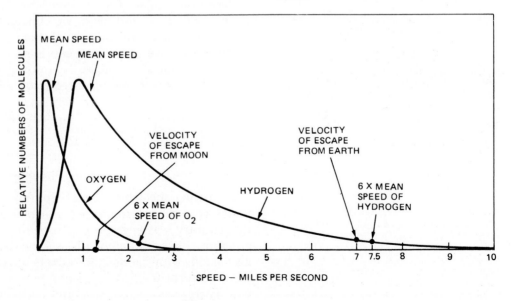

that the atmosphere is retained for at least four and one-half billion years; sufficient time for the development of life. Scientists have put on a safety factor of six. The condition for an atmosphere to be retained is such that the velocity of escape has to be greater than six times the average speeds of gases. More explicitly, six times $\sqrt{\frac{3kT}{m}}$ has to be less than $\sqrt{\frac{2G \cdot M}{R}}$. The mass of the molecule (m) now comes into account as well as the temperature (T) at the surface of the planet. The hotter the temperature of the surface of the planet and the lighter the mass of the molecule, the greater the chance for molecules to escape. Consequently, the velocity of escape for hydrogen and helium from the earth is very favorable; there is very little of these two gases remaining in the earth's atmosphere. However, oxygen, nitrogen, water vapour, and carbon dioxide can readily be retained because six times their average speeds is less than seven miles per second (escape velocity from the earth).

If we now go to the moon and compare the same quantities, we notice that the moon should not be able to retain for any length of time gases such as hydrogen and helium, oxygen and nitrogen. Those who watched the astronauts walking around on the moon noticed that they wore space suits to provide them with a breathing atmosphere, since there was obviously none that had been retained on the moon.

A quick comparison of escape velocities for other objects in the solar system shows that the superior planets all have escape velocities large enough to retain all gases, including hydrogen and helium. The escape velocity of Mars is less than half that of the earth, thus, there is a more critical problem for retention of atmospheres on Mars. Venus, on the other hand, has an escape velocity almost comparable to that of the earth, so Venus had an excellent opportunity to retain an atmosphere. There is a very thick carbon dioxide atmosphere on Venus, the origin of which is still a mystery.

Based on studies of the cosmic abundances of the elements oxygen, nitrogen, and neon, we conclude that there initially should have been roughly equal quantities of all three gases on the earth. We note that neon is no longer as abundant as nitrogen in our atmosphere. It is now generally believed that the earth's present atmosphere is of secondary origin. The earth's primary atmosphere was dissipated, presumably because the earth was originally much hotter, allowing outgassing to occur quite effectively.

Missions Possible

Following the launching of Sputnik in 1958, the United States government supported a strong effort to insure that this country was engaged in a broad-front space exploration program. First, the emphasis was on the technological feat associated with launching rockets successfully and having them perform their assigned functions once they were in orbit. There were successive improvements in the rocketry, leading up to progressively larger, multistaged rockets and more sophisticated payloads that were sent up into space. These culminated in the Apollo manned orbital missions which landed six times on the moon, beginning with Apollo 11 on July 20, 1969, and concluding with Apollo 17. Although these manned missions received the greatest attention in view of the human drama involved, it should not be overlooked that a great deal of technical knowledge was gained on the moon (and in fact, the last mission included a geologist as part of the two-manned team to study, first-hand, the geology and rocks in the vicinity of the landing site of the spacecraft). We plan to review briefly some of the highlights of the United States Space Program. It is not intended as a complete survey of all the space missions.

Apollo

Basically, the lunar program attempted to achieve the following:

The moon, or perhaps we should call it our step-sister planet (only 240,000 miles distant), has been an impressive sight throughout the ages. It has occupied man's mind for many thousands of years. Man's eternal dream to visit the moon seemed remote and virtually impossible until President Kennedy announced its exploration as one of the national goals. It is to our credit that this momentus achievement, perhaps one of the greatest of the century, was carried out on schedule.

One of the main results of the lunar missions was the mapping of its surface features in great detail, particularly the far side of the moon, which had been completely inaccessable to us (except for Soviet photographs). Some of the pictures of the far side of the moon show surface features which are different from the near side that eternally faces the earth (Fig. 5.4). The far side seems to be far more cratered. An

Figure 5.4. Lunar far side showing cratered surface with absence of Maria (NASA) photo).

extremely impressive feature is Mare Orientale, consisting of a 900-kilometer circular basin with at least three separate mountain ranges surrounding the center.

The astronomers in charge of deciding where to land finally had their wishes fulfilled by being able to have samples returned from various locations on the moon. All together, about a thousand pounds of rocks are now in the hands of the NASA Houston Rock Depository for such materials. The small but carefully documented chips of various rocks were distributed to a large number of investigators. The results of these findings now comprise a large volume of material: the geology, the morphology of the rocks, the chemical constituants, the nature of the crystalline formations, and the damage that has resulted to these crystals due to the long exposure of these rocks on the moon's surface (particularly from cosmic and other rays). All proved extremely interesting.

Lunar Rock Analysis*

The rocks brought back from the Apollo missions were stored at the Lunar Receiving Laboratory in Houston, Texas. Preliminary analyses were made, and then selected samples were distributed to a large group of specialists in the physical and chemical sciences. For the analysis, a broad gamut of instrumentation was available. Since the various Apollo missions landed at different sites, a large variety of lunar sample material was obtained. The listing of the returned rocks is shown in Table 5.2. The rocks brought back from the moon included fine crystalline vesicular volcanics, breccias, and loose soil. The breccias are rock and mineral fragments, glassy spatter held in a matrix of fine material and glass. Microbreccias seem to be scarce at the Apollo 12 site, but predominated at the Apollo 14 site. At Apollo 15 site, breccias are prevalent rocks, whereas crystalline rocks are characteristic of the mare plains around the lunar module. Around Apollo 16 and 17 sites, brecciated rocks are the most common types found. At a first glance, the lunar crystalline rocks can be described as basaltic in appearance and in composition. Sub-

HOLY COW!
384,000 KILOMETERS
I CAN'T GET OVER THAT!

TABLE 5.1
Facts About the Moon

Average distance from earth to moon	384,400 km
Diameter of moon	3,476 km
Mass of moon	7.35×10^{25} gm
Mean density of moon	3.34 g/cm³
Escape velocity	2.38 km/sec.
Orbital eccentricity	0.055
Inclination of orbital plane to ecliptic	5°9′
Inclination of lunar equator to ecliptic	1°32′
Temperature range	−190°C to +117°C

*Nicholas M. Short. *Planetary Geology*, Prentice-Hall, 1975.

TABLE 5.2

Rock Names	Grouping
Ferrobasalt (iron-rich)	
Titaniferous basalt (titanium-rich)	Chemical
Feldspathic basalt (plagioclase-rich)	variants
Olivine basalt (ilmenite)	Characteristic
Cristobalite basalt	mineral variants
Quartz basalt	
Gabbro and microgabbro (coarse-medium) crystalline rocks of basaltic composition	
Norite (hypersthene-plagioclase gabbro)	Petrologic and
Troctolite (olivine-plagioclase)	textural variants
Peridotite (coarser-crystalline, olivine-rich, pyroxene-bearing, and feldspar-free)	
Dunite (mostly olivine)	

sequent study showed that there were several varieties of these basic igneous rocks which could be more closely defined by their mineral content and textures. Table 5.2 shows some of the terms that are used, associated with the lunar rocks.

Another type of plagioclase rich igneous rock called Anorthosite is an important type of fragment found mainly in the breccias and soils at each site. These rocks contain various amounts of pyroxenes, olivine, and other minerals. The unfamiliar names given these rocks are not completely new, but are names that are associated with similar or related rocks found on the earth. There are identifiable differences between earth rocks and moon rocks, mainly in some of the metallic constituents.

Nearly all of the major rock types have been identified at each Apollo site. Over thirty minerals have been reported found in lunar rocks. Table 5.3 shows a listing of them. Most of these minerals are rare. However, six in this group of minerals make up the bulk and these are found on the following page.

1. Feldspars: calcic plagioclases. Most lunar plagioclases are strongly zoned, that is, they are rich in potassium and sodium in the outer regions. These rocks are not extensively twinned.
2. Pyroxenes: Calcium-magnesium-iron silicates are abundant mineral constituents.
3. Olivine: Magnesium-iron silicate. It is a minor constituent.
4. Silica phases these include cristobalite and tridymite.

Quartz is a very rare constituent in lunar rocks.

The Apollo 11 rocks showed an unusually high abundance of titanium, especially in some of the basaltic lava rocks. It is interesting that none of the above minerals contain any water, nor do they contain hydrogen as an essential element, except for some of the hydrogen which is introduced from

TABLE 5.3
Lunar Mineralogy

Abundant

Pyroxenes	$(Mg, Fe, Ca)_2 (Si_2O_6)$
Plagioclase	$(Ca, Na) (Al, Si)_4 O_8$
Olivines	$(Mg, Fe)_2 (SiO_4)$

Accessory

Ilmenite	$FeTiO_3$
Chromite	$FeCr_2O_4$
Ulvospinel	Fe_2TiO_4
Spinel	$MgAl_2O_4$
Cr-pleonaste	$(Fe, Mg) (Al, Cr)_2 O_4$
Perovskite	$CaTiO_3$
Dysanalyte	Ca, REE, TiO_3
Rutile	TiO_2
Nb-REE-rutile	$(Nb, Ta) (Cr, V, Ce, La) TiO_2$
Baddeleyite	ZrO_2
Zircon	$ZrSiO_4 + REE, U, Th, Pb$
Quartz	SiO_2
Tridymite	SiO_2
Cristobalite	SiO_2
Potash Feldspar	$KAlSi_3O_8 + Ba$
Apatite	$Ca_5 (PO_4)_3 (F, Cl) + REE, U, Th, Pb$
Whitlockite	$Ca_3 (PO_4)_2 + REE, U, Th$
Zirkelite	$CaZrTiO_5 + Y, REE, U, Th, Pb$
Amphibole	$(Na, Ca, K) (Mg, Fe, Mn, Ti, Al)_5 Si_8 O_{22} (F)$
Iron	Fe
Nickel-iron	(Fe, Ni, Co)
Copper	Cu
Troilite	FeS
Cohenite	Fe_3C
Schreibersite	$(Fe, Ni)_3 P$
Corundum	Al_2O_3
Goethite	$HFeO_2$

New Minerals

Armalcolite	$(Fe, Mg)Ti_2 O_5$
Tranquillityite	$(Fe, Y, Ca, Mn) (Ti, Si, Zr, Al, Cr)O_3$
Pyroxferroite	$CaFe_6 (SiO_3)_7$

the solar wind. Compositional differences within the crystalline rocks gave some clue as to how the lunar rocks found at the various sites might possibly be related, if at all. A study of the minor elements in lunar rocks showed a large number of anomalies when one compares the abundances of these elements to either terrestrial rocks or carbonaceous chondrites (organic-material-containing-meteorites, see Chap. 6).

To summarize, the following elements on the moon are in lower concentrations than those found on the earth and in carbonaceous chondrites. These include the more volatile elements, such as the alkalis, sodium, potassium, rubidium, as well as the minor elements of lead, bismuth, arsenic, mercury, copper, cadmium, barium, strontium, zinc, chlorine, and bromine. The following metallic elements are depleted on the moon in the same approximate proportion as they are on the earth, compared to cosmic abundances, i.e., gold, platinum, iridium, osmium, rhenium, nickel, cobalt, and germanium. The following elements are enriched in lunar basalts compared to solar abundances by about a factor of three to ten: Zirconium, hafnium, and yttrium.

Whether or not a rock belongs to the earth, the moon, or the chondrites, can be determined by plotting isotopic ratios of potassium to uranium versus potassium as shown in Figure 5.5. The curves enclose variations that were found within the samples. It is interesting to note that the chondrites showed the smallest amounts of variation, i.e., the circle which encloses all the chondrites samples examined is a very small one.

Among the lunar samples were a very interesting collection of glass beads of various shapes. Some were perfect spheres and others were elongated, all of various colors. When these beads were photographed at high resolution, it was found that minute impact craters could be discerned even on those already small spheres. These microimpact craters resulted from high-speed micrometeorites. Micrometeorites hit the earth as well, but get burned up in the earth's atmosphere. The moon has no atmosphere; therefore, everything that comes in makes an impact and leaves a permanent impression.

Since we are interested in the origin of the solar system, and the origin of life in particular, the possible presence of carbon or organic matter on the moon was of great interest. Indeed, some carbon was found indigenous to the rocks and must either have been incorporated in the material that formed the moon or landed there subsequently. Mare lavas contain much more carbon than is found in Highlands crystalline rock. Sample crystalline rocks from Apollo 16 commonly had between two to ten parts per million (ppm) carbon. Other samples had as much as 200 ppm.

To measure the ages of rocks, radiogenic age dating techniques were used largely by G.J. Wasserburg and his group at Cal Tech. The results gave the oldest rocks on the moon an age of 4.6 billion years. The age of crystallization for these rocks was 3.7 billion years ago.

Some of the main conclusions from the Apollo Missions are as follows:

1. The moon may be hot inside.
2. Heat flow is measured to be 3×10^{-6} watts per square centimeter, that is, about half that of the earth, a very unexpected result. (Measurements at 2 lunar sites were identical.)
3. Weak local magnetic fields were discovered, but no global field. There was evidence of strong ancient magnetic fields, active 3.2 to 3.9 billion years ago.

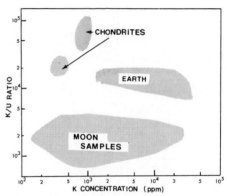

Figure 5.5. Plot of K/U ratio versus K concentration for lunar, earth, and chondrite meteorite samples. Note that it is possible to distinguish their origin on the basis of these measurements, since each sample falls within well-defined areas. There is a great deal more significance attached to this figure. One implication for the various lateral sizes of each group is that they might be related to the extreme temperature ranges and length of time these samples were exposed to heat. K = Potassium, U = Uranium (graph adopted from data by G.D. O'Kelly et al., and Short).

4. A rigid crust and outer mantle with no seismic or tectonic activity is one of the characteristics of the moon.
5. Moon quakes occur periodically at depth of 800 to 1,000 kilometers below the surface.
6. The accessible lunar rocks were formed under anhydrous, strongly reducing conditions.
7. There is a notable depletion of all alkali metals, siderophile and chalcophile elements.
8. An enrichment in refractory elements relative to chondrites and earth rocks was observed.
9. There is less metallic iron on the moon than the earth.
10. Indigenous carbon is presumably very low, between 1-25 parts per million.
11. All rocks returned from the moon are products of magmatic differentiation. No primitive or undifferentiated rocks have been found.
12. The thickness of the lunar crust may not be uniform and varies between 25 and 70 kilometers.
13. The moon formed about 4.6 billion years ago, the crust about 4.3, and highland basalts about 4.1 billion years ago.
14. Most lunar basins formed between 0.5 to 0.7 billion years after the formation of the moon.
15. The basins on the near side are largely basalt-filled. Those on the far side contained few lavas.
16. Mare-lava was extruded over a period of half a billion years, beginning about 3.7 billion years ago.
17. Mare lava rich in iron and magnesium contains highly varying amounts of titanium and is depleted in europium. There is evidence for melting of the lunar crust.
18. Old crust is saturated by impact craters of diameters greater than 50 kilometers. Nonmascon basins are old, irregular, and shallow. (Mascons are mass concentrations of denser material below the lunar surface.)
19. The mascon basins are young, circular, and deep. Basins having a diameter greater than a hundred kilometers have flat original floors.
20. Molten or partially molten material was abundant inside the second ring of large circular basins.
21. Mare basalts extruded from multiple centers. Last mare eruptive activity was from definable vents.
22. The regional systems of volcanic ridges are postmare in age. The inference that there is presently a rigid crust can be gotten from the evidence of the **mascons** and the presence of a *bulge* of the moon that leans toward the earth (Fig. 5.6). A solid or nonmobile mantle is indicated by the low number of weak internally originated moon quakes recorded by the seismometers. It is also generally agreed by the people who investigate the moon that the temperatures in the lunar interior today are generally below those of the melting points of most rock types. Why then is there still heat flowing out? One conclusion relating to the temperature of the moon and the Apollo sample analysis, is that parts of the moon

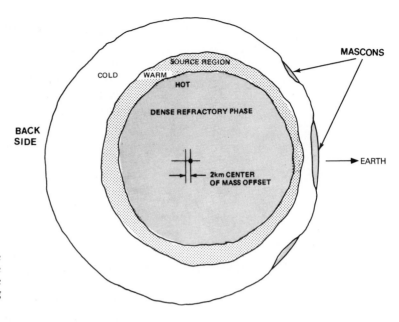

MASCONS

COLD   WARM   SOURCE REGION

HOT

DENSE REFRACTORY PHASE

BACK
SIDE

2km CENTER
OF MASS OFFSET

EARTH

Figure 5.6. Idealized cross section of the moon. Note the asymmetry and bulge of the moon *towards* the earth. Also note the presence of the mascons on the earth-facing side only.]

experienced remelting that began a few hundred million years after the crust solidified and lasted intermittently for the next six hundred million years.

The mascons, referred to earlier, are massive concentrations that occur below the lunar crust, but only on the side that faces the earth. There is a distinct difference between the far side of the moon (not visible from earth) and the near side that always faces the earth. The mascons are on the near

Figure 5.7. Large boulder on the moon with multiple cracks photographed by H. Schmitt on Apollo 17 mission (NASA).

Figure 5.8. Astronaut John W. Young, commander of the Apollo 16 lunar landing mission, leaps from the lunar surface as he salutes the United States flag at the Descartes landing site during the first Apollo 16 extravehicular activity (NASA).

side and are absent on the far side. Also, the appearance and number of craters are different on the far side. Why? Another mystery.

After all is said and done and all the material that we have collected is digested, the big mystery is still with us as before we landed on the moon: where did all the material come from that impacted on the moon? Why was there volcanic activity on the moon if, according to present theory, the moon was supposed to have been collected from cold material? Why is there a remnant magnetic field on the moon far in excess of what should be expected from a nonrotating, noncore planet? In other words, more puzzles were opened up by the space exploration than settled. This, however, is typical of all research—Pandora boxes inside each opened Pandora box!

Short Rocket Flights

While the Apollo program held center stage, a large number of other explorations of lower cost, but just as exciting for astronomers, were being continuously conducted. These involved rocket flights that went just a few hundred miles out into space and then returned, performing their function during those few precious minutes in which they were above the atmospheres. In those few minutes, they performed ultraviolet photography and X-ray detection of specific regions of the galaxy.

Other classes of spacecraft that were of an unmanned type were launched in the direction of various parts of the solar system. These, too, proved to be extremely rewarding. They included the Mariner missions to Mars, to Venus, and to Mercury. Mars, in particular, has now been studied very carefully, facilitating a complete mapping of its surface.

Mission to Mars

The Mariner Series

From 1965 to 1969, Mariner IV, VI, and VII provided man's first close-up glimpses of the planet Mars. These satellites, however, flew past the planet; hence their viewing period was brief, but exciting. Mariner IX, however, was inserted into orbit around planet Mars and was able to take a complete set of pictures covering one hundred percent of the Martian surface over an extended period. It took, altogether, 7,300 television pictures and transmitted them back to earth. It operated for a period of 349 days—an outstanding success and triumph for NASA and the science and technology behind this program.

The spacecraft was launched on May 30, 1971, and was inserted into orbit November 14 by means of a 15-minute motor burn. As was discussed previously, such a "burn" operation implies that its speed was adjusted so that its velocity was appropriate for retaining it in orbit around Mars. Similar procedures were involved in the Apollo mission around the moon.

74

Mariner IX arrived at Mars just in time to witness an enormous dust storm, which at first was considered an ill-omen, but later proved to be highly interesting, since the dust storm did clear eventually and showed a great deal about the dynamics of the atmosphere in action. It did, however, cause a one and one-half month delay in the image-mapping phase of the mission. Some of the pictures shown in this book are a result of this exciting technological feat.

Let us start with two of the unexpected bonuses which were of no small interest, namely the photography of the two satellites. Deimos and Phobos (Fig. 2.10). Phobos, the inner moon, was found to have a size of approximately 17 by 12 miles. The moons of Mars were discovered as two tiny dots of light about a hundred years ago by Hall, but no one had ever seen them in detail until the photos of the martian moons were relayed to earth via radio transmission from the satellites. Both Deimos and Phobos (Fig. 2.10) are fully cratered and irregular in shape. Phobos completes one revolution around Mars in 7.7 hours, less than the period of rotation of Mars. Deimos, eight by six miles in size, has an orbital period of 30.3 hours. Both satellites are also in rotation, each turning once on its own axis during one revolution about the planet Mars. Thus, they always keep the same side towards Mars, just as the moon does with the earth. How does this come about? For the same reason as the moon: it is because of the tidal effect of Mars on these satellites. Here we have the second concrete example of a tidal effect in action. Consequently, if one were to land on these satellites, one would have an excellent viewing station on the side facing Mars. The Mariner IX spacecraft took the pictures of these satellites at distances of about five thousand miles.

Surface Features on Mars

There are a large variety of distinct areas on Mars, each of which requires special consideration. There are *craters* on Mars which are definitely volcanic in origin. For example the one near Nodus Gordii (where multiple concentric fractures of the western ring and abundant rimless craterlets suggest that this crater was once a caldera) is strongly reminiscent of similar calderas on Hawaii (Figs. 2.7, 2.8, 2.9).

Detailed pictures of Mars' polar caps showed variations due to season changes (Fig. 2.7). Other changes were associated with dust removal, which exhibited cut terraces in the terrain. The detailed structures on the polar caps are highly significant and a great source for follow-up study.

There are some areas on Mars which are reminiscent of the lunar craters. These areas were first photographed by the earlier Mariner missions and had given the erroneous impression that Mars is perhaps like the moon, a lifeless planet. The complete mapping gave a far different impression.

A large number of features strongly suggest erosion processes, e.g., an intricate network of mighty canyons, which appears like a giant chandelier covering an area of about 330 to 260 miles, providing dramatic evidence of erosion in the area of Noctic Lacus.

A really spectacular area on Mars is a canyon whose length would stretch from coast to coast of the United States. It is four times as deep as the Grand Canyon and also correspondingly wider, with tributaries, side canyons and so forth. The only difference between Mars and the Arizona Grand Canyon is that there seems to be no present evidence of liquid surface water on Mars. Erosion seems to be the only plausible mechanism which could have formed such an enormous structure. Hence, there must have been periods on Mars when water flowed. Other pictures show wavelike patches strongly reminiscent of sand dunes in the Sahara.

Atmosphere

Measurements were made during the peak of the dust storm when the material entrained in the atmosphere could be sensed by means of an infrared spectrometer on board the Mariner IX. From these measurements it was deduced that the material was probably about sixty percent silicon dioxide, which is consistent with dust originating from basaltic rock. Surface characteristics measured when the atmosphere was clear, indicate a similar silicon dioxide composition, consistent with ample evidence of volcanism. Other measurements indicated that the dust was rising to about ten miles above the mean surface elevation, and that in some instances the dust levels were as high as thirty miles.

Temperature profiles were taken in various locations. These proved invaluable for analysis of atmospheric composition. Cloud layers could be seen in the north polar area, when photographed edge on. Cloud formations indicate the presence of both carbon dioxide and water condensation. Massive frontal actions were observed, and interactions with the underlying topography produced evident lee-wave cloud formations, whose wave spacings indicated a speed of about 120 miles per hour. The overall frontal movement shows motions of about 500 miles per day. Because of the low atmospheric pressure on Mars, which is less than 1/100 that of earth pressure, very high wind velocities are necessary to create enough force to pick up and move the surface dust particles. Clouds moving from north polar regions late in winter season all have the distinctive characteristics of earthly cumulus clouds heavily laden with snow.

Towards the end of the mission, clouds that formed over the Tharsis ridge and the Nix Olympia area were examined by the spacecraft television cameras and by the infrared spectrometer and were found to have the absorption characteristics of water-ice crystal clouds. The precipitable amount of water in the total column of atmosphere, extending from the surface to space, would have corresponded to about two-thousandths of an inch of water at most. Aside from water vapor, carbon dioxide, carbon monoxide, and ozone have also been detected in the polar regions by means of the ultra-violet spectrometer.

The maximum temperature at the equator of Mars is around 20°C. Compare that to the earth's equator and that of Venus.

The dilemma is: under what circumstances could fluid water have been found on Mars? The present state of the Martian atmosphere pressure is certainly not dense enough for fluid water to remain stable. Fluid water exposed on the surface would rapidly evaporate into the atmosphere, cooling the remaining fluid until it had solidified into ice. The water then would remain stable as invisible water vapor in the atmosphere or, if cold enough, as ice.

Examination of Martian features gave strong evidence that water might be present as permafrost or subsurface ice. The polar regions are particularly abundant with features that appear to be ice fields. Whether or not they are indeed water ice or carbon dioxide ice or a combination of both is still open to question and to further analysis. If there were a planet-wide warming trend, the atmosphere of Mars would have become considerably more dense than it is now, and fluid water could then have been retained on the Martian surface. It is possible that sometime in the past Mars had liquid water on its surface. In fact, there seems to be very little alternative explanation for some of the dramatic erosion and canyonlike features. The story of Mars is not yet completed.

The Viking Mission

Two Viking spacecrafts were launched from NASA, Kennedy Space Center, Florida, in September 1975. After a long interplanetary flight, they arrived over the surface of Mars and went into orbit. The landers separated from each orbiter and descended onto the Martian surface. A parachute slowed their descent from an altitude of about 21,000 feet to about 4,000 feet, at which time three rocket engines fired to bring them down to a slow, gentle landing on the Martian surface. Each lander contained experiments connected with biology

Figure 5.9. Viking lander. Note the extended scooping arm and the two cameras.

77

and molecular analysis of the constituents in the soil samples. A retractable claw with a ten-foot extension can scoop out soil samples and place them in an automated chemical laboratory for analysis. Two cameras scan the Martian surface and provide images in color and in black and white. Also, since two cameras were provided, they enabled us to obtain stereoscopic vision from the spacecraft. The main purpose was to detect possible life on Mars, which could be identified by the sophisticated equipment on board. Mineral analysis and molecular analysis were performed. Magnetic properties on the surface are to be checked, and the seismometer is supposed to detect Mars quakes, just as some of the equipment placed on the lunar surface was able to do. (In Viking 1, the seismometer is not functioning.)

The orbiters, in the meantime, take measurements of the water concentration at different parts of the Martian atmosphere and obtain information on the surface temperature of Mars. Furthermore, each orbiter acts as a radio relay link for the lander to send its messages back to earth.

In searching for life under what appears to be rather inhospitable conditions, it should be remembered that in May, 1974, scientists reported that soil samples taken far below the frigid surface on the earth's Antarctica contained frozen bacteria that may have been a million years old or more. Providing heat and nutrients to these bacteria terminated their dormancies and triggered them to both move around and reproduce. Such experiments encourage scientists to look for similar behavior on Mars. Whereas the moon is very much a dead planet, the hopes for Mars are that it is much more alive, and that these two early Viking landers are only the beginning of what we hope to be more extensive investigations of other planets and more extensive studies of Mars in the near future.

Figure 5.10. Panoramic View of Martian Landscape. 300° scan. Parts of Viking I are seen in foreground. (Courtesy NASA/JPL)

Vikings 1 and 2 Land on Mars

On July 20, 1976, the first successful operational spacecraft landed on Mars in an area known as the Chryse basin. The landing occurred at 5:12:07 A.M. PDT or 4:13 P.M. Mars local time. Within seconds of its flawless landing sequence, the lander took two pictures—a high resolution image of a footpad and adjacent surface material and a 300° panoramic survey of the horizon (Fig. 5.10), and book cover.

Parts of the lander are seen in the foreground of this spectacular picture. On the left side can be seen part of the meteorology instrument. This instrument is now transmitting to earth daily Martian weather information on this site, e.g., "Light winds from the east in the late afternoon, changing to light winds from the southwest after midnight. Maximum wind velocity was 15 miles per hour. Temperature range from $-122°$ F just after dawn to $-22°$ F. Pressure steady at 7.70 millibars." (Comparable earth pressure at ground level is about 1,000 millibars.)

A subsequent color picture of the Martian surface showed a decidedly pinkish hue. The atmosphere seemed to have a similar color, originating from the scattered dust particles in the thin Martian atmosphere. The dominant color of Mars (as seen from earth-based telescopes) which had earned it the title of the "Red Planet" has now been confirmed at close quarters. The suggestion was made that the likeliest mineral to account for this ruddy color is a hydrated iron oxide called limonite. From the color pattern alone, geologists were able to speculate on the existence of at least six distinct lithological rock types that are visible in the few kilometers covered by the color images. A large 3-meter size rock is towards the back of the spacecraft. The mechanical arm scooped up material from the Martian soil and deposited it in

Figure 5.10 (cont.)

the lander instrument chamber, where a number of tests are being processed which should provide some clues as to the possibility of past biological activity on Mars. The data is still coming in, and scientists are pondering its significance. No clear-cut answers are immediately forthcoming. The scientists would prefer to have more experiments and more time before making definitive statements.

Meanwhile, Viking 2 successfully landed on another site on Mars.

It has provided spectacular pictures and information from another part of Mars.

The Viking 2 orbiter has taken careful remote temperature measurements of Mars' northern ice cap, which establish that it is water ice, (not CO_2) of 1 meter to 1 kilometer in thickness.

Views of Venus and Mercury

At 10 o'clock A.M. on February 5, 1974, Mariner X passed within 6,000 miles of the planet Venus before heading on to its rendezvous with Mercury. It used the gravitational pull and orbital motion of Venus to catapult it, as it were, on to the planet Mercury, passing 436 miles above its rugged surface. It rendezvoused a second time with Mercury on September 21, 1974, at 1:20 P.M., when it passed some 30,000 miles over the planet's daytime hemisphere.

The photographs obtained from Mercury and Venus were nothing short of spectacular and, in addition, these were the first clear pictures ever taken of the planet Mercury, since Earth based telescopes had not been able to discern any surface features at all. The photograph of Mercury is a composite of many individual pictures (Fig. 2.3) transmitted from the spacecraft back to earth and then reconstructed and enhanced. It shows a planet that looks very much like the moon. One of the notable exceptions is the lack of Maria Basins.

Venus, on the other hand, showed spectacular details of cloud cover. A sequence taken in a seven-hour interval shows a very rapid motion of the clouds corresponding to a rotational period of four days, whereas Venus itself has a rotational period of 243 days. The detailed markings on the surface of the cloud covers reveal a rapidity with which the clouds on the upper layers of the planet seem to revolve around the planet. The temperature of the clouds were measured by means of infrared radiation and found to be $250°K, ±12°$.

The atmosphere of Venus is very thick indeed and has not allowed us a glimpse of its surface at all. Hydrogen was also measured on Venus, and some traces probably must have come from the sun itself. (Two Russian spacecraft landed on Venus and transmitted photos of rocks on its surface.)

The radio signals emitted by the spacecraft on its journey allowed information to be obtained on the gravity of Venus; that is, the pull that Venus exercised on the spacecraft as it passed by. From this data it was possible to determine that

Figure 5.11. Close-up of Venus' atmosphere. Note the fine details in the cloud layers. Picture taken by Mariner 10 in ultraviolet light, February, 1974 (NASA/JPL).

Venus is one hundred times closer to being a perfect sphere than is the earth. Also, they measured the mass of Venus with a precision which was five times more accurate than we had ever had before. The radio waves passing through Venus' atmosphere, emitted by the spacecraft as it went behind the planet, showed that the lower cloud layer rises from 22 to 32 miles above the planet's surface, and that this consists of quite different clouds from the higher cloud deck. The highest cloud deck extends to about 37 miles above ground level. This upper layer is very thin, broken, and rapidly moving as contrasted with the thick and probably unbroken lower deck.

Four distinct temperature inversions were noticed at altitudes of 35, 38, 39, and 50 miles. They are probably associated with specific cloud layers. Furthermore, electrically charged particles make up the ionosphere of Venus and peak at nighttime layers at about 75-87 miles, whereas a strong ionosphere in the daytime peaks at a little higher—90 miles. By contrast, the earth's ionosphere's layers have more layers in the daytime than at night.

Along Venus' equatorial zone are very fine cloud belts like jet streams (faint but quite distinct) that have Y- and C-shaped markings (Fig. 2.5). Earth-based ultraviolet photographs revealed these as consistent markings: a spreading pattern of clouds opening in the direction of rotation.

Mercury Encounter

At the Jet Propulsion Laboratory and other places where the progress was viewed hour by hour, fascination and excitement in obtaining pictures for the first time was great as the spacecraft approached Mercury. On Mercury they found craters that looked like the moon's: their scarps or cliffs were nearly two miles high and stretched as far as 300 miles across the surface. Hilly and furrowed terrain, unlike anything on the moon, covers about 200,000 square miles and looks as though it was formed over a long period of time by unknown forces from within the planet.

Major features of Mercury include basins, craters, scarps, ridges, and planes. The highlands are cratered as heavily as the lunar highlands. The largest basin, Caloris, is 800 miles across. It resembles the Mare Imbrium basin of the moon, except for its unusual pattern of cracks on its floor and extensive filling with lava flow. There is no evidence from Mariner that Mercury ever possessed an atmosphere, because the craters are not weathered. Melting and consequential sinking of heavy materials and release to the surface of lighter materials though might have given rise to an atmosphere. The final cratering must have taken place after an atmosphere had escaped from the planet.

Magnetic measurements made in the vicinity of Mercury produced a surprising result. Mercury affects the solar wind and has an offset magnetic field about 100 times smaller than the earth's field. This field produced a *bow shock* and fills the plasma cavity expected behind an airless body like Mercury. The source of the magnetic field is a mystery.

Chapter 6

METEORITES, COMETS, ORGANIC MATTER AND UNIVERSAL CHEMISTRY

The earth has been bombarded by material from outer space since its very inception (judging from the surface features of the moon, Mars, and Mercury). These objects show unambiguously that in the distant past the bombardment of planets by "debris" in the solar system must have been of an enormous magnitude. Where did all of this material come from? Why does the earth show less evidence than other planets? On the earth, weathering (erosion) by rain, ice, and glaciers, have been at work for a long enough time to eradicate most of the evidence of previous bombardments. Fortunately, there are some examples of more recent origin. One such crater is the Barringer Crater in Arizona. It is believed that other large circular depressions, perhaps even the Great Lakes in Canada, owe their origins to similar events which occurred in the more distant past. Table 6.1 is a partial list of identified craters.

The Great Meteor Crater Near Winslow, Arizona

This spectacular crater (Fig. 6.3) is located on the southern edge of the sprawling Navajo and Hopi Indian reservations. It is reached by an access road from U.S. Highway 66 between

TABLE 6.1
Selected Meteorite Craters

Name and Location	Diameters (Meters)	Energy Released (Megatons of TNT)	Rim Height Above Crater Floor (Meters)
Barringer, Arizona	1,240	2	190
Chubb, New Quebec Canada	3,400	40	380
Brent, Ontario, Canada	3,200	30	70
Clearwater Lakes, Quebec	26,000	17,000	30
Deep Bay, Sask, Canada	13,000	2,000	340
Reiskessel, Bavaria, Germany	24,000	13,000	————

Note: The energy released upon impact was calculated from equation: 1 Megaton of TNT is equivalent to 4.2×10^{22} ergs and the energy on impact is proportional to $4d^3 \times 10^{13}$ ergs (d is diameter in meters).

Figure 6.1. The flight of an incoming meteorite. Its path is traced out by the burning and excitation of its ablation products.

Flagstaff and Winslow, Arizona. From the air it can easily be spotted since it reminds one immediately of a typical lunar crater.

Meteor Crater—the world's first proven meteorite crater—is 4,520 feet from rim to rim, three miles in circumference, and 570 feet deep. Such man-made wonders as the Washington Momument and the massive Great Pyramid of Cheops of Egypt are dwarfed by its giant dimensions.

The meteoritic mass from outer space that gouged out Meteor Crater, probably a wandering asteroid, struck the earth, resulting in a possible energy release of a multimegaton hydrogen bomb. It splashed nearly half a billion tons of rock from the crater and probably destroyed all plant and animal life within a 100-mile radius.

If early man lived in Northern Arizona at the time, and it is very possible that he did, he probably watched in fear and awe the blinding flash and earth-shaking explosion of the meteorite's impact (Fig. 6.2). Recent dating tests using the new radioactive carbon isotope method, indicate that the meteorite struck at least 12,000 years ago, a time when great glaciers still covered much of the northern part of our continent. More recently, Meteor Crater has been a familiar landmark to both ancient and modern Indian tribes. For more than 1,500 years it has been linked to their tribal customs and legends.

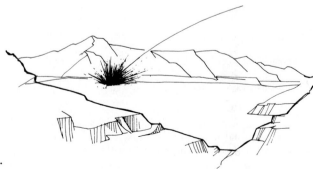

Figure 6.2. Impact.

Figure 6.3. The Barringer Crater near Winslow, Arizona. It is 1.240 m across and 190 m deep. To appreciate its immense dimensions, note the size of the cars in the parking lot in this aerial photo (photo by Peter L. Bloomer).

Discovery of Crater

Meteor Crater, also known as Barringer Crater, was first discovered by white men in 1871 and for many years was thought to have been of volcanic origin. However, in 1903 a Philadelphia mining engineer, Daniel Moreau Barringer, acquired the crater and initiated a series of intensive scientific studies that, shortly before his death in 1929, led to full scientific recognition of the fact that the crater was actually the result of the impact of a huge meteoritic mass from outer space. This spurred scientific investigations at the crater. Identification of its peculiar features, such as shatter cones and rare minerals formed by the impact, led to the discovery of a number of other craters of meteoritic origin in various parts of the world. These other craters, mostly less conspicuous because many of their distinctive features have disappeared through erosion, range in size and age from the Vredevert Ring in South Africa, 130 miles in diameter and 250 million years old, to the Sikhote-Alin group of 200 craters and pits, formed by a meteoritic shower in Siberia in 1947.

As a final note on this subject, it is worthwhile to remind ourselves of the irony associated with crater identification. Initially, the Barringer crater was erroneously considered volcanic in origin, while lunar craters, prior to the Apollo landing, were generally considered impact craters. There were some brave scientists like geologist A. Green of Long Beach State who stoutly defended the volcanic origin of some of the lunar craters. Now there seems to be no disagreement about the fact that, while most of the craters on the moon are of impact origin, a substantial number are volcanic in origin. Nature made a wise compromise!

Smaller Size Meteorites

Most people some time in their lives have either seen a meteorite, or pictures of one. Meteorites, most commonly on exhibit in museums, are huge iron boulders with roundish, irregularly shaped crevices (Fig. 6.4). The objects we are going to be discussing, however, are the meteorites that are smaller in size, but contain a far larger amount of information about our solar system, its origin, and about how life got started. With thousands of boulders and rocks on land, it is hard to distinguish a meteorite from all of the rest unless you are trained in observation. **Iron meteorites** can also be detected, if not too far underground, by the use of metal detectors. The **stony meteorites** make up about 86% of all meteorites that fall on the earth.

The idea that meteorites come from outer space has only been substantially recognized during this century. Over a hundred years ago this meteorite discussion would still have been considered extremely controversial, just like UFOs are at the present time. It took the observation of the actual fall of a meteorite and its subsequent recovery that firmly established its origin. During the last twenty years, the "space patrol" equipment in the Midwestern states was able to photograph meteorites successfully and trace out the orbits of selected meteorites.

Figure 6.4. Gooselake meteorite. Note the large crevices and holes in this iron meteorite. These holes are not caused by atmospheric heating during descent (photo courtesy Griffith Observatory).

Figure 6.5. Typical iron meteorite (courtesy Griffith Observatory).

A large number of meteorites, perhaps the majority of them, seem to lie between the orbits of Mars and Jupiter. One might speculate that the asteroid belt would have something to do with it. Figure 6.6 shows typical orbits of 3 meteorites.

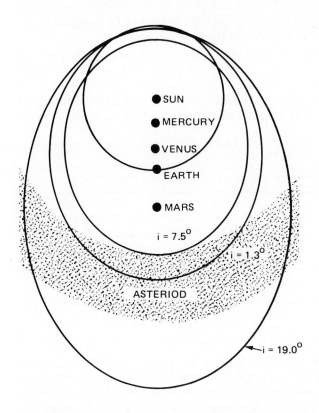

Figure 6.6. The orbits of 3 meteorites that were recovered on earth after impact.

Note how the (preterrestrial) orbits intersect the earth's orbit. The relationship of these orbits to the asteroid belt is shown. The best determined orbit of a recovered meteorite is the outermost one in this figure. It fell in 1959 in PRIBRAM near Prague. (Its inclination was 19° with respect to the ecliptic).

Table 6.2 shows the respective types of meteorites separated into types: iron, stony, and combination. Stony meteorites are easily recognized by the black, carbonlike fusion crust that surrounds them. This fusion crust is the result of an ablation, a baking process that occurs when the bodies entered the earth's atmosphere at supersonic speeds and heated up their crusts. Similar effects are seen when a manmade satellite enters the earth's atmosphere; the ablation effects on its surface and its heating are pronounced. However, ablation effects do not penetrate more than one or two milli-

TABLE 6.2

	Meteorites Seen Falling	Meteorite Finds
Irons	6%	66%
Stony-irons	2%	8%
Stones	92%	26%

meters, so that the more dramatic type holes that are sometimes seen in the iron meteorites (Fig. 6.4) could not have arisen from their fall through the earth's atmosphere, as is popularly believed. Holes as large as four or five inches in diameter can be seen in some of these iron meteorites. What fascinating story about their distant past are these holy objects telling us? They must have gone through some very violent types of eruptions to have that type of irregular structure—more like a cauldron than a simple cooker.

Of all the stony meteorites, the carbonaceous types are the most interesting. The stones are divided between chondrites and achondrites. The chondrites, in turn, are divided according to the percentage fraction of their carbonaceous content (Table 6.3). These kinds of chondrites have been known for

TABLE 6.3
Carbonaceous Meteorites
Typical Range of Carbon and H_2O Content

	Type I (%)	Type II (%)	Type III (%)
C	3–4	~2.5	0.5–1
H_2O	~20	9–13	1–2
Density	~2.2	2.5–2.8	3.4–3.7

over a hundred years and can be seen in various museums throughout the world (Table 6.4). From a preliminary analysis, their organic content is shown in Table 6.5. However, it was only during the last ten years, with the advent of sophisticated scientific equipment, such as gas chromatography combined with a highly-sensitive mass spectrometer, that has enabled us to obtain new and unambiguous identification of organic materials inside these carbonaceous chondrites. The word chondrite is derived from the word "chondrule," which signifies that it is made out of tiny spheres, one to eight millimeters in diameter usually surrounded by a carbonaceous, "gooey," tarlike material. A cross section of a typical meteorite (the Allende meteorite) is shown in Figure 6.7.

Figure 6.7. Cross section of a carbonaceous chondrite meteorite (Allende). Note the spherical chondrules (author's collection).

Figure 6.8. A typical carbonaceous chondrite. Note fusion crust (Griffith Observatory photo).

Figure 6.9. Widmanstätten pattern in an iron meteorite. Systems of bands are kamacite lamellae (Griffith Observatory photo).

TABLE 6.4
Carbonaceous Meteorites Arranged in Order of Type

Name	Country	Date of Fall	Weight (kg)	Carbon Content (%)	H_2O Content (%)	Type
Tonk	India	1911	0.01	2.70	21.66	I
Alais	France	1806	0.26	3.19	19.48	I
Ivuna	Tanganyika	1938	0.70	4.83	18.68	I
Orgueil	France	1864	11	3.10	19.89	I
Revelstoke	Canada	1965	0.001			I
Nawapali	India	1890	0.06	2.50	16.41	II
Santa Cruz	Mexico	1939	0.05	2.54	10.33	II
Cold Bokkeveld	South Africa	1838	4	1.30	15.17	II
Nogoya	Argentina	1879	2.5 ·	1.62	14.28	II
Erakot	India	1940	0.11	2.14	11.52	II
Mighei	U.S.S.R.	1889	8	2.48	12.86	II
Haripura	India	1921	0.32	4.00	13.70	II
Boriskino	U.S.S.R.	1930	1.17	2.06	11.97	II
Cresent	United States	1936	0.08			II
Bells	United States	1961	0.3			II
Murray	United States	1950	12	2.78	12.42	II
Al Rais	Saudi Arabia	1957	0.16	2.49	8.49	II
Murchison	Australia	1969	82.7	2.1	8.0	II
Bali	Cameroon	1907	0.01			III
Kaba	Hungary	1857	3	1.99		III
Mokoia	New Zealand	1908	4	.47	2.07	III
Vigarano	Italy	1910	16	1.12	2.88	III
Brosnaja	U.S.S.R.	1861	3.3	.56	4.02	III
Allende	Mexico	1969	1,000	0.29		III
Karoonda	Australia	1930	42	0.10		III

TABLE 6.5
Organic Matter in Meteorites
Preliminary Breakdown

Compound	Percent
1. Hydrocarbons—paraffins, naphthenes, and aromatics	1.25
2. Fatty acids	0.75
3. Aromatic acids and phenols	3.30
4. Amino acids	0.10
5. Unidentified	95.00

Figure 6.8 shows a picture of a typical chondrite meteorite. The cross section of an iron meteorite is shown in Figure 6.9 for contrast. Note the peculiar etchings; this is a characteristic of these extraterrestrial iron meteorites.

Stones from Heaven Fell at Allende, Mexico

On February 9, 1969, an impressive shower of meteorites descended on an unsuspecting area in Northern Mexico near the town of Pueblito de Allende, 30 kilometers east of Hildalgo del Parral. Its blue-white spectacular color astonished the inhabitants of Chihuahua, as it descended through the atmosphere. The word was flashed out. The next day the area was scoured and meteorites collected with the help of the local newspaper publisher. Figure 6.7 shows a cross section of a typical specimen of one of these Allende meteorites. Note in Figure 6.8, the outside fusion crust in one such meteorite.

Table 6.6 shows the chemical analysis of this Allende meteorite.* Its most abundant constituents are silicon oxide, magnesium oxide, and iron oxide which constitute more than 80% of its content. However, not to be ignored, is the carbon content which, although low, is 0.27%. It is this carbonaceous content which makes these meteorites interesting.

In general, there are 3 types of these carbonaceous chondrite meteorites, divided into groups according to their carbonaceous content, I, II, and III with I being the richest and III the lowest in organic compound content. (Allende meteorite is classified in group III.) Also note in Table 6.3 that the density of the meteorites increases from Type I to Type III.

E.A. King, Jr. and his group at the Lunar Receiving Laboratory were using this meteorite as exercise material prior to their receiving the lunar samples. They conducted extensive tests, including a study of their isotopic radioactive composition. Table 6.7 gives a list of the discovered radioactive isotopes.

Table 6.6
Chemical Analysis of Allende Meteorite

SiO_2	31	%
MgO	21.3	
FeO	31.9	
Al_2O_3	2.9	
CaO	2.8	
Na_2O	0.6	
K_2O	0.01	
TiO_2	0.17	
MnO	0.14	
N_i	1.40	
C_r	0.32	
→ C	0.27	
C_o	0.79	
Zr	0.0036	
Cu	0.008	

Data from E.A. King et al.

Table 6.7

Radioactive Isotopes in Allende Meteorite (1969)

$U, Th, K^{40}, Al^{26}, Co^{60}, Na^{22}$

Mn^{54}, Na^{24}

It is particularly noteworthy that the half life of some of these isotopes is extremely short, which implies that their activation had to have occurred just prior to falling into the earth's atmosphere.

Altogether, about 27 kilograms of meteorite specimen were collected within a period of a few days, no doubt indi-

*Science Vol. 163, p. 928, Feb. 28, 1969.

cating that many more, yet to be discovered, meteorites fell in that region. The original bolide probably broke up into many pieces prior to its fall.

The reason for our extended discussions of this particular meteorite is that it is a somewhat rare event to obtain a freshly fallen specimen. It fell at a *very* propitious time, considering the number of people available with highly sophisticated analysis equipment able and ready to study these meteorites.

Daily Bombardment

Despite the sparsity of identified large meteorite falls, the daily mass of meteoric material reaching the earth is reported to be about ten tons. This is material coming in at very high speeds. The amount of material coming in at low speeds, mostly micrometeorite material, is supposed to be about 400 tons.* If we assume that this amount of material has been coming in to the earth steadily for 4 1/2 billion years, it would have increased the earth's mass over that total period by 10^{-5} % (i.e., 10^{-7} × mass of the earth); a rather insignificant amount.

This amount of material spread uniformly over the total surface of the earth would occupy a thickness of about 1/2 meter.

The Impact Energy

The Barringer Crater is the oldest one in terms of discovery (identification), not in terms of its real age. Note the sizes of some of the other craters listed in Table 6.1. Some are at least 20 times greater than the Barringer Crater and are, in fact, comparable in size to craters on the moon. The inferred explosive energy released upon impact of the largest meteorite corresponds to 17,000 one-megaton hydrogen bombs—about the present world nuclear stockpile!

One can estimate the amount of energy released from an impact crater. There is a simple relationship that gives this quantity in terms of the crater diameter (d in meters). The amount of energy released is equal to $4 \times 10^{13} \times d^3$ ergs. The calculated energy released in each of those craters is shown in Table 6.1. It is also interesting to compare the velocity of the parabolic meteors in terms of the earth's escape velocity.

The heliocentric velocity of a parabolic meteor is about 42 km per second. The earth's escape velocity is 11.2 km per second.

Organic Matter in Carbonaceous Chondrites

We shall now discuss some recent results which changed man's outlook considerably. The work was by Cyril Pon-

*From Allen "Astrophysical Quantities," 3rd ed.

namperuma, who had led a group of chemists while he was at NASA Ames Research Center. This group analyzed data looking for organic constituents in meteorites and in lunar samples. In addition to the Allende meteorite, another significant meteorite fell in Australia in 1969, known as the Murchison meteorite. The analysis by the NASA Ames group was conducted thoroughly on this latter meteorite. Their findings were nothing short of spectacular. A whole range of aliphatic hydrocarbons and a large group of aromatic hydrocarbons were discovered. However, the most exciting discovery, which stirred everyone, was the identification of amino acids. There were no less than 27 varieties of amino acids in the Murchison meteorite.

There had been a number of previous reports about chemical analysis of organic compounds on meteorites. This older work was done by famous chemists in the past, such as Berzelius and Berthelot, who investigated the Orgueil meteorite.

The problem with these earlier investigations was that no one took them seriously, since the results seemed to be too "far out." It could always be claimed by skeptics that these meteorites were somehow contaminated. However, the more recent studies could not be treated this flippantly because there were distinct signatures associated with the organic materials which in no way could make them terrestrial compounds.

Amino acids, molecules arising from living systems, have a screw direction which if of the left-handed variety. Thus, terrestrial compounds would have predominately (left-handed) L isomers associated with their amino acids. The amino acids found in the meteorites, however, were of the right (R), as well as of the left-handed (L) variety. Therefore, contamination must be ruled out on this basis. There was additional corroborative evidence. Isotopic ratios of C_{13}/C_{12} also made the organic material stand out as being different from terrestrial compounds. Hence, scientists now have reluctantly, but overwhelmingly, accepted these findings.

Simulation of Production of Porphyrins in the Laboratory

Significant research was reported by Dr. Gordon W. Hodgson on the simulation of interstellar porphyrin synthesis. He used a plasma arc through which were passed various compounds such as ammonia, formaldehyde and carbon dioxide. Subsequent to the passage of these gases through the plasma, the compounds formed were quenched in a cool expansion chamber. The carrier gas used was argon. The significance of Hodgson's work is that it probably represents a good simulation of the manner in which organic compounds are produced in space when high temperature, ionized or radioactive gases are ejected from the DEBs (Chapter 18). A whole host of organic materials are presumably produced in DEBs on contact with catalysts such as magnesium oxides or carbon. It seems that neither the type of matrix nor the original gas conditions, are critical for synthesis.

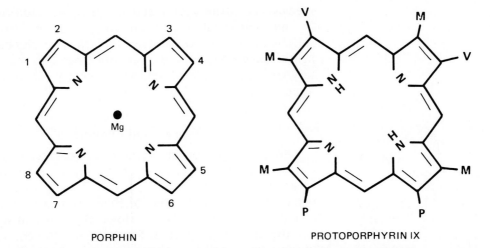

PORPHIN   PROTOPORPHYRIN IX

Figure 6.10. The basic Porphyrin structure. It consists of the characteristic ring as shown. Appendages can be attached at sites indicated by numbers or by the letters M, P, V. By changing these appendages a large family of porphyrins are generated. The central atom can also be varied. The important PROTOPORPHYRIN IX has two hydrogen atoms at its center. The porphin molecule on the left should have two hydrogen atoms at the center also. However, a magnesium atom was drawn in (the name of the molecule of course then changes) in order to illustrate the possible varieties. The chlorophyll molecule does have a magnesium atom at its center; its structure includes this basic skeleton, however, its appendages are slightly more elaborate.

The main point is that some sort of plasma jet is most likely involved in the production of compounds in space. The results show that a whole host of organic materials were synthesized or polymerized in the lab. Among these compounds were found the very important porphyrins.*

DEBs

DEBs is an acronym for *Developing Bodies*. These are bodies that are generated and ejected from the protosun and the major protoplanets. Each DEB in turn, in space, proceeds with its own development, which includes the ejection of plasma and gases through its porous shell. The resulting organic molecules and water condense out upon reaching the colder temperatures exterior to the DEB. Examples of such DEBs in our solar system are the billions of comets. It is postulated that the major organic and water content in the solar system is produced in this manner.

To some extent, the organic production could also have been directly possible in the atmospheres of Jupiter and Saturn, since the gravitational forces there were sufficient to retain all the light gases, particularly hydrogen.

The advantages of chemical production on or in DEBs is as follows: The DEB's core contains the atomic nutrients and its warm surface (400° K-1,200° K) provides the possibility of polymerization of smaller molecular constituents. Its remoteness from the sun serves to protect the more fragile molecular

*References: Conference on "Interstellar Molecules and Cosmo-Chemistry" sponsored by the New York Academy of Science in 1971. The proceedings were published, Vol. *194* of the New York Academy of Science.

species; its intrinsic radioactivity provides additional means for molecular polymerization. Its gravitational attraction is sufficient to retain the heavier molecular species but lose the lighter molecules, those that are not frozen, to the interplanetary or interstellar medium. See cometary identified species, Table 6.9.

Comets and Chondrites

The comets are ordinarily grouped together with other interplanetary debris. They are occasionally admired for their spectacular appearance (Fig. 6.11). Their discoveries, recurrences, and the predictions of their orbits are speculated on and discussed and analyzed. However, their real significance is unfortunately neglected. Furthermore, the connection between comets and meteorites is usually not made very apparent, despite the fact that the wake of **cometary orbits** generally contains large quantity of debris. When the earth, in its orbit around the sun, intercepts any of these orbits, it results in substantial showers of meteorites hitting the earth. These are micrometeorites producing spectacular fireworks (Table 6.8).

The times of "showers" are well enough known, since they can be predicted from a knowledge of the cometary orbits. Fluorescent spectroscopy is used to analyze the characteristic spectra of atoms, radicals and molecules in the cometary nucleus and tail. Table 6.9 shows the species that have been identified in comet tails and heads.

The observed species are strongly suggestive that larger molecules must exist in the comet. The observed radicals are most likely disintegration components. Such effects can be caused by the interaction of intense solar particle radiation

Figure 6.11. A comet as envisioned in the year 1066 on French (Bayeux) tapestry. It was considered an ill omen for the British and a good omen for the Norman invaders.

Figure 6.12. Modern man: Searching for black holes or other exotic objects.

TABLE 6.8
The Major Annual Meteor Showers*

Night Showers:	Radiant Coordinates R.A.	Dec.	Duration of Dectectable Meteors	Duration of Peak Days	Expected Hourly Rates
Quadrantids	231	+50	Jan. 1-4	0.5	50
Corona Australids	245	−48	Mar. 14-18	5	5
Virginids	190	00	Mar. 5-Apr. 2	20	5
Lyrids	272	+32	Apr. 19-24	2	10
Eta Aquarids	336	00	Apr. 21-May 12	10	20
Ophuichids	260	−20	June 17-26	10	20
Capricornids	315	−15	July 10-Aug. 5	20	20
Southern Delta Aquarids	339	−17	July 21-Aug. 15	15	20
Northern Delta Aquarids	339	00	July 15-Aug. 18	20	10
Pisces Australids	340	−30	July 15-Aug. 20	20	20
Perseids	46	+58	July 25-Aug. 17	5	50
Kappa Cygnids	290	+55	Aug. 18-22	3	5
Orionids	95	+15	Oct. 18-26	5	20
Southern Taurids	52	+14	Sept. 15-Dec. 15	45	5
Northern Taurids	54	+21	Oct. 15-Dec. 1	30	5
Leonids	152	+22	Nov. 14-20	4	varies
Phoenicids	15	−55	Dec. 5	0.5	50
Geminids	113	+32	Dec. 7-15	6	50
Ursids	217	+80	Dec. 17-24	2	5
Daylight Showers:					
Artietids	45	+23	May 29-June 19	20	60
Zeta Perseids	62	+24	1-17	15	40
Beta Taurids	87	+20	June 24-July 5	10	20

*Source: P.L. Brown, *Comets, Meteorites & Men.* Taplinger Publishing Company, New York, 1974.

TABLE 6.9
Identified Content of Cometary Spectra

H

O

OH

CH

CN

NH

NH_2

H_2O

H_2O^+ (Comet Kohoutek identified by Herbig and Herzberg)

C

C_2

C_3

CO^+

H_2^+

Na, K, V

Ni, Cu, Ca, Cr, Fe, Mn (observed in sun grazing comets)

CH_3CN }
HCN } (Microwave emission [Kohoutek])

CH^+

CO_2^+

N_2^+

OH^+

Ca^+

(solar wind) or perhaps by the ultraviolet and heat from the sun. It is also remarkable that comets have an enormously large hydrogen cloud surrounding them. The size of this cloud is about three times the size of the sun, thus making it the largest object in the solar system.

Since the escape velocity of hydrogen (i.e., its ability to make a clean get-away) is greater than the ability for the comet to retain this gas, the question has to be asked: How did the hydrogen get there?

One solution to the dilemma lies in the fact that Comet Kohoutek demonstrated the presence of H_2O^+ (ionized water). *There is, therefore, water in the tail of comets.* The disassociation products of water result in oxygen and hydrogen, as well as the OH radical. Note that OH has been identified in comets.

Consequently, the disassociation of water is probably the most plausible explanation for the origin of hydrogen. Perhaps similar processes occurred in the atmosphere on earth, resulting in the production of hydrogen and oxygen. The hydrogen, meantime, would have disappeared by escaping into the upper atmosphere and then off into space (Chapter 5). We shall review the properties of carbonaceous chondrites again and hope to show a connection with comets.

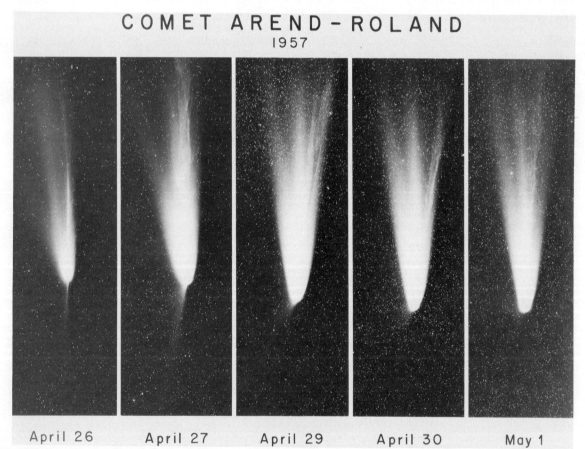

COMET AREND-ROLAND
1957

April 26   April 27   April 29   April 30   May 1

Figure 6.13. Comet Arend–Roland. Note the prominent gas jets or spikes projecting away from the comet's nucleus and towards the sun. Such action is presumably caused by the internal energy of the comet (Hale Observatories).

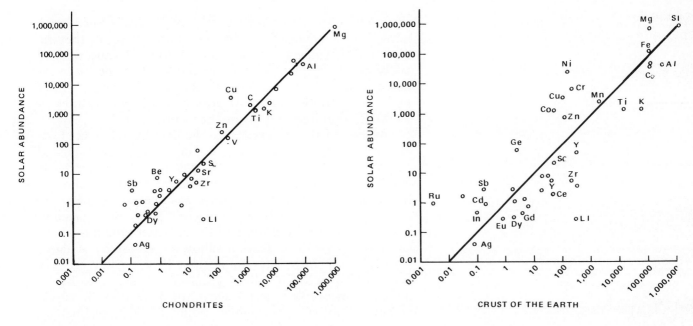

Figure 6.14. The relative abundances of metallic elements on the sun compared with those in chondrites and on the earth's crust. Elements above the line are more abundant on the sun, compared to either chondrites or earth. Note the good correspondence between solar and chondrite abundances.

Chondrules are tiny spheres from which the name of chondrites is derived. Note the various sizes in the cross section of Figure 6.7. They range anywhere from one to as large as eight mm. Some meteorites may have chondrules twice that size. The significance of chondrules lies in the fact that no rock on earth has such a structure. In addition, surrounding these chondrules is generally found carbonaceous material. There are, however, combinations of meteorite classifications. In fact, iron meteorites have been discovered containing graphite or occasionally diamond. It should also be noted that the abundances of the elements within the meteorite are of the same general proportion as the abundances found in the atmosphere of the sun.

Figure 6.14 shows very clearly such a relationship, where at least 30 elements are plotted. A similar plot of abundances of the elements in the sun compared to those in the crust of the earth does not show such a close relationship. The relative abundances of elements in meteorites is closer to that of the sun than that of the earth.

The earth, undoubtedly, has undergone considerable changes, such that the available surface material may not be a true representation of the overall abundances of the elements on earth. Meteorite material perhaps allows us to obtain a better overall unchanged cross section. After all, we have the whole meteorite to work with, not just the crust, which is the case for the earth.

Iron meteorite cross sections, once polished and etched, show a very curious pattern known as Widmanstätten. Is it characteristic of its prior history, such as pressure, heat, and strain? This Widmanstätten pattern (Fig. 6.9) consists of parallel arrays of plates of low nickel alloy Kamacite. Such structures can be simulated in the laboratory. However, they require initial temperatures of at least 1,400°C!! Thus, we may safely conclude that these iron meteorites had once been exposed to fairly hot temperatures. But where and how? Outer space is relatively cool. How does one get temperatures of 1,400°C? That question has not been answered.

The ages of the meteorites can be determined from abundance ratios of various isotopes. The average age points to around 4.5 billion years which is consistent with other determinations of rocks found on the moon. Another technique that was used to date the meteorite was to examine the radioactive gases resulting from radioactive decay of potassium, uranium, thorium, and some of the daughter products whose half lives are of the order of a billion years. A study of about seventy stony meteorites found that their average age was between 3.5 and 4.5 billion years. There seems to be no present controversy as to the age of the meteorites, because a number of different techniques result in the same final answer.

As these meteorites in outer space have been exposed to cosmic rays, it is possible to determine secondary ages related to the time of breakup from some initial larger body. In this case, the penetration of the radiation makes a difference. There is another age that can be obtained from the study of the isotopes, and that is the time it took to form whatever bodies these came from. This comes about from the fact that the decay half-life of some of the atoms is relatively short (e.g., a hundred million years). Consequently, if the daughter products are still within the meteorites, the only way they could have gotten there is during the initial decay process, 1/2 billion years ago. From this, we obtain an age of probably between 50 and 200 million years, during which time the original atoms existed somewhere before they left that particular place to exist all by themselves inside a meteorite in outer space. At the beginning, the meteorite material was both radioactively hot and temperature hot.

Tentative Conclusion (In the form of a question)

Are the carbonaceous chondrites perhaps parts of the parent body (nuclei of comets), the site of previous organic chemistry and organic synthesis—the DEBs? The tail of the comet is then its partial store of chemicals strung along like clothes on a line!

The Chemical Elements

The nature of the chemical elements and their production can be deduced by studying the combinations of nuclei and electrons. The nucleus consists essentially of neutrons and protons; the protons have a positive charge, and neutrons have none. The mass of the atom is substantially that of the nucleus, since the electron mass is about eighteen hundred times less than that of the proton. Each element has a different number of neutrons and protons in the nucleus and a corresponding number of electrons in the outer shells such that the total number of electrons is equal to the number of protons in the nucleus, thus constituting a neutral atom. Whenever one changes the number of electrons in the outer orbits, the chemical properties of the atom are changed. If one or more electrons are removed from the neutral atom, the atom is said to be ionized. It is possible to strip away all the electrons of the atom and leave a bare and naked nucleus. It is generally believed that inside the hot stars this is the natural state of things. In modern nonscientific terminology, bare nuclei are "streaking" around inside the star! However, on earth and on the outer surfaces of the stars, the electrons combine in the proper way with the nuclei of the atoms constituting neutral atoms most of the time. Examples of highly ionized regions are the sun's corona, where some iron atoms may have as many as fourteen electrons missing.

The Periodic Table

The periodic table of the atoms is built up by successive addition of protons and neutrons to the nucleus and by adding the corresponding electrons as shown in Table 6.11. The atomic number corresponds to the number of protons in the nucleus. The atomic weight corresponds to the sum of the neutrons and protons, e.g., Helium 4 consists of two protons and two neutrons, and Helium 3 consists of two protons and one neutron. Both Helium 3 and 4 will have two electrons in their outer orbits so as to constitute a neutral atom. Thus, chemically they behave in a very similar way, since the chemistry is governed solely by the number of electrons and the state of excitation of the electrons in the outer orbits. Water (H_2O) can also be produced by substituting a deuterium (D) atom for the hydrogen atom. A deuterium atom consists of a proton and a neutron; i.e., its mass is two rather than the ordinary hydrogen atom whose mass is one. The "heavy" water molecule D_2O is similar, but slightly different, in its chemical properties from ordinary water. It was destined to play an important role in the atomic reactor development. The term **isotope** of an element refers to elements that contain the same number of protons but different numbers of neutrons: thus the chemistry of isotopes is virtually identical, but their atomic weights are different, e.g., Uranium$_{238}$ and Uranium$_{235}$ are two isotopes of Uranium. The fact that the chemical properties of these two isotopes are very similar made it extremely difficult and costly to separate them. The separation of these Uranium isotopes was, however, an essential process, because only isotope 235 is readily fissionable by slow neutrons, splitting the nucleus in two, releasing energy, and ejecting two or more excess neutrons. It can produce either peaceful atomic reactors or the more awesome nuclear bombs, via chain reactions induced by the release of neutrons. Note that U_{235} has 143 neutrons and 92 protons.

Many of the elements found in the periodic table in their natural abundances are made up of various isotopes. The importance to the scientific and medical field of some of the isotopes has been explored during the last twenty-five years. Thus, natural lithium, for instance, consists of a mixture of lithium 6 and lithium 7 isotopes. Strontium, for example, has isotopes 86 and 87, etc. There are a number of isotopes of carbon of which the most abundant has an atomic weight of twelve. The isotope carbon 14, which is radioactive, plays an important role in dating objects containing carbon and can yield ages up to 15,000 years.

Radioactivity involves processes whereby elementary particles are ejected from the nucleus, changing the atomic weight or charge or the atomic number of the chemical element. The radiation that is emitted could be an α-particle (which is nothing but the core of the helium atom), or it could be an electron or a positron (which is the positive analog of the electron) or a gamma ray, which is a very high energy photon. The study of this radiation, their lifetimes, and their characteristic features is of recent origin (during the last thirty or forty years). In addition to light, we also obtain some very high energy atomic particles from outer space. These highly energetic particles, called **cosmic rays**, impinge on the earth's atmosphere continually.

Among the important information to be noted in the list of chemical elements are the abundances of the elements. Cosmic abundances of the elements are in the following order: hydrogen, helium, carbon, nitrogen, oxygen, and neon. Whereas helium is not important chemically, note that hydrogen, carbon, nitrogen, and oxygen, which are by far the most abundant elements, constitute those elements which combine most readily to form the millions of possible organic molecules which are necessary for the creation and sustenance of life.

The story of helium is an interesting one, even though it has no significance for life per se. Its discovery was made on the sun before scientists actually knew of its existence. Helium was discovered on the sun in 1868 by the French astronomer Jansen. It was called helium after the Greek word helios (sun)—an element that had never been seen before on the earth. It wasn't until 27 years later, in 1895, that Sir William Ramsey produced a gas in the laboratory whose spectroscopic lines matched or fitted the fingerprint of the lines that were seen on the sun by Jansen. Twenty years later, similar excitement arose when what was thought to be a new element (because its lines could not be fitted to any of the lines in the laboratory), Nebulium was discovered on the sun's corona. In the 1920s, Ira Bowen identified this so-called Nebulium as ionized oxygen atoms with 1 or 2 electrons missing. Later, iron atoms with fourteen missing electrons were discovered (Table 6.10). The important implication of this latter discovery is that the sun's corona has an effective temperature of 1 million to 2,000,000 degrees, whereas the sun's surface temperature is only 6,000° K!!

TABLE 6.10
Atoms Identified in the Solar Corona

Element	Atomic No.	No. of Electrons Missing
Argon	18	9, 13?
Calcium	20	11, 12, 14
Iron	26	9, 10, 12, 13, 14
Nickel	28	11, 12, 14, 15

TABLE 6.11
Chemical Elements

Element	Symbol	Atomic Number	Detected in Sun	Needed in Biology	Element	Symbol	Atomic Number	Detected in Sun	Needed in Biology
Hydrogen	H	1	√	√	Iodine	I	53	—	√
Helium	He	2	√	—	Xenon	Xe	54	—	—
Lithium	Li	3	√	—	Caesium	Cs	55	—	—
Beryllium	Be	4	√	—	Barium	Ba	56	√	—
Boron	B	5	√	√	Lanthanum	La	57	√	—
Carbon	C	6	√	√	Cerium	Ce	58	√	—
Nitrogen	N	7	√	√	Praseodymium	Pr	59	√	—
Oxygen	O	8	√	√	Neodymium	Nd	60	√	—
Fluorine	F	9	√	√	Promethium	Pm (II)	61	—	—
Neon	Ne	10	√	—	Samarium	sm (Sa)	62	√	—
Sodium	Na	11	√	√	Europium	Eu	63	√	—
Magnesium	Mg	12	√	√	Gadolinium	Gd	64	√	—
Aluminum	Al	13	√	—?	Terbium	Tb	65	√	—
Silicon	Si	14	√	√	Dysprosium	Dy (Ds)	66	√	—
Phosphorus	P	15	√	√	Holmium	Ho	67	—	—
Sulphur	S	16	√	√	Erbium	Er	68	√	—
Chlorine	Cl	17	—	√	Thulium	Tm (Tu)	69	√	—
Argon	Ar (A)	18	√	—	Ytterbium	Yb	70	√	—
Potassium	K	19	√	√	Lutecium	Lu (Cp)	71	√	—
Calcium	Ca	20	√	√	Hafnium	Hf	72	√	—
Scandium	Sc	21	√	—	Tantalum	Ta	73	√	—
Titanium	Ti	22	√	—	Tungsten	W	74	√	—
Vanadium	V	23	√	√	Rhenium	Re	75	—	—
Chromium	Cr	24	√	√	Osmium	Os	76	√	—
Manganese	Mn	25	√	√	Iridium	Ir	77	√	—
Iron	Fe	26	√	√	Platinum	Pt	78	√	—
Cobalt	Co	27	√	√	Gold	Au	79	√	—
Nickel	Ni	28	√	—?	Mercury	Hg	80	—	—
Copper	Cu	29	√	√	Thallium	Tl	81	—	—
Zinc	Zn	30	√	√	Lead	Pb	82	—	—
Gallium	Ga	31	√	—	Bismuth	Bi	83	—	—
Germanium	Ge	32	√	—	Polonium	Po	84	—	—
Arsenic	As	33	—	—	Astatine	At	85	—	—
Selenium	Se	34	—	√	Radon	Rn	86	—	—
Bromine	Br	35	—	—	Francium	Fr (Fa)	87	—	—
Krypton	Kr	36	—	—	Radium	Ra	88	—	—
Rubidium	Rb	37	√	—	Actinium	Ac	89	—	—
Strontium	Sr	38	√	—	Thorium	Th	90	—	—
Yttrium	Y	39	√	—	Protactinium	Pa	91	—	—
Zirconium	Zr	40	√	—	Uranium	U (Ur)	92	—	—
Niobium	Nb	41	√	—	Neptunium	Np	93	—	—
Molybdenum	Mo	42	√	√	Plutonium	Pu	94	—	—
Technetium	Tc	43	—?	—	Americium	Am	95	—	—
Ruthenium	Ru	44	√	—	Curium	Cm	96	—	—
Rhodium	Rh	45	√	—	Berkelium	Bk	97	—	—
Palladium	Pd	46	√	—	Californium	Cf	98	—	—
Silver	Ag	47	√	—	Einsteinium	Es	99	—	—
Cadmium	Cd	48	?	—	Fermium	Fm	100	—	—
Indium	In	49	√	—	Mendelevium	Md	101	—	—
Tin	Sn	50	√	—	Nobelium	No	102	—	—
Antimony	Sb	51	√	—	Lawrencium	Lw	103	—	—
Tellurium	Te	52	—	—					

Chemical Elements: Itemized

In order to appreciate the importance of chemical elements, we shall first study a table which lists all of them. Table 6.11 lists those elements which are found in the sun, and those that are essential for life. Table 6.12 shows the most abundant elements in the cosmos. Table 6.13 gives the abundances of the elements in the earth's atmosphere, and Table 6.14 lists the abundances of the elements in the earth's crust, sea water, and human body. Armed with this knowledge, one can attempt a better overview of the distribution of the chemical elements in the universe and locally in our solar system.

The field of relative abundances has fascinated scientists for many years. There are many speciality books on the subject. The object of these studies is to obtain a better basic understanding of cosmology. If the relative abundances are similar, one can say it has a common origin; if they are different, one seeks an explanation for the differences. No matter how you slice it, the search always leads back to the field of cosmology, the origin and nucleosynthesis of the elements in the stars, and possible explanations of why their abundances differ. There are a number of features that really stand out. The first one is the relative abundances of the most abundant elements in the universe: hydrogen, helium, carbon, nitrogen, and oxygen. Ignoring helium, which does not participate in any chemistry, it is obvious that the most abundant elements also are the most important for water and organic chemistry, without which there can be no life as we know it.

TABLE 6.12
Relative Cosmic Abundances by Percentage (weight)
of the Most Abundant Elements

Element	Symbol	Atomic Number	Cosmic Abundance (by weight)	% (weight)
Hydrogen	H	1	100,000	73.4
Helium	He	2	34,000	24.96
Oxygen	O	8	1,040	0.76
Carbon	C	6	400	0.294
Iron	Fe	26	223	0.164
Neon	Ne	10	160	0.117
Nitrogen	N	7	130	0.095
Silicon	Si	14	93	0.068
Magnesium	Mg	12	64	0.046
Sulphur	S	16	51	0.037
Argon	Ar	18	25	0.018
Nickel	Ni	28	11	0.008
Calcium	Ca	20	8	0.006
Sodium	Na	11	4	0.003
Manganese	Mn	25	1.4	0.001
Phosphorus	P	15	1.0	0.0007

Abundances are based largely on spectral data from Sun. (Data adapted from Allen.)

TABLE 6.13

Composition of Earth's Atmosphere by Weight

Gas	$\times 10^{-6}$
N_2	755,230
O_2	231,400
H_2O	600–17,000
Ar	12,900
CO_2	500
Ne	12.7
He	0.72
CH_4	1.0
Kr	3.3
CO	0.06–1
SO_2	2
H_2	0.04
N_2O	0.5
O_3	0.02–0.2
Xe	0.39
NO_2	0.008–0.03
Rn	0.01?
NO	Trace

As a digression, let us consider whether chemical elements, as in stones or wood, are able to communicate with other elements in other bodies. If you think about this a little bit, you will realize that it may seem rather strange, but human beings are nothing more than a composition of a large variety of chemical elements also. Hence, a set of atoms and molecules do communicate with another set of atoms and molecules. That is true, is it not—or is it?

Also included in this chapter is information on the essential elements found in living organisms, in order to obtain

TABLE 6.14

Composition of Universe		Composition of Earth's Crust		Composition of Seawater		Composition of Human Body	
Percent of Total Number of Atoms							
H	92	O	45	H	66	H	63
He	7.8	Si	27	O	33	O	25.5
O	0.060	Al	8.0	Cl	0.33	C	9.6
N	0.0083	Fe	5.8	Na	0.28	N	1.4
C	0.030	Ca	5.0	Mg	0.033	Ca	0.31
Si	0.003	Na	2.3	S	0.017	P	0.22
Ne	0.007	K	1.7	Ca	0.006	Cl	0.03
Mg	0.002	Mg	2.8	K	0.006	K	0.06
Fe	0.004	Ti	0.9	C	0.0014	S	0.06
S	0.0015	H	0.14	Br	0.0006	Na	0.03
		C	0.19			Mg	0.01
All Others < .01		All Others < .1		All Others < .1		All Others < .01	

some conception of the importance of these elements in life-forming organisms. It seems that there are very few of the abundant atomic elements that are not somehow utilized in living cells. (See Tables 6.11, 6.14, and 6.15.)

TABLE 6.15

Elements Necessary for Life

Seven elements are needed to make the molecular building blocks of living matter:

Carbon
Nitrogen
Oxygen
Hydrogen
Phosphorus
Sulphur
Magnesium

These elements are needed in: Amino acids
Sugars
Fatty acids
Purines
Pyrimidines
Nucleotides
Porphyrins (chlorophyll)
for photosynthesis

The other rare elements indicated in Table 6.11 are incorporated in many specific enzymes, proteins, hormones, and pigments. They are needed for metabolism, protein digestion, electron transfer, regulation of acidity, amino acid metabolism, nitrate utilization, DNA biosynthesis, (lipid digestion, phosphate transfer, aldehyde oxidation, and a host of other cellular functions. We are generally vitamin conscious, but essentially ignorant of the many trace elements which are absolutely necessary for the maintainance of life.

All these elements were manufactured inside a star (our sun?). Is this relevant astronomy?

The Precious Source of Organic Molecules—Oil

There are three aspects associated with this topic which we are about to touch on. One, the enormous variety of organic compounds in oil. Two, its possible origin. Three, some of the trace molecules or gases that are mixed in with the oil.

First, the **trace compounds.** These, of course, are a nuisance to the petroleum industry. However, they are a delight for cosmo-chemist detectives attempting to determine the origin of oil. Virtually, all present theories postulate that oil originated as the decay product from once-living compounds. This is possible, in part, but not very likely for the original material, because there is the "chicken versus egg dilemma." Since living matter required organic molecules to begin with, which came first—living matter or the organic molecules? I think it was the organic molecules. If this is so, one still has the problem of origin. Some hypothesize that water and oil originate at the bottom of volcanoes. Others postulate that they are created by lightning discharges in atmospheric gases by a sort of Miller-Urey type experiments. They are manufactured in comets (DEBs) in large quantities. (See Chapter 18.)

There are two bits of evidence that make it very hard to explain their origin as decay products of living matter. One, is the fact that helium gas is only found in association with oil fields, as in Texas. There is no helium in any living system. Two, is the research conducted by Earl W. Baker and colleagues on petroporphyrins. Apparently, a large variety of porphyrins are found mixed in with the oil to the chagrin of the oil companies. Naturally, one supposes that these are somehow related to derivatives or decay products of other porphyrins and their related products, such as chlorophyll. Some of them might be. However, Baker et al., discovered that a whole class of these porphyrins can in no way be related to them because of their structure (Fig. 6.15). They contain a benzene ring attached to one of the pyrolle structures. The porphyrin molecule, Chi (χ), identified in outer space and discussed in Chapter 13, contains four of these benzene rings. A porphyrin with one benzene ring is generally known as a rhodo-type porphyrin. Is it an intermediate between the tetrabenz-porphyrins of outer space and biological substances? Presumably, under very special conditions, benzene rings can be broken by the application of heat and water. It is gratifying to find some remnant of this more basic tetrabenzporphyrin: even if it is just an intermediate, it is very possibly the missing link. To repeat the main thrust of the argument: this rhodo-type petroporphyrin can in no way be related to any decay product of a biological porphyrin, because on earth there are no benzene rings on any of its biological porphyrins. It may very likely be the evidence needed to establish the connection to its original source.

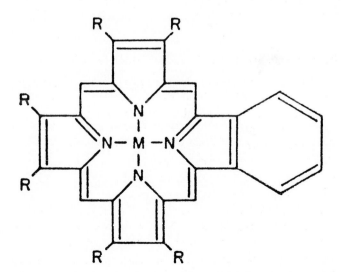

Figure 6.15. Rhodo-type petroporphyrin (see Earl W. Baker et al. **Journal Am. Chem. Soc.** *89,* 3631 [1967]).
Note the lone benzene ring attached to the porphyrin structure. Such molecules do not occur in biologically derived porphyrins.

Historical Note: The Credibility of Witnesses: Stones from Heaven, Who Ever Believes That Can Be True?

No less a person than Thomas Jefferson displayed the same incredulity on hearing of the Weston, Connecticut meteorite (December 26, 1807) which had been investigated by Professors Silliman and Kingsley of Yale. He remarked that it was easier to believe that Yankee professors would lie, than that stones would fall from heaven.

One of the commissions of the French Academy, which included among its members the chemist Lavoisier (though only twenty-five years old at the time), declared the meteorite of Luce (1768) to be a variety of pyrite. Concerning the stone meteorite shower of Barbotan (France, 1790), which was well confirmed by the mayor and the city council, the French scientist Berthelon wrote: "How sad it is to see a whole municipality attempt to lend credibility, through a formal deposition, to folk tales that arouse the pity not only of physicists but of all sensible people." In Germany, X. Stutz (about 200 years ago), wrote: "Of course it is said that in both cases (meteorites of Agram, Croatia, 1761, and Eichstadt, Bavaria, 1785) the iron fell from the sky. Even the more enlightened minds in Germany may have believed that in 1751, in view of the terrible ignorance then prevailing of natural history and practical physics. But in our times it would be unforgiveable to regard such fairy tales as likely."

Chapter 7

THE ACTIVE, EVOLVING EARTH— TECTONICS

The subject of the earth covers a lot of territory. One obviously cannot do justice to all topics related to the earth in a book on Astronomy. However, those aspects that have a direct bearing on the theme of the course are briefly discussed. They include chemical composition of the earth's crust, ages of rocks, and the evolution of the earth itself as an example of a typical body of our solar system. The earth, being easily accessible, provides the best clues to the origin of the solar system.

> As is usually the case,
> After travelling through space,
> Earth is still the very best
> Cosmic theories' acid test.
>
> (F.M.J.)

The Atomic Elements of the Earth's Crust

As a continuation from the previous chapter, we shall first briefly review the most abundant elements in the earth's crust (Table 7.1). Note that oxygen is the most abundant

TABLE 7.1
Elements in Earth's Continental Crust

Element	Symbol	% by Weight
Oxygen	O	45.2
Silicon	Si	27.2
Aluminum	Al	8.0
Iron	Fe	5.8
Calcium	Ca	5.0
Magnesium	Mg	2.8
Sodium	Na	2.3
Potassium	K	1.7
Titanium	Ti	0.9
Hydrogen	H	0.14
Manganese	Mn	0.1
Phosphorus	P	0.1
		———
Total		99.2
(Rest-rare minerals)		.8

element in the crust. There is a great deal of fascinating historical information locked up within the rock minerals. Their chemistry reveals substantial heat treatment in their distant past. The peak temperature and the extent of time to which rocks were exposed to the heat treatment may perhaps be the most useful information that could be extracted. Some rocks were also under intense pressure at the same time. Their past was pure torture. It would require similar treatment to identical chemical rock constituents in order to duplicate and discover their prior history.

The Earth in Evolution, Plate Tectonics—Continental Drift

The geology of the earth, its internal structure, and its innermost properties contain, in a large measure, the secrets and the evidence for the early evolution of the solar system. Unfortunately, this evidence is difficult to accumulate, and, as far as the inside of the earth is concerned, rather difficult to come by. In fact, the only technique presently available for mapping in a rather crude way the innermost regions of the earth is the method of seismology. This method uses sound waves of different frequencies which can travel the 8,000 miles from one side of the earth and back again, if necessary. By studying the speeds of these waves, the manner in which they are reflected, and the details of the two types of waves, namely the *shear waves* and the *pressure waves*, one can umambiguously determine boundaries or whether the waves are travelling through a solid, a liquid, or a gas. One cannot distinguish between a liquid and high pressure gas, though unfortunately. The key results are that the earth contains a solid core surrounded by a fluid core (or perhaps high pressure gas), then by solid mantle (Fig. 7.1). The density distribution inside the earth is shown in Figure 7.2. In addi-

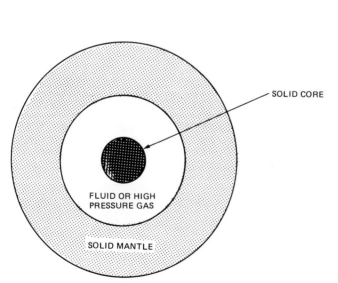

Figure 7.1. A schematic diagram of a cross section of the earth, showing the solid mantle, the fluid core, and the solid innermost core.

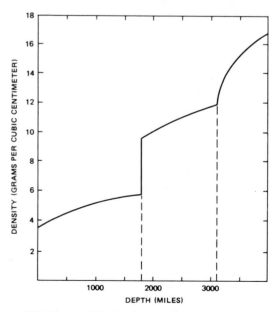

Figure 7.2. The earth's density as a function of depth. This data was deduced from seismic measurements.

108

tion, during the last 20 years or so, a very complete mapping of the rift valleys, the trenches, and the "zones of fire" as the earthquake belt is called, has indicated that the earth is still in a very active mode: the continents are drifting apart.

Abundances of Rare Metals in the Earth

Table 7.2 is a compilation of rare metals. It compares the maximum recoverable amount (A) with the relative cosmic abundances (B). This comparison deserves further analysis. First, one has to realize that Skinner's estimates could be off by an order of magnitude (a factor of 10), but not by 3 orders of magnitude. If we are to have faith in the cosmic abundance part of the table, then we come to a fascinating conclusion: There are enormous quantities of gold and plati-

TABLE 7.2
Rare Metals

Element	A Maximum Recoverable Tonnage from Ore Deposits Millions of Metric Tons	B Cosmological Abundances (Relative Scale)
Nickel	1,200	400,000
Copper	1,000	8,000
Niobium	340	40
Lead	170	50
Thorium	100	5
Tantalum	40	1.6
Tin	25	16
Uranium	27	1
Molybdenum	20	3.2
Tungsten	17	8
Silver	1.3	2.7
Mercury	0.34	6.3
Platinum	0.084	64
Gold*	0.034	3.2

Table A is based on the assumption that mining will not be deeper than 10 km below the surface of the crust. (Data from B.J. Skinner, American Scientist, *64*, 258/1976.)

Table B is derived from data by Allen "Astrophysical Quantities." This table is shown to remind ourselves of the *finite* quantities of minerals available on earth.

About 3% of all available copper is already mined. Having mined out all of these minerals does not mean the end of life. It means more recycling of these minerals is necessary or usage of more cosmologically abundant minerals such as iron, magnesium, or aluminum. As Skinner predicts: Back to another *iron age*?

*Table A also implies, based on about 10^9 oz. of gold in various bank vaults, that about half the gold in the earth's crust is already extracted. This is not so. See Text.

num yet to be discovered in the earth someplace—about 1,000 times more than has presently been discovered! This information should be good news for the gold miners and bad news for the gold hoarders. (Fort Knox holds about 1/4 of the world's present supply.) Of course, those treasures could well be deep inside the earth. However, relative amounts of the heavy, rare elements, Ta, W, Mo, and uranium, have been correctly estimated in the earth's crust. It is very likely that a number of extremely rich veins of gold and platinum still remain undiscovered. Since the other heavy element estimates in the Earth's crust are consistent with cosmological abundances, unlike gold and platinum, we cannot expect to find large unsuspected Uranium ore deposits in the crust. Uranium ore supplies have to be considered if future fission reactors are to become more plentiful and cost competitive. If indeed these predictions turn out to be correct, then astronomy is useful in an economic sense.

Nuclear Time Clocks

We shall now discuss briefly the problem of age determinations since the subject has direct astronomical implications. How old is a given rock on the earth, on the moon, or a piece of meteorite? Just as a person's age might be estimated by the state of the skin, the lack of hair, his teeth, a subtle method is used to determine the age of a rock. The time markers within a rock are specific radioactive atoms, which decay. This spontaneous decay of atoms, such as potassium 40, rubidium 87, uranium 238, and thorium 232, are excellent time clocks. Their decay, or daughter, products are well known and can be detected. In fact, one can perform measurements in the laboratory on all these compounds and thereby establish their rate of decay. The only assumption one makes in this technique is that nothing within the rock was disturbed since its inception: no daughter or parent products were introduced at any time. Consequently, from the rate of the decay and by knowing the remaining parent-daughter atoms within the rock, one can extrapolate back to the age of the parent atom, or the time its clock was started.

Let us consider briefly an analogy to illustrate the technique. Imagine that you had deposited $100 in your bank account and that one dollar was removed automatically (as a service charge) from that account every day. Suppose that one day you looked at your bank account and you saw that you had $42 left. Even if you had failed to keep track of the elapsed number of days since the money was deposited, you would immediately be able to deduce that 58 days had elapsed. This analogy illustrates a similar technique used for radioactive atoms.

The half-life of an element is used as a criterion for its decay rate. The definition of a half-life is the time required for one-half of the original atoms to have disintegrated into daughter products. Thus, taking the example of uranium 238, if one starts out with a million such atoms, then, after four and one-half billion years only half a million atoms of U_{238}

will be left. Nature has kindly provided us with a large number of radioactive species to work with. However, only the very long lived ones are of any use in this type of age determination, since one requires some leftover atoms of the original parent in order to establish a meaningful age.

It was this technique that was used to obtain a measurement of the age of our solar system based on rocks found in meteorites and in a few lunar samples. The oldest rocks found on earth so far do not exceed 3.3 billion years. (It can be safely assumed, however, that the earth is 4 1/2 billion years old, based on the meteorite and lunar samples measurements.)

Geothermal Temperature Gradient

Scientists have long realized that the inside of the earth is hot. The argument is *how hot?*

What is the most dramatic evidence for the internal heat? Volcanoes eject molten lava at temperatures sometimes exceeding 1,200°C.

Numerous hot springs (e.g., Yellowstone Park) provide hot water, and the deeper we penetrate into the earth's crust, the hotter the rocks become. Very deep mines may have unbearably hot temperatures. Water in deep rock formations is warmer than underground water from shallow depths. The evidence for the increase of temperatures as one drills deeper into the earth's crust is undisputed. The temperature increases roughly about 1°C for every 100 ft. of depth, or about 50°C per mile. The temperature does not increase in a uniform manner, particularly near the mid-ocean ridge boundaries or near oceanic trenches. Thus, anywhere the geological formations are peculiar, anomalous temperature changes occur as well. Recent work by D.I. Turcotte and G. Schubert indicates that at depths of about 300 kilometers, temperatures as high as 1,500°C are encountered. If one extrapolates this rate of temperature increase, the center of the earth's temperature is somewhere between 100,000 and 200,000°C. Such high temperatures are not readily accepted by present-day geologists. We shall return to these apparently high temperatures a few times in our discussions. A high temperature may be a measure of an equivalent high potential energy source whose heat production capability is equivalent to these high temperatures. For example, the core of a fission reactor has an equivalent high temperature because of its energy generating capacity. As long as energy is extracted at the proper rate, the core temperature stays below the melting point of its containment capsules. Once its energy is no longer removed rapidly enough, its core temperature would rise quickly and cause a complete melt down of the core. The earth's core may be analogous to this man-made device.

The Earth's Crust

Geologists presume that the continents are underlain by a comparatively light granitic crust about 25 miles thick, and

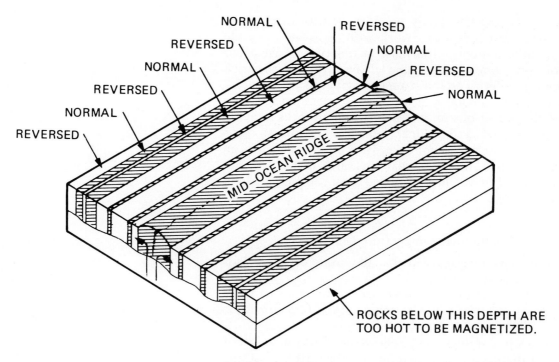

REVERSED NORMAL REVERSED NORMAL REVERSED NORMAL NORMAL REVERSED NORMAL REVERSED NORMAL

MID-OCEAN RIDGE

ROCKS BELOW THIS DEPTH ARE TOO HOT TO BE MAGNETIZED.

Figure 7.3. Sea floor spreading and the "frozen" record of the earth's past magnetic fields. Note how the molten hot material (lava) is pushed up from inside the earth and how it becomes deposited in successive striped layers as it solidifies. The resulting magnetization pattern is completely symmetric on both sides of the ocean ridge. The record of the earth's magnetic field present at the time the molten lava is extruded becomes permanently recorded as soon as the lava solidifies.

the oceans underlain by a crust which is only 5 miles thick. The oceanic crust is composed of denser basaltic minerals. The boundary between the crust and the mantle is called the Mohorovicic discontinuity—abbreviated, Moho. The outer rigid lithosphere consisting of a shell of between 40 and 90 miles in thickness, comprises the crust and the rigid upper-most part of the mantle.

Material is being pushed out and deposited on either side. Thus, the ocean basins consist of relatively newer material; progressively older material exists on either side of the ocean ridges. A plot of the magnetic fields perpendicular to such an ocean ridge showed the surprising result that in the distant past, the direction of the earth's magnetic field changed many times (Fig. 7.3). By plotting these changes on either side of the ridge, one can get a measure of the manner by which the material was pushed out from the inside. As the hot lava cooled, the magnetic material oriented itself along the then existing magnetic field. It then "froze" in that direction, and a permanent record was established. Thanks to this magnetic record, one now has a rather fascinating story which requires interpretation.

Examining a map of the continents, it is readily seen that South America and Africa could fit very well together. The concept of these two continents having once been joined in the past and then drifting apart is a rather old one. As long ago as 1620, Francis Bacon discussed the possibility that the

Western Hemisphere had once been joined to Europe and Africa. In 1688, P. Placet wrote an imaginative memoir entitled "The Corruption of the Great and Little World," where it is shown that before the deluge, America was not separated from the other parts of the world. Some 200 years later, Antonio Snider was struck by the similarities between American and European fossil plants of the Carboniferous period (about 300 million years ago) and proposed that all the continents were once part of a single land mass. His work of 1858 was called "Creation and Its Mysteries Revealed." By the end of the nineteenth century, geology had entered seriously into the discussion. At that time the Austrian geologist Eduard Suess had noted such a close correspondence of the geological formations in the lands of the Southern Hemisphere that he fitted them into a single continent which he called Gondwanaland. In 1908, F.B. Taylor of the United States and in 1910, Alfred L. Wegener of Germany independently suggested mechanisms that could account for large lateral displacements of the earth's crust and thus show how continents might be driven apart. Wegener's work became the center of a debate that has lasted to the present day. Although the evidence for the continental drift was overwhelming by the turn of the century, it took an additional 60 years until, at one meeting, geologists finally accepted Wegener's theory. Part of the reason for their long delay in accepting Wegener's ideas was that a very prominent geophysicist by the name of Bullard had calculated the amount of energy necessary in order to move these continents. He found that there was not sufficient energy available to perform this enormous task. Bullard's calculation was apparently sufficient to prevent acceptance of Wegener's theory for a long time.

The following discussion represents the author's own work. More extensive discussions of his theories are found in Chapter 18.

Present geological studies show the trends of how the continents have moved as well as the rifts which lie deep in the oceans, the trenches, and finally the reconstructed map of the continents all placed together in its original configuration ~ 250 million years ago—that is where the situation is at the moment. The author has examined this problem and suggested a simple solution; that the original size of the earth was roughly one-half its present size. The exact original diameter was 1/1.86 of its present diameter. Plotting out the shapes of the continents, one can place all of the continents on a sphere of that smaller radius (Fig. 7.6). We also know that the earth's rotation is slowing down at the rate of one-thousandth of a second per century. If one were to project this backwards in time, it would amount to a speed-up of about 11 hours during the 4 1/2 billion years of the earth's existence. Thus, the earth was obviously rotating faster initially. Also, the total amount of material comprising the earth must roughly be unchanged. Consequently, one can calculate, based on the conservation of mass and the conservation of angular momentum, what the conditions must have

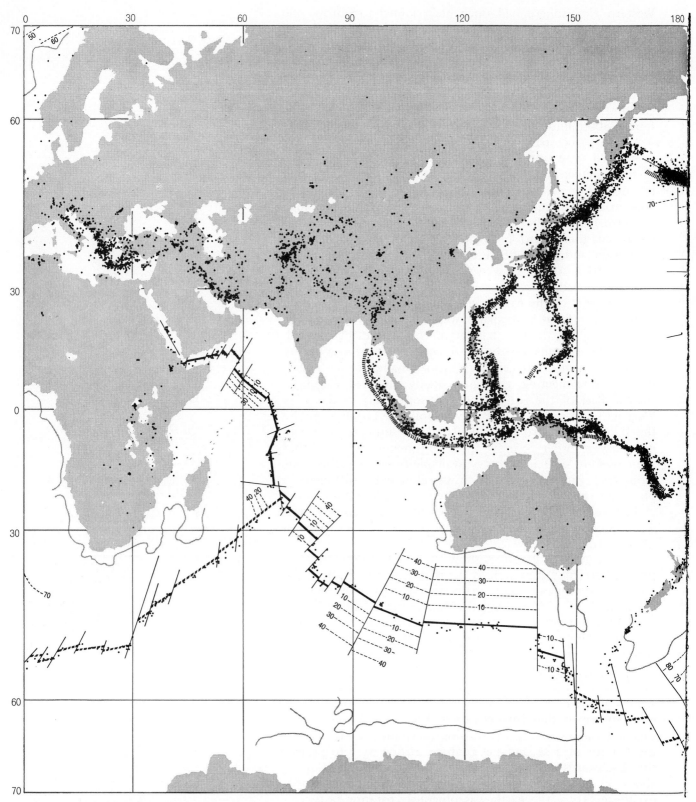

Figure 7.4. WORLDWIDE PATTERN of sea-floor spreading is evident when magnetic and seismic data are combined. Mid-ocean ridges (*heavy black lines*) are offset by transverse fracture zones (*thin lines*). On the basis of spreading rates determined from magnetic data J.R. Heirtzler and his colleagues established "isochrons" that give the age of the sea floor in millions of years (*broken thin lines*). The edges of many continental masses (*gray lines*) are rimmed by deep ocean trenches (*hatching*). When the epicenters of all earthquakes recorded from 1957 to 1967 (plotted by Muawi

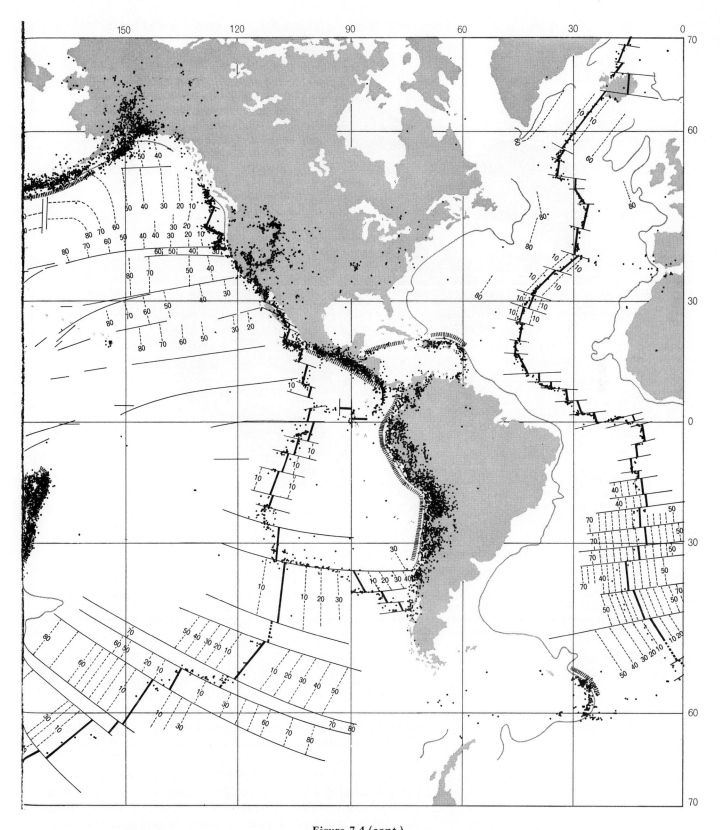

Figure 7.4 (cont.)
Barazangi and James Dorman from U.S. Coast and Geodetic Survey data) are superposed (*dots*), the vast majority of them fall along mid-ocean ridges or along the trenches, where the moving sea floor turns down. From *Sea-Floor Spreading* by J.R. Heirtzler. Copyright © 1968 by Scientific American, Inc. All rights reserved.

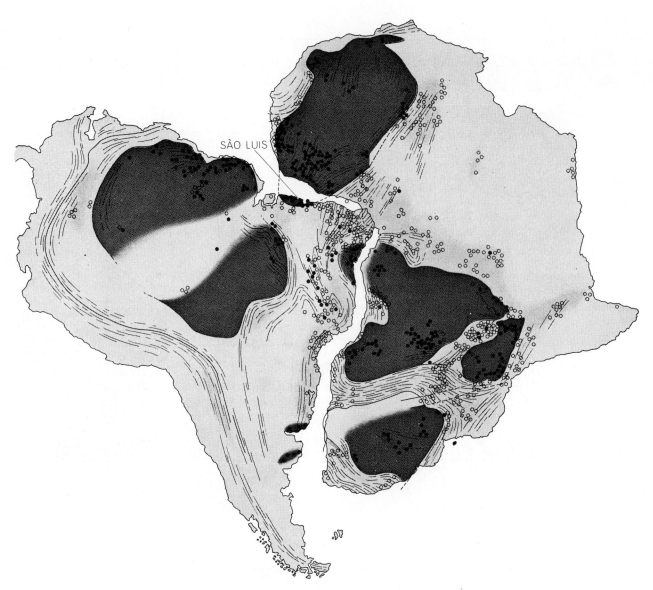

SÃO LUIS

Figure 7.5. Tentative matching of geological provinces of the same age shows how South America and Africa presumably fitted together some 200 million years ago. Dark-areas represent ancient continental blocks, called cratons, that are at least 2,000 million years old. From *The Confirmation of Continental Drift* by Patrick M. Hurley. Copyright © 1968 by Scientific American, Inc. All rights reserved.

been like originally, particularly if one works backwards to the original size of the earth. Its mean density was about 35.6. Initially, the earth was an extremely hot object whose crust was cooling down. Breaks in the crust allowed the material to be pushed up, and provided a continuous expansion that we still see going on today. It is interesting to note that the extent of the present liquid core is exactly the size of the original size of the earth. There also is complete internal self-consistency as far as the conservation of mass and angular momentum are concerned, projecting the earth to this smaller original diameter. There is geological evidence that 3 1/2 billion years ago, the surface temperature of the earth was 50°C, far hotter than it is today. Based on the author's study, we have the answer to one of the critical geologic dilemmas: the source of the original energy: The

ORGINAL SIZE OF EARTH

SIZE OF LIQUID CORE

Figure 7.6. The earth now and 4 1/2 million years ago. Note that all the continents can be fitted with reasonably good precision on a sphere of about 1/2 size of present earth. *Conclusion*: The earth expanded. *Implication*: A large internal energy source must exist inside the earth. It is presumably the solid inner core.

answer is that the center of the earth initially would have had an energy source whose *equivalent temperature* was about five million degrees. That is sufficient energy to provide for the expansion of the earth to its present radius, as well as to provide the energy necessary for mountain building, moving the continents, causing the volcanoes to evolve, and so forth. It is a very simple calculation to show how much energy is necessary to work against gravity in building up to the present size earth from half its size. There is no other source of energy available other than that which was placed there originally! Present theory presumes, for instance, that internal heat is a result of nuclear disintegration of limited quantities of radioactive species. Such theories could only account for a few thousand degrees at most, whereas millions of degrees are necessary for all the tectonic and geologic activities associated with the expansion of the earth.

This is an answer to Bullard's dilemma.

As final proof, observe the reconstructed pictures of the earth showing *all* the continents combined to form an almost perfect sphere (Figs. 7.7, 7.8, 7.9). It would be extremely difficult to find an alternative explanation. It is too much of a coincidence for all the continents to fit together on the size

117

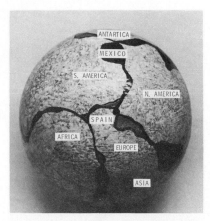

Figure 7.7. Reconstruction of the continents on globe 1/1.86 present size. Dark areas are overlap or gaps. Note the matching of continental margins on other parts of the continents not previously considered.

Figure 7.8. Fitting of continents on original size of earth.

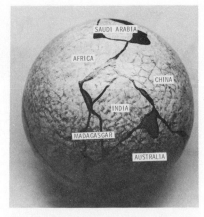

Figure 7.9. The reconstructed earth 4 1/2 billion years ago, as seen from different vantage points on the original size globe. The orientation of the globe is chosen in order to exhibit all the different continental margins.

sphere which corresponds to 1/1.86 of present size. Corroboration of this theory would involve geologic matching of other parts of the continents which this picture predicts were once joined.

The Earth Expansion

While nineteenth century thinking revolved around a shrinking earth, as recently as 1933, O.C. Hilgenberg believed that the mass and size of the earth had grown. An astronomer, J.K.E. Halm, suggested that the earth's density has been decreasing from an original 9.13 (density compared to water) to its present 5.5 L. Egyed also supported the theory of the earth increasing in size. He believed that the ocean areas expanded because the continental plates do not appear to allow for this expansion. A very astute observation. Figures 7.10 and 7.11 show the ocean areas laid out without the presence of their usual water content. It very clearly exhibits the stretching and tearing of the ocean bottom. The surface stretch marks on the ocean floor are pronounced in both the Atlantic as well as the Pacific Oceans. Moreover, in the Atlantic Ocean, it is apparent that the stretching occurred laterally away from the mid-Atlantic ridge as well as in the transverse direction.

Another geologist, S.W. Carey, speculated that an improvement in his jigsaw reconstruction for 200,000,000 years ago would result if, by fitting the continents together, the earth's diameter were reduced to three-fourths its present size. Geologists generally stopped short of the idea of reducing the size of the original earth to the liquid core as will be discussed subsequently.

Evidence for the earth's slowing down is contained in the fossil records. Paleontologists have been able to count the

Figure 7.10. A part of the Atlantic Ocean floor. Note the mid-Atlantic ridge. These two Figures (7.10 and 7.11) show the type of stresses and strains that the earth is undergoing by having its surface pushed apart and material extruded from the inside out. (Map courtesy of *National Geographic Society*.)

Figure 7.11. A part of the Pacific Ocean floor. Note the sea floor pattern. (Map courtesy of *National Geographic Society*.)

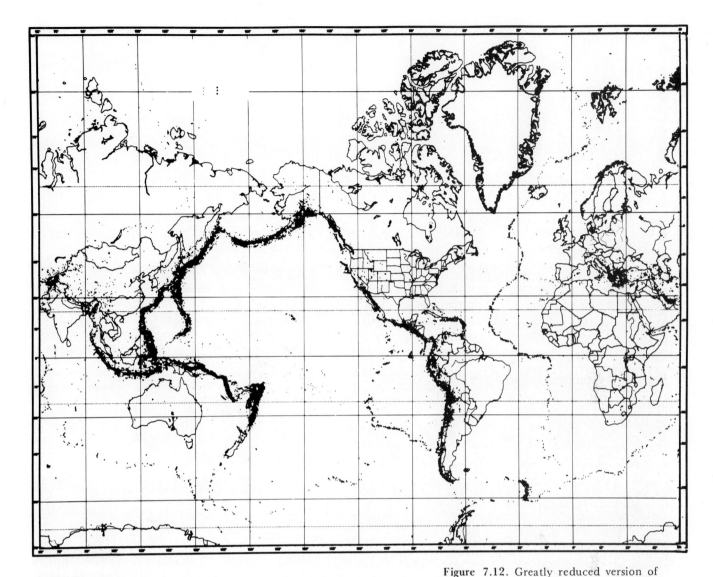

Figure 7.12. Greatly reduced version of the new World Seismicity map prepared by The U.S. Geological Survey shows the location of about 23,000 earthquakes around the world (U.S. Dept. of Interior).

daily growth rings in corals and other fossils which suggest that the earth had about 400 days in the year during the Devonian Period, roughly 375,000,000 years ago.

Other dramatic evidence of the earth's potential internal energy is its ability to move enormously large blocks of plates. Such dramatic events occur periodically along plate boundaries. The ring of fire zone (Fig. 7.12) which extends all along the Pacific Coast, through the Aleutians, and down into Japan, dilineates the area where this movement occurs (earthquakes). Spectacular examples at any one location may occur only a few times during an individual's lifetime.

The San Andreas Fault is an example (Figs. 7.13 and 7.14) along which sudden and dramatic movement occurs every hundred years or so. In 1906, the San Francisco earthquake demonstrated movement along the northern portion of this fault. The most recent movement of this fault in the Southern California area occurred in 1857. There are a large number of smaller faults associated with this larger one, which also occasionally cause earthquakes. None are as powerful,

RECENT EARTH MOVE-
MENTS ALONG FAULT
HAVE DISPLACED
STREAM CHANNEL
FROM A TO B

REPEATED MOVEMENTS
OVER THOUSANDS OF
YEARS HAVE DISPLACED
CHANNEL FROM A TO C

B

C

500 FEET

A

• •SAN ANDREAS
FAULT

Figure 7.13. Aerial view of the Carrizo Plain area, California showing displacements of stream channels caused by earlier movements along the San Andreas Fault (U.S. Dept. of Interior).

however, as the motion directly along the San Andreas Fault. The expected Richter scale reading each time will be in excess of 8; that is 100 times more powerful than the Sylmar earthquake in 1971.

Unfortunately, we do not have records extending back in time for more than 200 years in the California area. In Japan, major earthquakes occur every 100 years or so and, since the San Andreas Fault lies along the same ring of fire, a similar interval between quakes can be anticipated. Geologists are presently studying this fault area very carefully.

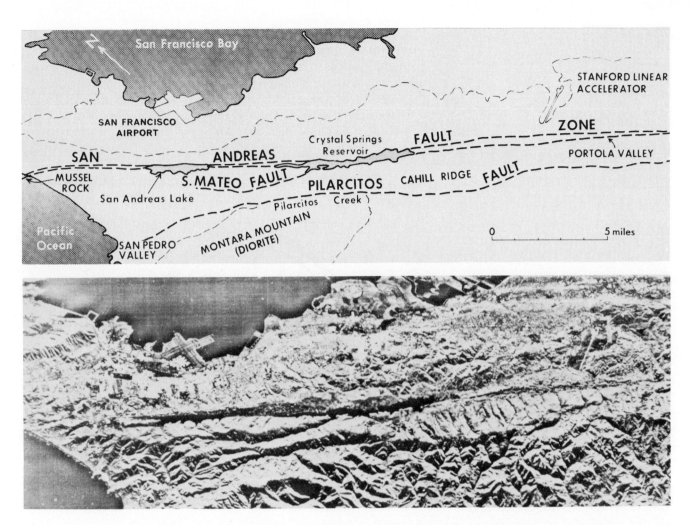

Figure 7.14. San Andreas Fault (radar imagery) (U.S. Dept. of Interior).

The San Andreas Fault is anticipated to release its built-up energy in the Southern California region within the next few years. It can be expected at any time.

Plate Tectonics and Its Relevance to Astronomy

There is a direct correlation, which we shall now outline, concerning the relevance of the earth's activities in relationship to the origin of the solar system. The earth, being close at hand, provides us with the best tools available. The following evidence should be considered together:

1. The projected internal temperature of 100,000°C, extrapolated from measurements near the earth's crust.
2. The internal energy necessary for expansion of the earth's diameter, for providing plate movement, geothermal energy, and mountain building.

Consider Figure 7.15: it is easily possible to calculate the amount of energy necessary to expand the earth from the original radius to its present one. The work that was expended in the expansion was done against the gravitational attraction of the earth's core. A very simplified approach is to consider the work done against this gravitational force F.

Work = Force × distance. An approximate expression for this work is $\frac{GM_1 M_2}{d^2}$ × distance; which is of the order of $\frac{GM^2}{R}$. It is *this* energy which is equivalent to about 5,000,000° K (within a factor of 10).

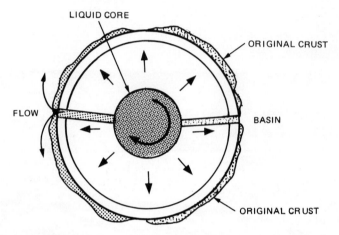

Figure 7.15. The earth's crust being pushed apart.

Project Hindsight

A great many people still believe that the earth is shrinking. This erroneous concept was espoused in the sixteenth century by Giordano Bruno, who compared the crust of the earth to the skin of an apple which wrinkles as the drying apple shrinks.

In 1833 Adam Sedgewick proposed that mountains are formed as the earth cools and contracts. Such notions are also commonly held by today's population.

One of the leading physicists of the nineteenth century, Lord Kelvin, had calculated the time required for the earth to cool to its present state. He estimated this to be 20 to 40 million years. His calculation of such an extremely short time-scale disturbed the geologists of the day a great deal.

Charles Darwin had taken issue with an earlier estimate by Kelvin where he allowed the earth to have a maximum age of 400 million years. According to Darwin, such a time span was insufficient to account for the evolutionary changes indicated by fossil records. Such arguments may not have swayed Lord Kelvin, since his estimates were based on solid calculations! Kelvin's mistake was merely that his assumptions were erroneous.

About 40 years ago, using nuclear dating techniques, geologists were able to obtain a preliminary measurement for the earth's age. It was about two billion years. A well-known astrophysicist at the time, Eddington, strongly opposed this idea, based on the age of the sun, which he had calculated to be far less than a billion years old.

Eddington's calculation was based on the then popular concept that the sun derives its energy exclusively from gravitational contraction. Since the sun's luminosity and size were known, it was relatively simple to calculate the amount of time it would take for the sun to shrink to about zero radius. This is *not* the way nature produces its energy however, as we shall discuss in Chapter 12.

Magnetic Fields

Additional Remark

If one were to add electric charges to any spinning system, magnetic fields would be generated. If the charges were positive, the magnetic field is in one direction. If the net charges were negative, the magnetic field direction is reversed, even though the direction of spin is the same.

Conclusion

One can change the direction of the magnetic field generated by a rotating charge configuration by either changing the direction of spin or by changing the sign of the net charge.

Q. Is this relevant?

A. Very possibly.

Clue: There are magnetic fields associated with sun spots (Chapter 12) which alternate in direction on successive sun spots. There is a magnetic field on the earth which has changed direction hundreds of times in the past.

Q. Could we discover a correlation here?

The basic physics is this: a rotating net charge distribution generates a magnetic field. Perhaps the net charge inside the fluid (it may be a plasma) earth core becomes successively different and even reverses sign subsequent to mass ejection processes. The mass ejection (volcanic activity) may result in an overshoot of one charge, which nature tries to correct on successive ejections, but never quite achieving exact neutrality except when the earth's magnetic field passes through a zero reading.

Chapter 8

OUR SUN

The Sun Viewed as a Star

We are indeed fortunate to have one star close at hand to supply us with all our energy requirements and, as a fringe benefit for astronomers, to educate us about stars in general. We shall concentrate on some of the important observed solar phenomena and discuss some of the outstanding features of this, our star.

Galileo had already discovered that there were **sunspots** on the surface of the sun, since these are easily recognizable and dominant features (Fig. 8.1). What is known about sunspots?

The total number of sunspots visible at any one time varies a great deal. Figure 8.2 shows a record of the number of sunspots as a function of time. Note that peaks and valleys occur roughly at intervals of about eleven years. We have such observations for the last 200 years. The peaks corresponding to sunspot maximum are not of equal height. Solar sunspot activity seems to be greater during certain periods and greatly diminished at others. How relevant is this phe-

Figure 8.1. Our sun with sunspots! (Hale Observatories)

126

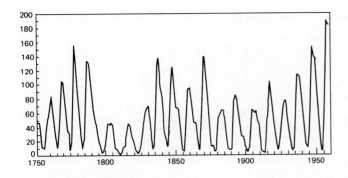

Figure 8.2. Number of sunspots versus time, plotted over a 200 year time span. Note the periodicity of the peaks.

nomena to us? During periods of sunspot minimum, there may be a correlation with the weather patterns. Such a correlation is not proven and is only poorly understood. At any event, during periods of sunspot minima, certain parts of the earth experience severe droughts. 1976 seems to have been a time close to sunspot minimum activity, and indeed there have been severe droughts in the Sahara and some parts of the United States. Another characteristic feature of sunspots is that they have magnetic fields associated with them which alternate in direction. There are two groups of sunspots; one in the northern latitudes of the sun and the other in the southern part. Sunspots never occur at the north and south poles, but are always associated with the middle latitude region. The sunspots then migrate towards the equator of the sun. The period of rotation of the sunspots varies between 24 and 27 days, roughly corresponding to the rotation of the sun. A given sunspot may be seen for perhaps two rotations and then will disappear back into the sun.

The outstanding feature about the sunspot magnetic field is that the polarity alternates between adjacent sunspots, but oppositely in the northern and in the southern part. If the northern sunspot group leads with positive polarity, then the southern group will lead with a negative one. After eleven years the cycle will reverse, such that the northern group will lead with a negative and the southern with a positive one. Thus, the sunspot cycle is not really an eleven-year cycle, but a twenty-two year cycle.

No theory or mechanism has ever been successfully worked out that will explain the polarity reversals, the twenty-two year cycles, nor the temperature differences between sunspots and photosphere.

The surface of the sun is called the photosphere. The gaseous material above this, the atmosphere of the sun, is called the chromosphere. The region beyond that is called the corona. A rich harvest of spectral lines is obtained when one examines the sun's radiation by means of a spectrograph (more about this in Chapter 11). More than 700 of these lines were studied by Fraunhofer in the early nineteenth century. There are presently over 25,000 solar lines catalogued that bear his name. A number of observatories throughout the world continually monitor the sun, a sort of sun skypatrol. They take pictures at various wavelengths using narrow band

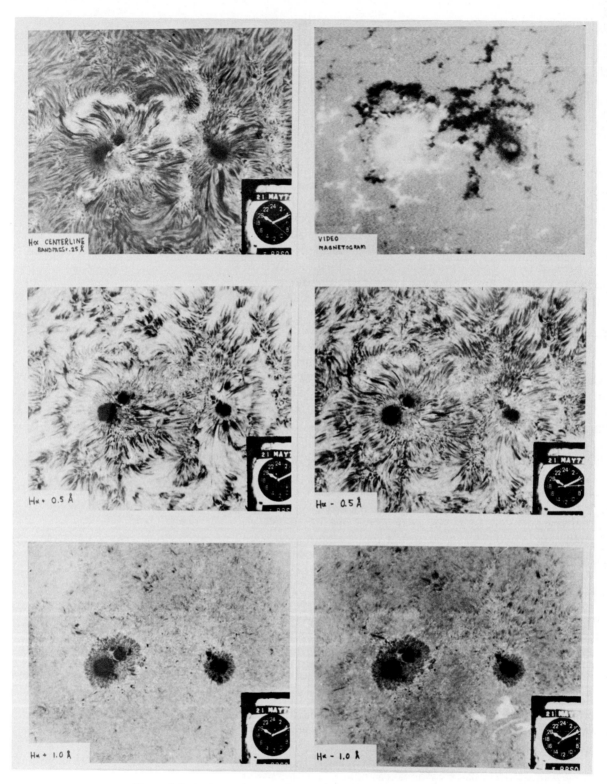

Figure 8.3. Active regions on the sun (Big Bear Solar Observatory).

spectral filters, particularly at wavelengths associated with very strong atomic transitions in common solar atoms. As a result, different solar features are enhanced. If the picture is taken with a "hydrogen filter," one sees essentially the hydrogen distribution on the sun. More dramatic pictures are sometimes obtained with a "calcium filter." Figure 8.6 is a very sharp, high resolution photo taken in 1970 at the High Altitude Observatory, near Boulder. The photograph of the photosphere, shows very fine details of the sunspots. Note the hairlike features radiating from a sunspot group. Also the **granular cells** on the surface of the sun are very clearly exhibited. The size of the sunspots vary. They typically range between 20,000 to 30,000 miles in diameter (sizes of Uranus and Neptune perhaps?). Some are between 60,000 and 90,000 miles in diameter (not too different from Jupiter or Saturn). Some groups survive as many as four to five rotations before they disappear within the sun. Sunspots have been seen to break up into smaller spots. Sunspots are never found at latitudes greater than plus or minus 45°; their heliographic latitudes are generally 30°. When a sunspot group is formed near the region of the sun's equator, one can be sure the sun's activity is at a minimum. However, before this group has a chance to fade away, another group, indicating a

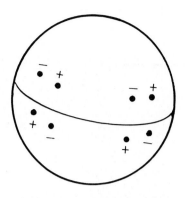

Figure 8.4. Schematic diagram of sunspots on the sun. Note the alternating sunspot polarities on the northern and southern hemispheres.

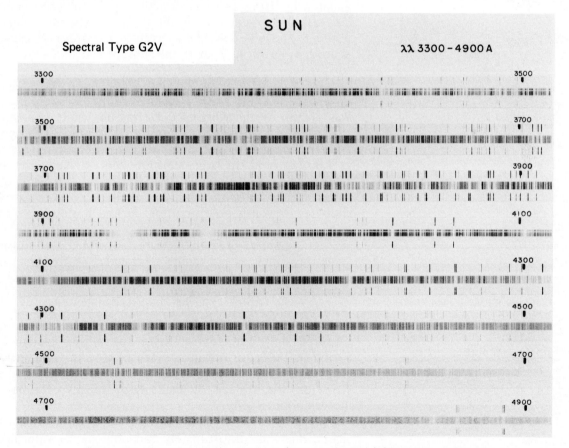

Figure 8.5. Part of the solar spectrum (Fraunhofer lines) (Hale Observatories).

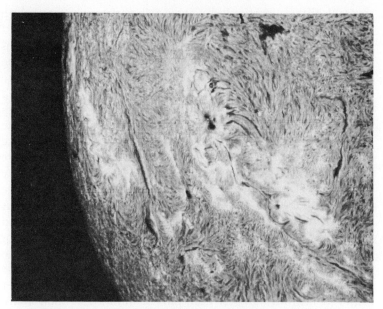

Figure 8.6. Picture of portion of sun (taken at one wavelength). (Climax High Altitude Solar Observatory)

new cycle, already begins to form at higher latitudes. Figure 8.7 shows an unusually clear sunspot as well as material apparently being emitted directly from the sunspot itself. Whereas the temperature on the surface of the sun is between 5,500°K and 6,000°K, the average temperature of a sunspot is around 4,500°K. That is, the sunspot acts like a "refrigerator."

Inspection of Figures 8.3 and 8.7 suggests that there are magnetic fields at work associated with the sunspots. This was proven by the work of G.E. Hale in 1908, who showed that there was a magnetic intensity of about 100 gauss associated with a small spot, and that these fields can be as large as 4,000 gauss at the larger sunspots. Since a magnet has both a north and a south pole, it shouldn't be too surprising therefore, that the sunspots usually occur in pairs, where one sunspot has its south pole pointing up and the other its north pole.

There are more dramatic features associated with sunspots; sometimes they even become spectacular. Active areas associated with sunspot groups are usually called **faculae.** Large eruptions associated with such groups are referred to as **prominences.** These can be seen best by means of a **spectro-heliograph.** Some very dramatic solar eruptions have been captured on photographs. There was a very active solar period in 1946, for instance, when photographs taken at the High Altitude Climax Observatory showed very unusual activities on the surface of the sun by means of time-lapse motion photography.

Finally, we come to discuss the most spectacular of all sights, one that unfortunately can only be seen during the rare period of a total solar eclipse; a period that is no more than eight minutes at any given locality. Pictures taken then show the outermost regions of the **corona** of the sun. Al-

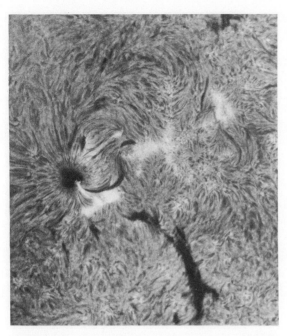

Figure 8.8. An enormous flare erupts from the solar surface.

Figure 8.7. A dramatic eruption can be observed directed away from the sunspot. It appears as if material is ejected directly from the sunspot itself (photo courtesy Dr. L. Lamore).

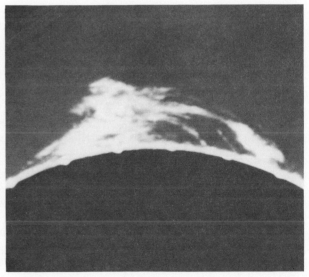

Figure 8.9. The corona during total eclipse (Hale Observatories).

Figure 8.10. Coronograph picture of flares and prominences. The sun shows activity on its surface (Hale Observatories).

Figure 8.11. Dramatic flare eruption to a distance of about 200,000 miles (Hale Observatories).

though the outer corona can only be seen during a total eclipse, the inner corona can be photographed by means of an instrument called a **coronagraph.** The unusual nature of the outer corona is the fact that its equivalent temperature is between about one and two million degrees. Emission lines appear in the corona, whereas mainly absorption lines are seen on the surface of the sun. The million degree temperature associated with the outer corona is not one that would be observed if one had a thermometer there, but one that is associated with the high energies of the electrons in the corona. The high equivalent temperature is deduced from the fact that many electrons in the coronal atoms are torn loose.

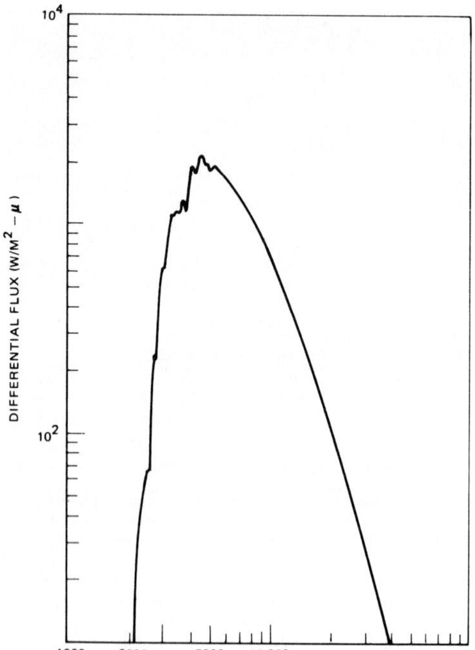

Electromagnetic Radiation from the Sun

The radiation from the sun is distributed over a whole range of wavelengths or colors. The peak of this color distribution is at 5,500Å. The complete spectral range of the sun's radiation is shown in Figure 8.12. It shows that below a certain wavelength, very little radiation is emitted by the sun, and likewise above certain wavelengths (2-3 microns) the radiation received is minimal. It should also be kept in mind that at the surface of the earth we do not receive the complete output from the sun. The earth's atmosphere reflects about 30% of the incident radiation and absorbs ultraviolet and certain long wavelengths. The total energy received outside the earth's atmosphere (i.e., the solar constant) is approximately 126 watts per square foot, or about 1,360 watts per square meter; more than half of this energy reaches sea level. It is this energy from the sun that drives the life cycles described in Chapter 9, it also keeps the earth warm (the atmosphere acting as a blanket to retain some of the heat at night).

Figure 8.12. The distribution of energy from the solar flux as a function of wavelength.

Variations in the sun's output do not exceed one percent at any time, despite variations in the visible surface activity seen on the sun. We can be fairly certain that the sun, during its lifetime of 4.6 billion years, could not have made any erratic departures in its light intensity, since it would have significantly altered the status of life on earth.

The intensity distribution of electromagnetic radiation from the sun in color is peaked in the green-yellow region. It is probably no accident that our eyes are most sensitive to the same region of the spectrum. In addition to light, the sun also emits a host of other particles. This comes under the category of **solar wind**.

Solar Wind

The solar wind consists of protons and electrons of equal number. The proton carries a positive and the electron a negative charge. The velocity of these particles, at the position of the earth, is about 300 kilometers per second when the sun is in its quiet phase. It can increase to as high as 800 kilometers per second during the sun's active phase. This solar wind is supersonic, having a **Mach** number between 5 and 7. During the active period of the sun, when sunspot groups are developing and solar flares are occurring, the solar wind characteristics become highly variable, and they are closely related to solar flare phenomena.

Some readers may be familiar with electricity, where the term current is a measure of the flow of electric charges. It is customarily measured in units of amperes. A television set, for example, would draw about 5 amperes, a 100-watt bulb about one. The proton flux, which is equal to the proton density times its directed velocity, corresponds to an electric current of about 10^{-11} amperes per square centimeter. At the position of the earth, this is not enough current to heat the filament of a light bulb, not even a flashlight. It might be enough current to tickle the fancy of lightening bugs.

Anyone contemplating trips to the sun has to keep in mind that the solar wind particle density increases as one gets closer to the sun (besides getting hotter). It becomes as large as 10^7 particles per cubic centimeter. Figure 8.13 shows the directed velocity of the solar wind as a function of distance from the sun, as well as the effective temperature associated with these particles. Also shown is the variation that one encounters during the active and quiet sun phases. The effective temperature extrapolated to the outside surface of the sun is about a million degrees—about the same value as the temperature of the corona.

During the time of solar flare activities, one observes the emission of various types of particles as well as electromagnetic radiation from the sun. Whereas the electromagnetic radiation travels with the speed of light and takes eight and a half minutes to reach the earth, the particles take longer, anywhere from a few hours to a few days. Furthermore, since the photons can travel in straight lines (light does not get

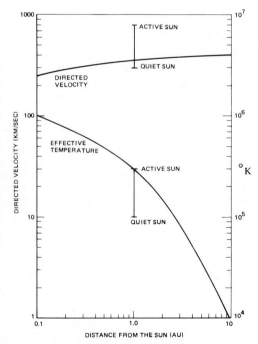

Figure 8.13. The solar wind velocity and effective temperature as a function of distance from the sun.

133

bent in a vacuum), the electrical particles emitted by the sun are influenced by magnetic fields and can be bent. There is a magnetic field associated with the sun and the sunspots. There is another magnetic field associated with the earth. Because of the earth's magnetic bending effect, only about ten percent of the bright large solar flares are followed by charged particles which reach the earth.

Although the earth's atmosphere does a fairly good job in shielding us from most of the UV radiation, the astronauts on the moon had to be concerned about solar wind excesses, since the moon obviously had no atmosphere to protect them. There is some correlation between the times at which solar flares occur and the eleven-year solar cycle.

The Constituents of the Solar Flare Particles

Solar flare particle radiation is made up of 90% protons, whose energy is in excess of 1 **Mev** and approximately 10% alpha particles in the same energy range. It also contains some heavier nuclei and enough electrons to maintain electrical neutrality. The energy of the electron is in the kev range. For a word of explanation about the technical terms, *Mev* and *kev*, see Technical Note No. 2, which refers to the energies of the particles. One **Mev** is the energy that a charged particle obtains when it falls through a potential of a million volts. Similarly, a thousand electron volts between charged plates would accelerate an electron to that energy.

The occurrence of flares is more probable when a large persisting group of sunspots is present on the surface of the sun.

It should also be mentioned that the sun emits a large number of protons whose energies are greater than those that have been mentioned here. Energies as large as 500 Mev have been obtained from the sun on occasion.

Contrast the particle flux emitted from the sun with particles that have been detected from other sources, coming under the title of cosmic rays.

Elements on the Sun

More than 60 elements have been identified on the sun by means of spectroscopy (Table 6.11). Also, at least 18 molecules have been identified in the sun's cooler regions. The relative abundances of the elements on the sun were already discussed in Chapter 6 and compared with abundances in meteorites.

Sun's Surface under High Magnification

The surface of the sun has a mottled, peculiarly grainy appearance (Fig. 8.14). The size of these **granules** is between 300-1,000 km in diameter. They appear to have a hot inner region and a cooler outer region. Their structure is uneven and not circular. They persist for varying periods on the sun's surface, usually about 8 minutes in duration, before disappearing. By means of narrow band spectral filters with adjustable pass bands, the motion of the gas atoms can be followed with earth-based telescopes. Complicated outward and inward flow of gases, slow pulsations of solar regions and other exotic effects are being studied.

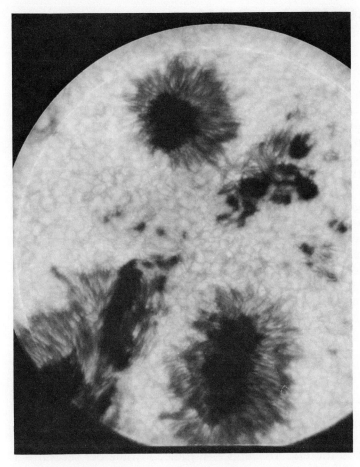

Figure 8.14. Excellent, high magnification photo of sun's surface (Climax Solar Observatory).

Chapter 9

THE SOURCE—(SUN'S) ENERGY MAKES IT WORK

In this chapter we wish to illuminate in greater detail the effect of the sun's energy in making life possible; above all, we shall trace the energy flow and the cycles which are driven by means of the sun's energy. The subjects to be discussed deal with a broad overall picture of the sun's role in maintaining the life cycle.

The sun provides energy for all of life's processes. Before we get into some of those details, it might be beneficial to obtain an overview of how the energy is utilized on earth and while doing so, we shall list all the energy sources that we presently know. One very essential distinction that must be made first, however, is the difference between power and energy. What do we pay for when we pay our electric bills—power or energy? About half the population thinks it's power, but it is really energy. Power is the rate at which energy is utilized. Power is equal to energy divided by time.

$$\text{Power} = \frac{\text{Energy}}{\text{Time}}$$

(or Energy = Power × Time)

The conventional units of energy are Joules and the unit for power is watt. Another unit for energy (in the c.g.s. system) is the erg. 10^7 ergs = 1 Joule; 1 Joule per second = 1 watt. Electric bills are charged for kilowatt-hours, i.e., the use of 1,000 watts for 1 hour, 100 watts for 10 hours, or 1 watt for 1,000 hours.

Examine Table 9.1 carefully in order to get an overview of all the valuable energy sources. The primary source *is* the sun. The secondary sources are derived *from* the sun, with the only exception being the lunar gravitational tidal energy. Some might think that the nuclear fuel is not solar energy (if all material initially came from inside the sun, however, it must surely be counted as solar energy). However, the distinction between solar and nuclear energy in the context in which it is customarily used, obviously separates the two forms of energy. Table 9.1 shows the manifestation of energy and its flow.

Figure 9.1 connects all forms of energy together to illustrate possible energy flow patterns. Present technology uses mainly heat, either nuclear or fossil fuel, to expand a gas. In the gasoline engine, heat is supplied by chemical means, when a spark sets off an explosive gas-air mixture. The resulting gas

TABLE 9.1
The Magic Flow of Precious Energy
The Stuff of Life

Primary Source: The SUN.

      Output: 4×10^{26} (joules/sec.).

         or 4×10^{26} watts (of this, the earth receives 10^{17} watts).

Secondary Sources: A. (Derived from SUN).

Earth's internal heat source (3×10^{13} watts).

Rotational energy of earth (kinetic energy): 2×10^{29} joules.

Atmospheric motion—Winds (secondary solar energy).

Lunar and solar gravitational energy—Tides.

Secondary Sources: B.

Nuclear fuel—Fission of uranium 235, plutonium.

         Nuclear fusion processes (explosively so far).

Fossil fuel—Oil, coal, natural gas, wood (cellulose).

Manifestations of Energy and its Flow

1. a. Photo—Chemical reactions; e.g., photosynthesis (e.g., smog), ozone.

   b. Photoelectric—Direct conversion of sunlight to electrical energy via photovoltaic (solar cells) devices.

2. *Chemical reactions*

   a. e.g., oxidation (burning of fuel).

   b. Cellular chemical activities and energy production.

3. *Electrical*

   a. Generators, motors, convert work to electricity and vice-versa (moving charges).

   b. Electrical energy storage devices, e.g., capacitors, electrolytic batteries.

      Charge separation technology.

   c. Electromagnetic fields—Radiation.

      Example 1. Primary source of solar energy input on earth (about 100 watts/sq. ft.).

      Example 2. Radio and television electromagnetic energy (transmission via radiation or along wires).

4. *Mechanical (work)*

   a. Kinetic energy—Energy by virtue of motion (e.g. car travelling at 55 m.p.h., or flywheel).

   b. Potential energy—Mainly gravitational energy by virtue of position; e.g., with respect to center of earth.

5. *Heat*

   Intrinsic energy associated with the random motions of atoms and molecules in gases, solids, or liquids.

---

expansion drives a piston, as shown in the diagram. As the piston is being pushed forward, a force is applied. The work that is performed by the piston is equal to the applied force times the distance the piston moves.

$$\text{Work} = \text{Force} \times \text{Distance}$$

(Energy → Work)

Note that this force can rotate a drive shaft, which in turn can either rotate the wheels of a locomotive, the wheels of a car or a hydraulic pump, or that of an electric generator. The expansion chamber indicated in Figure 9.1 can be a steam engine. It can also be replaced by a turbine type device which is similar to the one shown in Figure 9.1 for pumping water from a lower level to a higher level.

Note that one can drive this system also by reversing the flow of water and dispensing with the heat engine. We will discuss this later as an example of hydroelectric power generation.

Let's follow this diagram a little further. You will note that the electric power generated can be transmitted to perform the following: drive another electric motor, heat an incandescent or a fluorescent light bulb, generate heat by means of a resistive element, R, or charge a battery. If we disconnect the generator from our electrical circuit and in turn connect in a solar panel which consists of photovoltaic solar cells, all electrical devices can be operated in a similar manner. Present-day technology, however, is such that the solar cells are far too expensive, approximately $5 per square inch. So, economically, they are not viable to compete with the other processes. Incentives should be given to manufacturers to lower the price. One could use other types of solar cells than those presently employed, e.g., semiconductor spray coatings of large areas by vapor deposition techniques. The sacrifice of efficiency is not serious, because there are enormously large, available, sunlit desert areas.

Energy Storage

The diagram also shows one type of low efficiency electrical energy storage device: the battery for electrical energy. The other (not shown) is a condensor or a capacitor. Both are handicapped by their heavy weight in relation to the energy stored. The reason that six-passenger electric cars are not commercially viable and competitive with gasoline energy is that the electrolytic battery does not store sufficient energy for its weight and required size. Lowering the weight of the electrolytic battery for a given energy storage by perhaps a factor of 5, at reasonable cost, would completely eliminate the gasoline engine. One could charge up batteries at home, at night, when the electrical consumption is diminished in any event, and then use the car during the daytime. Pollution could be more easily controlled—directly at the power plant where the electricity is generated. One would also eliminate the smog problem completely. The greatest source of smog is

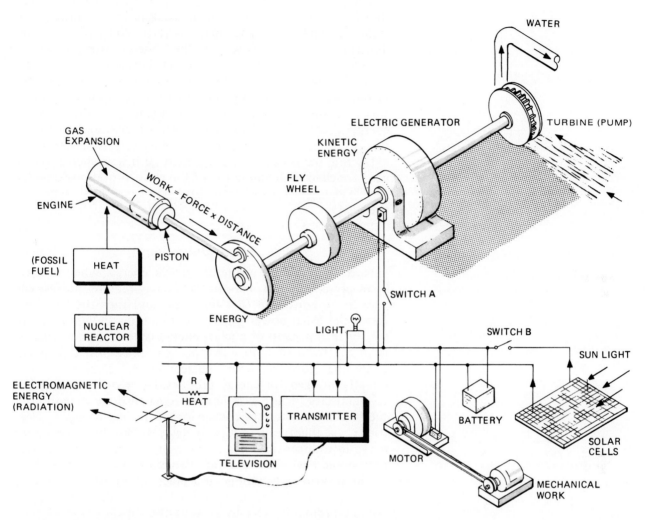

Figure 9.1. Twentieth century Homosapiens energy utilization—its transformations, flow, and electrical distribution. This all-inclusive diagram shows:

a. Major sources of energy.
b. Its transformation from one form to another, including work and electrical appliances.
c. Upper part of diagram indicates three possible sources of input energy: (1) Nuclear. (2) Fossil fuel. (3) Hydro-electric (shown operating in reverse direction, i.e., water is being pumped against gravity).
d. Not shown. Possibility of reversing energy flow. (Exception: one cannot achieve [high grade] nuclear energy from [low grade] heat. [Fusion reactors are unsuccessful so far!]).
e. The use of electrical energy, including its conversion to work by means of electric motor.
f. If switch A is open and switch B closed, solar energy could, in principle, supply all electrical needs.
g. Note energy storage devices.
   1. Kinetic (flywheel).
   2. Water reservoirs.
   3. Electrical-batteries.
   4. Fossil fuel, certain chemicals.
   5. Nuclear fuel.

the engine itself, which chemically combines the excess nitrogen and oxygen in its explosive burning process and produces nitrous oxides products, which subsequently undergo further photochemical changes upon exposure to ultraviolet sunlight.

The pumping of water to higher potential energy levels as shown in Figure 9.1, is used at the Niagara Falls hydroelectric facility at nighttime. The energy is retrieved by reversing the direction of water flow. Another energy storage device, shown in the Figure 9.1, is a flywheel. This is a kinetic energy storage system, occasionally used to smooth out surge demands. Keep in mind, however, that the earth spinning on its axis contains an enormously large quantity of this type of energy (2×10^{29} Joules). However, it is not so easy to tap this rotational energy. The only time we've ever succeeded in extracting the very minutest quantity of it was when a rocket was launched in the direction of the earth's rotation (Chapter 5). "Tidal generators" may also tap into this source of energy.

Energy Utilization

Note the poor use made of nuclear energy, when utilized in its present format. Present technology requires nuclear energy to be converted first into heat and then the heat performs the usual power generation functions shown in Figure 9.1. Fifteen percent of nuclear energy is never used because it is in the form of radioactive particle emissions. It is a sad waste that such highgrade nuclear energy cannot be more directly utilized for energy production, or direct conversion to electricity. There was limited research done that showed the feasibility of direct conversion of nuclear energy to electricity via thermionic emission devices. However, they were never introduced into the reactor on a large scale; besides, thermionic devices have an efficiency of only about 10-20%.

The overriding economic and practical problems in getting a large power system manufactured and installed in a timely fashion ordinarily acts to prevent the introduction of substantial improvements in the state of the art. New inventions have to be checked out and life tested. Few are willing to invest the time, effort, and resources to develop systems that are more efficient (or safer) in energy utilization. Bear in mind that there are many factors that go into the design of power plants and that overall efficiency or simplicity may not be one of them. Also, once a working system is produced, licensed, and government inspected, there seems to be a tendency towards conservatism: No change, "Leave well enough alone" is a motto used by many engineers.

Let us examine the manifestations of energy and its flow in more detail. Note that the photochemical reactions, photosynthesis, are the primary—the most important, energy flow systems on earth. They provide living systems with energy and us with food (fuel). Porphyrin structures within all green plants and blue-green algae have the ability to extract the sun's energy and utilize it in chemical processes. It is the beginning of the food chain. All food is a form of energy. We can be sure that photosynthesis is essential for life. The ability to extract energy from the sun gives groups of organic molecules a great advantage over other molecules that do not. It allows them to tap into the sun's energy supply and perform other functions.

Next in importance are the chemical processes that are carried on within each living cell. They are relegated to special components within a cell, known as the mitochondria. They perform energy production and utilization relatively efficiently, at low temperatures (20-40°C).

A study of biology, particularly those aspects that deal with the utilization of energy within a cell, would be beneficial for most of us. Nature leads the way, and man (a component of nature) imitates.

Electrical energy is, of course, the cleanest and most easily handled form of energy. We shall discuss it further later on. Mechanical energy is manifest throughout the solar system. The rotation of the earth, as mentioned before, is a form of kinetic energy. Any energy which is related to motion or rotation comes under this category.

There is another form of energy that is associated with position, namely gravitational energy. An example would be if you were to climb a mountain or a hill, you would have to expend work or energy in order to climb this hill. On the way down, you will retrieve the energy that was expended on the way up. We discussed similar examples in Chapter 3.

Heat energy is really the lowest form of energy, although it is used the most for supplying the needs of society today. Heat energy results from the random motions of atoms and molecules. This energy can be extracted as shown in Figure 9.1. However, the efficiency of this extraction is severely limited, and some heat can never be converted into useful work or electrical energy. This limitation on the use is incorporated as a law of physics, which we shall discuss separately (Tech. Note No. 8).

Examine Table 9.2, which shows a recycleable energy system which is nonpolluting and of maximum efficiency. It makes use of the most abundant molecule on the earth's surface: water. The hydrogen-oxygen water cycle is the best utilization of energy. Its end product is pure water that is drinkable. It also makes sense in terms of recycling. It is used

TABLE 9.2

The Hydrogen-Oxygen Cycle

Production: $2 H_2O$ + Energy in $\rightarrow$ $2 H_2$ + O_2

Utilization: $2 H_2$ + O_2 $\rightarrow$ $2 H_2O$ + Energy out
$\downarrow$
Pure and drinkable

on a limited scale in spacecraft where a device known as a fuel cell can produce electricity by combining hydrogen and oxygen. The "waste" product of this energy production is absolutely pure water, which is utilized by the astronauts! If this can be done in a small closed system, it is obvious that we should also be able to apply it to the somewhat larger but similarly closed system, the earth's biosphere.

So far, man has considered the atmosphere, world resources, and the water, as limitless. With the world's population now at over 4,000,000,000, the finite aspects come more clearly into focus. The quantity of pure water, the quantity of available energy, and the amount of organic material (including food) on earth is, after all, *finite* and, in fact, can be listed. Our biosphere, comprising all living things, organic material and water, the ecological system, should be thought of as an engine with the sun supplying the essential working fluid (energy) to drive this eco-engine. That's the perspective we must have and that is relevant astronomy.

Energy Conversion

All forms of energy can generally be converted from one form to another. The most useful form is electrical energy, since it is clean, nonpolluting, and easily transportable by wires (Fig. 9.2). Gas can also be transported over large dis-

Figure 9.2. High power electric transmission lines. Large amounts of power can be easily and quietly transmitted via wires.

Salt River Project, Arizona. A view of the Pinnacle Peak Transmission Lines crossing the Arizona desert. These lines carry power from Glen Canyon to the Salt River Valley. Bureau of Reclamation photo by E.E. Hertzog.

tances at relatively low cost, once pipes are in place. Engineers continually transform energy from heat to electricity, the conversion of oil to mechanical energy. Hydroelectric power uses hydrostatic water pressure (arising from gravitational potential energy) and the resulting water flow to drive turbines, which in turn generate electricity (Figs. 9.3 and 9.4). Note that the water pressure difference was initially obtained by rain water. This required the sun's energy, because the water had to evaporate from oceans and lakes to

Figure 9.3. The sun's energy utilized on earth. It produces clouds, rain, and energy via hydroelectric (really converted solar) power.

Aerial view of Hoover Dam and Lake Mead. The world-famous dam, completed in 1935, spans the Colorado between Nevada and Arizona, providing multipurpose benefits; flood protection, river control, water storage, and conservation for irrigation and low-cost hydroelectric energy. Bureau of Reclamation photo by E.E. Hertzog.

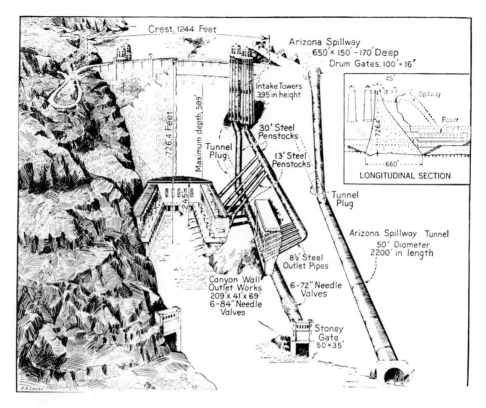

Figure 9.4. How Hoover Dam works. (Bureau of Reclamation—Dept. of Interior.)

be transported by clouds and redistributed via river run-offs. It ends up at the edge of a hydroelectric dam as a source of ready potential energy. It is important to trace the manner by which energy flows, because at this stage of man's development, food and energy are what will make man fight: his life depends on them. Is this relevant enough?

Thermodynamics

We shall now discuss two laws of thermodynamics which were discovered over a hundred years ago and which are pertinent to our discussion. The first law of thermodynamics is a law of bookkeeping. It says that energy can be transformed from one kind to another, as long as there is a strict accounting. In other words, *you cannot destroy it or create it.* The second law of thermodynamics is more subtle, in that it restricts the way energy can flow in cyclic processes (rotating machinery), which involve heat input and heat output. This law relates to the types of engines with which all of us are most familiar. These include the steam engine, gasoline engine, and the refrigerator. The second law says: *none of these engines can ever be operated at 100% efficiency.* One cannot obtain work, which is another form of energy, at 100% efficiency by extracting all the energy from heat. There will

144

Figure 9.5. Four Corners Steam Generating Plant. Bureau of Reclamation photo by Mel Davis.

always be some waste in the process (Tech. Note No. 8). The usual gasoline engine operates at 20-30% efficiency. However, the useful work possible at the rear wheels is no more than 30% of engine output. Most cars are very inefficient energy users.

The best possible theoretical efficiencies possible are of the order of 50%. The steam engine generating plants (Fig. 9.5), which have been with us for a hundred years or more, have indeed been researched heavily, and you cannot squeeze an additional 1% efficiency out of them, no matter how hard you try. However, the waste heat that is not used in the conversion process is usually dumped instead of utilized. Energy could certainly be used more efficiently! It is also worth noting that one can operate all the electrical energy at 100% efficiency in converting electricity to heat, but not the other way around.

Solar Energy

Let us get back to the sun as a primary source of energy. We receive at the earth's surface about 100 watts per square foot perpendicular to the incident radiation (Fig. 9.6). How much do you pay in your electric bills? Take a good look. In 1976, residential homes paid between four and five cents per kilowatt-hour or thousand watt hours. That is, at the cost of about 4 to 5 cents, one may burn a thousand watt bulb for one hour.

Television normally uses up about 500 watts; hence, its cost is roughly two and one-half cents per hour. By keeping the cost in mind, we should calculate how much free energy we are getting from the sun. To be sure, the sun's energy is

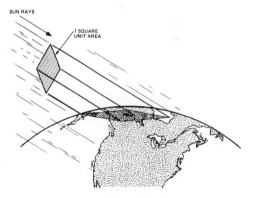

Figure 9.6. The incident solar radiation flux is about 100 watts per sq. ft. Note here the energy (measured perpendicular to the beam) can be spread over a larger surface area on earth, thereby reducing the amount of energy incident per sq. ft. As the earth turns on its axis, no single spot on earth receives continuous maximum solar input. At the polar regions, for instance, during certain parts of the year, the sun does not set; however, its altitude is always low.

145

not immediately ready to be plugged into a light socket. However, the lowliest of plants utilizes 1% of the solar energy directly.

Carbon Cycle

Green plants have the capability of fixing carbon-dioxide and water to produce the larger hydrocarbon molecules. It requires the sun's energy to do this. These plants, in turn, can be reprocessed along the food chain. Each process, unfortunately, works at a diminished efficiency. For instance, the efficiency of conversion of solar energy for usable energy in humans amounts to about one part in a ten thousand. This comes about as follows: The plants utilize approximately 1% of the solar energy. From plant to animal, there is a 10% conversion efficiency, and from animal to man there is about another 10%. These efficiencies combine to between 1/10 of 1% and 1/100 of 1% conversion efficiency from sunlight to energy in man. When you now raise your hand, working against gravity, the energy that you expend ultimately comes from the sun! The sun drives the eco-engine (Figs. 9.7 and 9.8).

The Use of Sun's Energy via Living Organic Molecules
(Plants)

Photosynthesis

Visible Sunlight + H_2O + CO_2 → carbohydrates, other organic compounds.

Sunlight photons absorbed by chlorophyll cause charge separation. The plus charge is associated with the oxygen atom and the minus charge with the hydrogen atom. The negative charged hydrogen atom reduces the carbon dioxide to sugars, e.g., a sugar such as sucrose is composed of two hexose molecules. Here is a method to utilize energy from sunlight via photosynthesis:

1. Grow sugar cane.
2. Add yeast and let it ferment.

extract about 1% of solar energy.
end product: Ethanol (Ethyl Alcohol).

1.3 kilograms of sugar yield 1 liter of alcohol.
(1974) cost: price of sugar cane + 5c for conversion from sugar cane.
Note, alcohol can be added to gasoline to stretch its supply.

Example: In 1974, Brazil produced 9 million metric tons of raw sugar, which they converted in part to 740 million liters of alcohol. 250 million liters were used to extend their gasoline supply by 2%.

146

Figure 9.7. The life-food chain driven by solar energy. Efficiencies of solar energy utilization are shown below each stage. Photosynthesis extracts less than 1% of solar energy. Steer extracts 10% of energy from grass. Man extracts 10% of available energy from meat protein thus utilizing (1/100) % of solar energy for his energy needs. By eating vegetables only, greater efficiency of available resources is achieved (e.g., India).

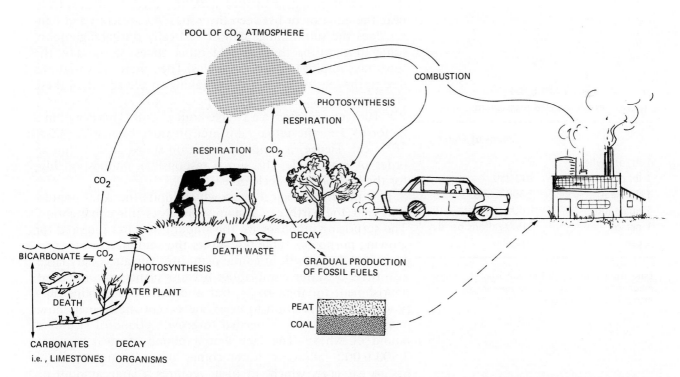

Figure 9.8. The carbon cycle. Carbon, in the form of CO_2, becomes recycled at various stages. Some of these recycling processes take millions of years. One can disturb the equilibrium drastically if CO_2 becomes suddenly overproduced.

147

This sounds very attractive, but here are the hidden costs: Labor, high cost of nitrogen fertilizers, plentiful water, good land. Brazil and parts of Africa seem promising areas, though, for exploiting this method of solar recyclable energy production.

Hydrological Cycle

The sun's energy does more than just driving photosynthesis in plants (and keeping us warm). The other cycle that the sun controls is the **water cycle**, without which life also would not be possible. We can very readily check the numbers on this process, since it takes 540 calories to evaporate one cubic cm of water (the calorie being another unit of energy, Tech. Note No. 6). One energy unit is very familiar to the general public, the Calorie (1 large Calorie = 1,000 small calories). People on diets watch their food intake by counting Calories. What are they really watching and counting? The body requires a certain amount of energy; roughly two million calories per day.

It is easy to calculate the total amount of energy received by the earth from the sun. Multiply the energy received per square foot by the total projected earth's surface area, πR^2, where R = earth's radius. That is the energy the sun sends us, assuming idealized situations with no clouds, no absorption, and so forth. It is 10^{17} Joules per second (Tech. Note No. 7).

The other factor that one takes into account is the angle the incident radiation makes with the earth's surface. Only near the equator or between the zones of Capricorn and Cancer does the sun impinge almost vertically during high noon, some time during the year. At other times of the day, the sun's rays impinge at varying angles. Then there are variations due to the seasons and latitude. Taking an average of all these effects, one concludes that it is possible to evaporate roughly 2×10^{18} cc of water in a twelve-hour period. This is within a factor of 3 of the actual rainwater provided by nature (3.6×10^{17} cc). Hence, a simple calculation shows that within an order of magnitude, the sun is responsible, unquestionably, for the hydrological cycle on earth.

It is this hydrological cycle which limits the total population that the earth can sustain. How does this come about? The surprising numbers are the amount of water required for growing purposes. Table 9.4 shows the amount of water necessary for the growth of edible plant life. The amazingly large quantities of water come about because plants not only need nourishment for their roots, but also water for cooling purposes. It is a revelation to everyone except the farmers how much water, indeed, is needed to grow a pound of rice or a pound of wheat. The fact that a pound of meat requires 2,500-6,000 gallons of water comes about because the cow has to eat grass which, in turn, requires a large amount of water, and the efficiencies for each process, of course, are never greater than 10%. Thus, the production of a quart of milk requires a thousand gallons of water. A hundred

TABLE 9.3

Total land area	$= 1.48 \times 10^{18}$ cm^2
Arable land area	$= 3 \times 10^{17}$ cm^2
Total area planted	$= 1.3 \times 10^{17}$ cm^2
Ocean area	$= 3.63 \times 10^{18}$ cm^2

TABLE 9.4
Fresh Water Requirements

	Gallons of Water
1 lb. dry wheat	60
1 lb. dry rice	200-250
1 lb. meat	2,500-6,000
1 quart milk	1,000
1 person	2,000 gallons per day
1 car	100,000

Data from Paul R. Ehrlich and Anne H. Ehrlich, *Population, Resources, Environment*, W.H. Freeman & Co., San Francisco, 1970.

thousand gallons of water are required to manufacture one car! Not that the car has to drink all this water, but in the process of manufacturing the car, a large amount of water is being used. The overall water cycle is shown in Figure 9.9 where all processes such as precipitation, evaporation, and runoffs are indicated by simple numbers. The numbers represent cubic kilometers per day.

Now, where is all this water? 97% of all the water on earth is in the oceans, and that is salt water and not immediately usable. Of the 3% that is drinkable, 98% is in the earth's icecaps. (If these icecaps were to be melted down, the ocean height would increase by about 100 meters and cause severe flooding of low lying land areas.) Only 2% of the 3% of all the pure water is being circulated by clouds and rain, etc. That is, only a very small fraction of all the available potentially pure water is utilized in the life processes. To give some perspective, as projected by Ehrlich, by 1980 the United States would need 700 billion gallons of water, and only 650 billion gallons are available. Thus, shortages of water are inevitable. Some of the reserves in our water tables have already been severely depleted—water tables in Arizona and even India are far below where they were decades ago.

Ehrlich maintains that each person requires about one acre of land both for water and food supply. The fact that so very few of us live on one acre of land is the result of a complex food distribution system where a few grow the food and transport it to the many. This still does not eliminate the need for one acre of land per person. Assuming a hundred

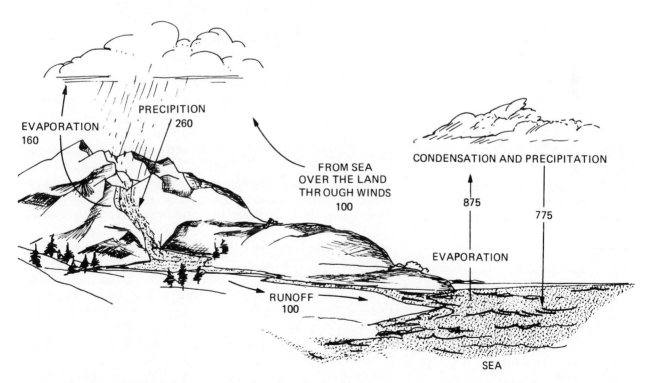

Figure 9.9. The hydrological cycle—**Units are in cub. km per day** (adapted from P.R. Ehrlich and A.H. Ehrlich, *Population, Resources, Environment*).

149

Figure 9.10. Proposed Harding Ice Field, Kenai Fjords, National Monument (National Park Service photograph by M. Woodbridge Williams).

TABLE 9.5
World Population

Date	Population	Doubling Time
6000 B.C.	5×10^6	
1650 B.C.	500×10^6	
1850	1,000	200 years
1930	2,000	80
1976	4,000	46

Population Doubling Time
Underdeveloped Countries: 19 to 31 years

United States	63 years
Austria	175
Denmark	88
Norway	88
United Kingdom	140
Russia	63
Spain	88
Japan	63
Italy	117

Source: Paul R. Ehrlich and Anne H. Ehrlich, *Population, Resources, Environment,* W.H. Freeman & Co., San Francisco.

people would require a hundred acres, you could put all of the one hundred people on *one* acre, but the other ninety-nine acres would still be required for water and food-growing purposes. That is the situation we are faced with at the moment. A large portion of the population lives in overcrowded cities and only a small fraction is engaged in the food production process. Knowing this limitation, and knowing the total amount of land available (Table 9.3 lists the amounts of arable [plantable] land and Table 9.5 the total number of people), it is apparent that we are very close to the limit of the total number of people the earth can sustain (Tech. Note No. 7).

Table 9.5 shows the past population increase and what to expect if it is allowed to increase at the rate at which it is now going. It is obvious that an impossible situation will eventually arise. The earth just cannot support that many people. There is no way that one can overcome this dilemma (Table 9.6). Growing more food will not do it, because the limitation is apparent by looking at the amount of energy received from the sun, and there is just no way you can increase this, absolutely no way. One might squeeze another 1% here, another 10% there; one might plant a few more acres here or there, but within a factor of 2, we have already achieved the limit of the total number of people the earth can adequately support. Any excess now will result in severe hardships. The fact that some people are living well is now at the expense of others who are living poorly.

TABLE 9.6
No. of People Earth Can Support

One person requires one acre of land for adequate food and water.

$$\frac{\text{Arable land}}{\text{Land per person}} = \frac{1.3 \times 10^{17} \text{ sq. cm}}{4 \times 10^7 \text{ sq. cm}} = \frac{3.2 \times 10^9 \text{ people}}{} = \text{present limit}$$

Conclusion: World population has reached its limit or very close to it. Any catastrophic departures in available rain or food supply would result in immediate famine and death of a large fraction of the population.

Hydrocarbons

Another limitation is the total quantities of hydrocarbon available for possible utilization. The total quantity of organic matter on the earth's surface is a finite quantity. All that nature is doing is transforming one set of molecules into another set, breaking them up, building them up, or having these molecules stored in one form of living system or another, be it vegetable, animal, or man. The recycling of organic molecules is a continuous process, driven again by the master driver, the sun's energy. *From dust to dust—transform we must.*

Origin of Hydrocarbons

In view of the importance attached to hydrocarbons (fossil fuel) as a source of energy as well as a source of life, we might reconsider in this chapter the possible origin of these compounds. There are a number of theories concerning the origin and production of hydrocarbons. There is one theory that postulates an extraterrestrial origin and another local production. It is certainly possible to produce limited quantities of hydrocarbons by means of discharges (lightning) in a reducing earth's atmosphere. However, the extraterrestrial production processes discussed in Chapters 6 and 13 are far more efficient and hence most likely the dominant mechanism for providing the earth with organic compounds and water.

At this point, there is an interesting dilemma. It is the chicken versus the egg problem. Which came first? At the present time, it is assumed that the oil is the result of degradation products of living systems. If the oil is the degradation product of living things, where did the living things, which are again partly organic materials, obtain their organic molecules?

Perhaps the oil came first, and the fact that some remnants of primitive living systems can sometimes be found mixed in with the oil, particularly porphyrins, will be the result that *water* plus oil perhaps constituted the original primitive *organic soup.* Since some of the oil presently being pumped up is of more recent vintage, perhaps one should consider the possibility that some of the oil was brought to the earth in relatively recent times. Where does the oil come from?

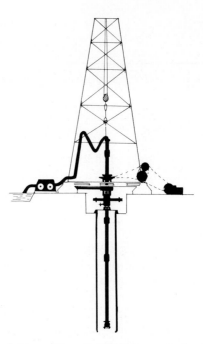

Figure 9.11. *Drilling for precious oil.* Fossil fuel is basically nonrenewable. Hundreds of millions of years are required to lay down coal beds, for instance. World's oil supplies will be exhausted some time in the twentieth century.

Do we dare suppose that the earth was bombarded by organic material and water in the distant past? The only objects in the solar system that have the potential of containing large amounts of organic materials and water are the comets and the cometary tails. Indeed, organic remnants have been identified spectroscopically in the comet's tails as well as water in great abundances; consequently, as proposed by the author, this is not as far-fetched as it initially seems. It would be ironic, indeed, if man were to initiate Armageddon for purposes of possession of minerals on certain parts of the earth when indeed the solar system is full of the magic oil (in frozen state) all over its vast expanses.

Recycling Disequilibrium

Here is another analogy in the manner in which the sun dispenses its energy to drive the various cycles.

Consider the money supply in the world. Provided no new paper money is printed, the money circulates. It is occasionally stored, just as fresh water is stored in Arctic ice and below ground. Hydrocarbons are stored in coal, oil, in the top soil and in living matter. The amount in transit or circulation is small compared to the total available. As soon as all reserves, however, are in one location, then an enormous disequilibrium can set in—look out! One should not place all of one's assets on a single number at the roulette wheel!!

Examples of biological disequilibrium occurred before in the earth's evolution. The trilobites and dinosaurs are examples of overproduction of a single species. Species man is approaching a

152

similar dilemma rather rapidly, once he constitutes a critical fraction of all available circulating organic matter (and in addition, alters the biosphere with his careless behavior).

Examples of unequal water distribution also creates havoc on earth. Such extremes as having all water either in vapor form or in solid ice would probably prove fatal to life or at least make it possible for only the heartiest of bugs to survive.

Partial extreme conditions, but happily not to the ultimate limit, have occurred on earth previously: Ice ages of varying severity appear periodically. Major ice ages occur every 200,000 years, minor ones at 10,000-20,000 year intervals.

Fission and Fusion

We shall briefly review the nuclear energy sources since they comprise one of our many options. The basic principle involves the fission of atomic cores of specific nuclear species, particularly Uranium 235. Such fission is induced by slow neutrons. Subsequent to each fission, the nuclear cores split and release between 150-200 Mev of energy. In addition, they also release between two and three neutrons which in turn have the ability to induce fission in additional nuclei. This lends itself to the possibility of a self-sustaining reaction, one which can either be slow and controlled or cataclysmic (Fig. 9.12). The operation of controlled nuclear fission

Figure 9.12. Fast energy production via nuclear fission (Nagasaki, Japan, August 9, 1945) (Official U.S. Air Force photograph).

153

devices is illustrated in Figures 9.13 and 9.14. These diagrams illustrate schematically how energy is extracted from nuclear reactors.

Subsequent to each uranium fission, the kinetic energy of the fission products interacts with the uranium matrix heating its atoms. It is this heat which is transferred via the water-moderating fluid and used in further conversion via conventional steam turbine engines to produce electricity.

The water serves the additional purpose of interacting with the fast neutrons that are emitted from the fission processes, slowing them down to enable additional fission processes to take place. Figure 9.15 shows a typical nuclear generating station at San Onofre.

With the success of the nuclear reactor, scientists had hoped that similar success would be obtained by simulating the so-called **stellar fusion processes** (Chapter 12), converting hydrogen into helium first in the laboratory and subsequently expanding this technique for commercial use.

Had this process been perfected, virtually inexpensive, limitless energy would be available. Unfortunately, despite the expenditures of over one billion dollars and efforts of over twenty years, success is still elusive. Interesting new concepts such as laser fusion are now being researched. Perhaps more original and novel ideas could be used here as well.

Note: The sun is already engaged in the fusion (or is it fission) production of energy, providing free transmission to the earth of 10^{17} watts. Man is just not clever enough to utilize it more effectively and extensively, except for farming (food production).

Geothermal Energy

The earth's internal heat source provides another possible supply of enormous amounts of energy, which has only been very feebly tapped. Figure 9.16 is a cross section of the earth's crust and mantle showing a particular region from where potentially large quantities of energy can be extracted.

Solar Energy Is Our Limit

The total solar power intercepted by the earth is 10^{17} watts. This is the earth's energy budget or living allowance. It cannot be increased by plea bargaining, compromise, finagling, religious rites, or by pious pronouncements. That's all we get. The earth's inhabitants can use it as they see fit. But as was shown in a previous calculation on the hydrological cycle and people water requirements, we have now reached our limit in human population. The primary reason that it cannot be pushed higher is the limit of the sun's energy budget. (Living space considerations are still secondary.) That's it. (Those who argue against population control or for unlimited food supply tend to ignore the analysis of the sun's energy budget.)

See also Tech. Note Nos. 7, 8, and 10.

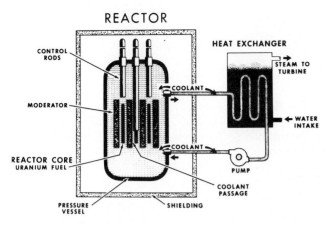

REACTOR

Figure 9.13. Nuclear Reactor. Basically, a reactor is an atomic furnace in which the fissioning or splitting of atoms of nuclear fuel can be controlled and put to useful work. The diagram shows the location of fuel, moderator, control rods, and coolant in a typical power reactor. These components are enclosed within a "pressure vessel" which serves to contain the various parts of the reactor. The coolant, heated to high temperature by the nuclear fuel, flows through a heat exchanger where it turns water, in a secondary system of pipes, into steam. The steam then is piped to a turbine which operates an electrical generator (ERDA photo).

Figure 9.14. Cut-away view of a nuclear steam supply system based on a pressurized water reactor. Note size of man entering door at right (Combustion Engineering, Inc.).

Figure 9.15. San Onofre Nuclear Generating Station. The San Onofre Nuclear Generating Station provides 430,000 kilowatts of electricity for the Southern California Edison Company and San Diego Gas and Electric Company—enough power to supply a city of well over half a million population. A pressurized water nuclear reactor is housed in the steel containment sphere near the center of the picture. The power station is located at San Clemente, California, on the Pacific Ocean. Southern California Edison Company.

Geothermal Resource Investigations, Imperial Valley, California
Generalized Section Through the Salton Trough

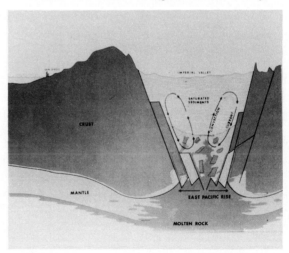

Figure 9.16. Geothermal Energy Source: Note the heat flow from the mantle to the lower portion of the trough.

Other Sun-Driven Cycles

We have discussed only the water and carbon cycles. The sun is responsible for a large number of additional cycles. These include the nitrogen, phosphorus, and oxygen cycles. There are cyclic processes involving complex molecules and rather sophisticated chemical reactions in which the sun's energy plays a role.

The chemical and photochemical interactions in the upper atmosphere that are driven by the sun's radiation are quite extensive and certainly affect life on earth in a critical manner. Also, not mentioned are the various photodissociation processes involving ozone, O_3 oxygen O_2, and the break-up of H_2O, into OH and H, plus interaction of these molecules with man-made impurity molecules such as NO.

Conclusion

The success of hydroelectric power generation lies in the fact that we are working *with* nature, using the natural solar energy cyclic processes. It is, therefore, cheap, clean, and efficient. In contrast, the burning of hydrocarbons (oil) to obtain energy can be likened to early man burning down his house together with his farm animals because the roasted animals tasted good! Besides, it helped him to retrieve precious metal such as nails used in the construction of his house.

Our so-called civilization cannot be very advanced if it has failed to put its house in order on a global scale (and burns it to boot). The struggles the world over are for power (not electrical), for resources, energy, minerals, and food supplies. So far, *planning is a limited local option.*

It does not require great vision to forecast the very near future, based on the figures presented here.

Is anyone out there listening?

Does anyone really care?

Is there enough brainpower around to organize a more effective way to deal with these problems? If the answer is yes, implementation of any workable plan seems hopeless.

Time *has* probably already run out. We are now living at or beyond nature's available resources and there will be a day of reckoning. There is a price to be paid eventually—we can be sure of that.

Chapter 10

STELLAR MAGNITUDES
AND STELLAR BRIGHTNESS,*
BLACK BODY, E.M. RADIATION

Figure 10.1. Typical sample of stars in galaxy whose brightness we wish to measure. Open star cluster NGC 2682. 200-inch photograph (Hale Observatories).

Scientific progress can only be made if we quantify the information that we seek. We have to put numbers into our discussion. Our first problem will be to find a method whereby we can identify the quantity of light emitted by each star (i.e., a means for easily measuring the amount of light emitted from any star in the galaxy). The technique that we shall adopt for this process is a rather simple one, one which has been used for over two thousand years! It is based on defining **magnitudes**. The magnitude scale is simply a means for comparing the brightness of stars.

Health Warning: There is a very small amount of algebra in this chapter. Those with weak hearts may wish to have smelling salts close at hand. They can usually be discarded after the second reading. A survey of over 2,000 students disclosed: that not a single fatality has been reported so far to the National Institute of Healthy Mathematical Disfunctions and Algebraic Disordered Arrays.

Let us look at the numbers shown in Figure 10.2. It is a schematic representation of magnitudes. The brighter the star, the smaller its numerical value of magnitude. For stars brighter than magnitude 0, negative numbers are used, e.g., Venus at its brightest has an apparent magnitude of -4.4. The following is the definition of **brightness ratio**: If two stars have a magnitude difference of five, their brightness ratio is *one hundred*. The brightness ratio of two stars whose magnitude difference is one, is $\sqrt[5]{100} = 2.512$ (the fifth root of 100).

Example 1: A star of magnitude 5 is 2.512 times fainter than a star of magnitude 4. Example 2: A star of second magnitude is $(2.512) \times (2.512)$ brighter than a star of fourth magnitude.

To be more sophisticated about it, we write this in an algebraic formula as follows:

$$\frac{b_m}{b_n} = 10^{\frac{2}{5}(n-m)} \qquad (10.1)$$

$$\text{where } b_m = \text{brightness of a star } m$$

$$b_n = \text{brightness of star } n$$

The ratio of brightness of a star of magnitude n compared to the brightness of a star of magnitude m is given by that simple formula. We'll check this formula to see whether this will work out for five magnitudes (you will see indeed that it comes out to be one hundred).

Example 3: m = 5
        n = 10

$$\frac{b_5}{b_{10}} = 10^{\frac{2}{5}(10-5)} = 10^2 = 100$$

Also, convince yourself that $(2.512)^5 = 100$

Unfortunately, this method does not provide us with the real **intrinsic brightness** (B) of a star, because these brightness ratios do not take into account the fact that stars are at different distances. Imagine having a lot of hundred watt bulbs all at different distances from you. Each will have a different apparent brightness. How do we compare intrinsic stellar brightnesses? The obvious answer is to place all of the light bulbs (all of the stars) at the same distance from the observer. Of course, we do this in our mind. It is physically impossible to move the stars. We place all of the stars at a distance of ten **parsecs** or 32.6 light years (about 1.92×10^{14} miles).

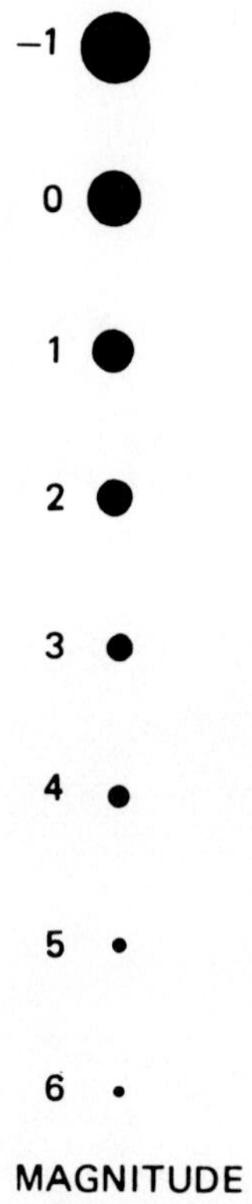

MAGNITUDE

Figure 10.2.

The Distance to Nearby Stars—Method of Parallax

For purposes of comparing stellar brightness, one requires knowledge of stellar distances. Consequently, we now have to delve into the mystery of how that can best be done. Although even the nearest stars are at enormous distances from us, it is possible (but not easy) to use geometrical means to determine their distances. As with any other triangulation method, the largest possible baseline is required. Even a baseline comprising the total width of the earth is not sufficient to obtain a measurable angle subtended by the star. In order to increase the base even further, we resort to the orbit of the earth around the sun, which gives us a baseline of 186,000,000 miles instead of 8,000. Even with such a base, the angle subtended, Figure 10.3, is less than a

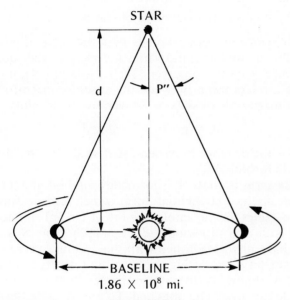

STAR

BASELINE
1.86 × 10⁸ mi.

Figure 10.3.

second of arc for the nearest star, Proxima Centauri. The definition adopted is as follows: The distance in parsecs is such that

$$d = \frac{1}{p''}$$

Where d is the distance in parsecs

p is the angle subtended at the star between the sun and the earth, measured in seconds of arc.

1 parsec = 3.26 light years

1 parsec = 206,265 A.U.

This will be discussed in greater detail in Chapter 17.

(See also Tech. Note No. 13, p. 311.)

By consensus, this is the distance at which astronomers decide to place all the stars in order to perform a comparison of stellar brightness. Once this is done, one can then talk in terms of both **apparent magnitudes** (m) and **absolute magnitude** (M). In order to distinguish between these terms, one uses small and capital letters, respectively. The absolute magnitude provides a number which relates to the intrinsic brightness of the star. At a distance of 10 parsecs, the star's apparent magnitude is equal to its absolute magnitude (by definition). The formula needed to compare the intrinsic brightnesses B_a and B_b of stars a and b is given in terms of their absolute magnitudes as follows:

$$\frac{B_a}{B_b} = 10^{\frac{2}{5}(M_b - M_a)} \tag{10.2}$$

Where M_a = absolute magnitude of star a

M_b = absolute magnitude of star b

Finally, since everyone knows that the light intensity of light bulbs (as well as stars) varies inversely as the square of the distance from the observer (Tech. Note No. 4), it is easy to derive a relationship between the absolute magnitude and apparent magnitude of stars. It is given by the formula:

$$M = m + 5 - 5\log d \tag{10.3}$$

where d is the distance in parsecs. (Let's call this the absolute magnitude formula.)

The **log term** is another (shorthand) method of expressing a number in its exponential form which can be found in **logarithm tables**. For example, the log of ten is 1, the log of a hundred is 2, of a thousand is 3, etc. (Tech. Note Nos. 1 and 12). We have now established with this formula a very simple and elegant way for getting the absolute magnitude of a star, provided we know its distance (or its parallax). The apparent magnitude can always be obtained. To repeat, once the stellar distance d is known, one substitutes its numerical number and its apparent magnitude m into the absolute magnitude formula, and, behold, one has the absolute magnitude M (Tech. Note No. 22, provides an example).

However, what one really requires is the **luminosity** (L) of a star. There is no star like the sun to give us the proper comparison, so let us use the sun as *the* comparison star. We know the absolute magnitude of the sun is 4.8. Hence, substituting 4.8 into the comparison equation and comparing it with the sun, we have the means of comparing the luminosity of all stars with the sun. The luminosity of the sun is 4×10^{26} watts. The luminosity of all other stars can now be calculated by the comparison formula, provided we have the basic distance and the apparent magnitude information:

$$\frac{L}{L_\odot} = 10^{\frac{2}{5}(M_\odot - M)} \tag{10.4}$$

Where L = Luminosity of star

$L_\odot$ = Luminosity of sun

$M_\odot$ = 4.8

M = Absolute magnitude of star

This is an important astronomical tool which is absolutely necessary in order to obtain the amount of energy sent out by individual stars in our galaxy.

A comparison study of stars shows that some stars are as much as 50,000 times brighter than others. Let us look at this in more detail. Why do the stellar luminosities vary by so much? How do these stars differ? One of the more obvious differences is the fact that the stars differ in color and most likely also differ in size. How does the color and the size affect the luminosity? Is there perhaps some other property that we ought to consider? Yes, there is: the *temperature* of the star. The temperature, which is related to its color, together with the star's size, make up the two critical parameters that govern the amount of energy a star is able to radiate. Later on, we will have to think a little more deeply as to where this energy really comes from and what enables these stars to keep shining for billions of years, a most fascinating and crucial topic discussed in Chapter 12.

Is this topic relevant? Without the constant uniform radiation from the sun for 4 1/2 billion years, life would not be possible! That's relevant enough for most people.

Meanwhile, let us explore on a very elementary, yet basic level, the mechanism by which the radiation comes out from the surface of the star. The only thing we see from a star directly is its surface or its gaseous envelope. To do this, we have to resort to Physics and study the **Black Body Radiation** laws.

Black Body Radiation

Astronomy was able to make its most rapid progress when it utilized some of the results that physicists had obtained previously. Among these advances in astronomy was the application of the laws of radiation that were studied by physicists in the late nineteenth century. The interest was in the experimental and theoretical interpretation of radiation emitted by a hot body. In particular, theoretical physicists concentrated on the radiation obtained from an idealized situation. One can simulate a black body by using a metal box, placing a heat source underneath it, and examining the radiation emitted from a tiny hole in this box (Fig. 10.4). If

Figure 10.4. Black body radiation. All the colors (wavelengths) of the rainbow are produced. The colors are observed by means of either a prism or a diffraction grating (not shown).

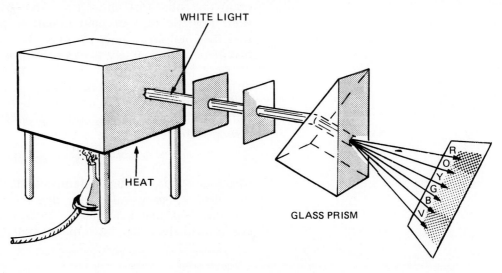

WHITE LIGHT

HEAT

GLASS PRISM

one shines a light into the hole, most of the radiation would be trapped and, conversely, the radiation that comes out from such a body has an idealized distribution in wavelengths. Since it is a perfect absorber, it is also a perfect radiator, hence the name black was associated with it. This **Black Body Radiation** is studied as a function of the wavelength of the emitted light that is shown in Figures 10.5 and 10.6. By changing the temperature of the black body, a number of different curves are obtained such that the higher the temperature of the black body, the higher the peaks of the curve and the more the peaks are shifted toward shorter wavelengths.* Wien discovered that there is a mathematical relationship between the wavelength maxima (λ_m) where the maximum intensity of the radiation occurs, and the temperature T of the black body. It is a simple relationship (now known as Wien's Law).

$$\lambda_m \times T = \text{constant} \qquad (10.5)$$

Thus, we can see that the hotter the temperature, the shorter the wavelength at which this maximum occurs. The actual shape of this curve had puzzled physicists in the nineteenth century a great deal. They had difficulty in producing a theoretical argument for predicting the shape. The discovery of a correct mathematical formulation for it proved to be a revolution in physics. It was done by Max Planck at the turn of the century.

For those who are not familiar with reading graphs, a few words of explanation for Figure 10.6 may be necessary. These distribution functions are very similar to, say, life expectancy curves, income distribution curves for general population, etc. Think of the ordinate (vertical scale) as the number of people (or income), and the abscissa (horizontal scale) as the age distribution. You see, there also would be a maximum point, corresponding to the peak of the people distribution curve (or of their income) as a function of their ages. Using this example, if one now were to ask what the total population is, it would correspond to the area under the curve. Or if we graph the number of people at different ages, again the total area under the curve gives the total population. For the case of light radiation, physicists discovered that the total area under the curve is proportional to a single parameter only, namely the *temperature*. (An analogy for age distribution would be to consider life expectancy curves at different epochs.) The radiation analysis was done by Stefan and Boltzmann, who discovered that the energy emitted per square centimeter per second is proportional to the fourth power of the temperature as given:

$$E = \sigma T^4 \text{ (ergs per cm}^2 \text{ per sec.)} \qquad (10.6)$$

where σ (sigma) is the Stefan-Boltzmann constant and T is the absolute temperature (in degrees Kelvin).** Thus, by knowing just one parameter, namely the temperature, one can immediately tell how much energy is radiated by an

*For a definition of wavelength λ, see page 164.
**Degrees Kelvin = degrees Centigrade + 273.

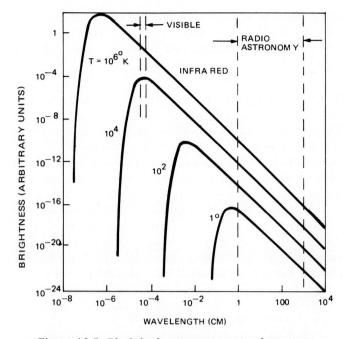

Figure 10.5. Black body spectrum over a large range of temperatures. Note the large range of brightness changes and the spectral regions where most of the electromagnetic radiation is emitted for the various indicated temperatures. The lowest curve would correspond roughly to the so-called three degree black body radiation. Also note that the visible spectrum only constitutes a small fraction of the total radiation. See Figure 10.6 for another scale of this same phenomena, over a more limited temperature range.

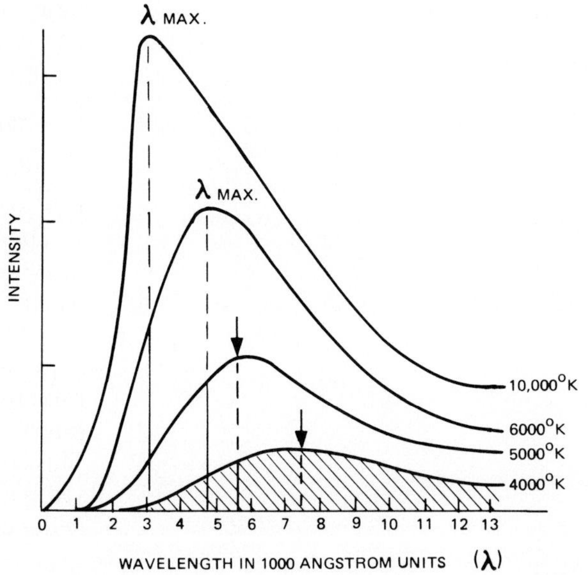

Figure 10.6. This shows the intensity of the black body radiation as a function of temperature. Note the peak of each curve is shifted to shorter wavelengths as the temperature of the black body is increased. These peaks are marked by arrows or with the symbol λ_{MAX}.

idealized black body. Of course, the implication for all this is that we would now assume that stars approximate these idealized black bodies. Then by knowing the surface temperature of a star, one would immediately be able to deduce the energy radiated by the star per square centimeter. What do we do next with this result? If we multiply the energy radiated from one square centimeter by the total surface area of the star (Fig. 10.7), we get the total energy radiated by the star for all wavelengths. So, if the area is $4\pi R^2$, with R as the star's radius, then the total energy radiated by the star, which we call the luminosity (L), is given by:

$$L = 4\pi R^2 \times \sigma T^4 \tag{10.7}$$
Luminosity Equation

This is an immediate expression for the luminosity of a star, given its surface temperature and its radius. We could easily turn this procedure around and use this equation to get the radius of the star, since it is relatively easy to get the surface temperature of the star. How do we get the luminosity? We use the previous expressions (Eq. 10.3), involving apparent magnitude and the star's distance, to get the absolute magnitude. From the absolute magnitude, we get the luminosity (Eq. 10.4) and then taking the luminosity and putting it into Equation 10.7, we can calculate the radius of the star. This may seem complicated, but it is one of the well-known techniques used to predict a star's size. Note that even with the

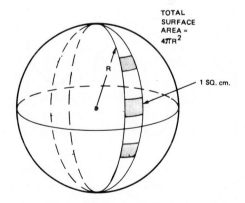

Figure 10.7. A sphere of radius R showing a number of square areas, each one 1 square cm in extent, emitting black body radiation.

largest of telescopes, a star can never be seen as a disc, the way we see the sun from the earth. A space traveler on Pluto would not easily see the sun as a disc either: it would subtend an angle of only $\frac{1/2°}{40} = \frac{1°}{80}$. However, even a small telescope on Pluto would see the sun's disc. Not so, however, for distant stars.

There is one method, nevertheless, by which astronomers have been able to obtain the star's radius directly and that is by examining the light by means of interference techniques. This involves putting sets of mirrors outside the telescope and adjusting the distances between these two mirrors, where, in principle, light from two different sides of the star would interfere once they got together at the end of the telescope. This technique only works for the very closest and largest stars. However, it confirmed the calculated diameters deduced by the luminosity method just described.

Electromagnetic Spectrum

In this section we wish to present a cohesive picture of one aspect of physics which has an enormous impact on astronomy. That is, the radiation emanating from celestial objects. In fact, the only information we receive from the universe, with very few exceptions, is in the form of electromagnetic radiation. The properties of such radiation will first be explored here.

The black body or any hot radiating surface, emits electromagnetic energy whose intensity distribution as a function of wavelength can be studied in great detail, using either prisms or diffraction gratings. One observes the well-known colors of the rainbow. The visible part of the electromagnetic spectrum comprises only a very small part of its totality. All electromagnetic waves propagate at the speed of light in a vacuum.

Figure 10.8 is a very simplified diagram defining wavelength, it is the distance between crests of a wave. The frequency corresponds to the number of cycles that pass any one point per second. The simple relationship between wavelength and frequency is such that the product of wavelength and frequency is equal to the speed of light.

$$\lambda \times \nu = c \tag{10.8}$$

where c = speed of light
    λ = wavelength
    ν = frequency

A slightly more sophisticated picture of the manner in which electromagnetic waves are propagated is shown in Figure 10.9. The electromagnetic waves actually, as the term implies, have both electric and magnetic oscillating fields associated with them, vibrating perpendicular to each other and to the direction of their wave propagation. The amplitude of these fields changes as shown in the figure. We shall not be concerned too much with the magnetic properties of

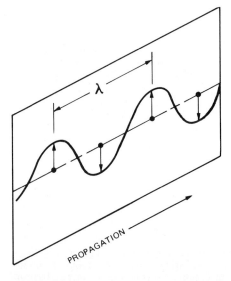

Figure 10.8. The propogation of a polarized electromagnetic wave indicating the change in electric vector amplitude and the definition of wavelength, lambda (λ). Note that a polarized wave has its oscillation confined to one plane.

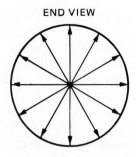

END VIEW

UNPOLARIZED LIGHT
VIBRATION OF ELECTRIC VECTOR

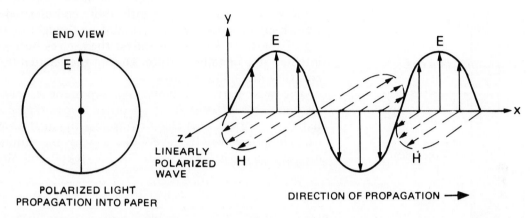

END VIEW

POLARIZED LIGHT
PROPAGATION INTO PAPER

LINEARLY
POLARIZED
WAVE

DIRECTION OF PROPAGATION ⟶

Figure 10.9. Schematic diagram of the propagation of a polarized electromagnetic wave. Both the electric and the magnetic field vectors are shown as they change in intensity while the beam is propagating, as shown.

such waves, but largely with the electric properties, since it is these electric properties that essentially interact with atoms in gases or solids and manifest themselves in a number of phenomenon.

Figure 10.10 shows a larger conceptual picture, indicating that electromagnetic waves really span an enormously large range of phenomenon. Did you know that X-rays, TV, visible, infrared, microwaves, and radio waves all belong to the same family of electromagnetic waves? Notice that the visible part of the spectrum comprises only a very small portion of this large range. Radio and TV waves are indicated. The numbers on the figure represent the wavelength in centimeters. Notice that the wavelength range corresponds to 22 orders of magnitude—from the size of the nucleus, the shortest gamma rays, to the very longest radio waves possible. Each part of the spectrum has its own technology associated with the production of these waves and their detection. Consequently, different names are associated with each range. The X-rays and gamma rays discovered in 1895 are so energetic that they are able to penetrate matter and allow us to take the familiar X-ray pictures. The sun's ultraviolet radiation is screened out largely by the ozone layer in our atmosphere. The visible portion, to which our eyes are sensitive, comprises the largest fraction of energy emitted by the sun. Some of the infrared

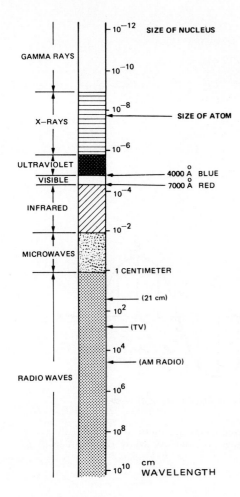

radiation is blocked by the earth's atmosphere, which acts like a protective blanket. The earth's atmosphere is very transparent to microwaves, but there are certain radio wavelengths which are reflected by the atmosphere more readily than others. Our ability to communicate by means of radio waves over large distances is based on the fact that the ionized layers in the earth's atmosphere are able to reflect some of these radio waves during part of the night cycle.

Again, to repeat, all electromagnetic waves propagate with the same speed in a vacuum. Only when these waves interact with glass or other materials (dielectric media) does the velocity inside the media change. The more modern picture of these waves gives them a slightly more complicated connotation. Eletromagnetic waves can also be thought of as consisting of photons. Photons manifest themselves best when they interact at a metallic surface. During their actual travel, light acts very much like a wave.

The wave-particle duality is the present day concept of photons as well as that of all other elementary particles in nature, i.e., every particle in nature has the dual properties of particle and wave: It travels like a wave but interacts with matter like a particle. (Shades of Mr. Jekyll and Mr. Hyde?)

Figure 10.10. This shows the electromagnetic spectrum. Customary designations are shown for the names associated with specific wavelength ranges. Also note the size of the atom and the size of the nucleus on this scale.

Chapter 11

LIGHT SECRETS OF THE ATOM (ATOMIC SPECTRA)— STELLAR ZIP CODES—H-R DIAGRAM

Light Fantastic: Spectral Analysis of Stars

Light is broken down into its component colors by either a prism (Fig. 10.4) or a diffraction grating. A **spectrograph** or a **spectrometer** merely embodies one of these optical components. Not too many years after this instrument became a familiar piece of laboratory equipment, astronomers attached it to a telescope.

The first application of the spectrometer *for stars* was performed by Huggins in 1863, who examined the spectra of Sirius and of Capella. He was amazed to discover that in addition to a continuous spectrum, there were dark (absorption) lines superimposed. This opened up new vistas for astronomy, because new techniques were now available for identifying the elements in the gaseous atmosphere surrounding the stars.

First, let us study the laboratory situation. By using discharge lamps (which are not too different from fluorescent

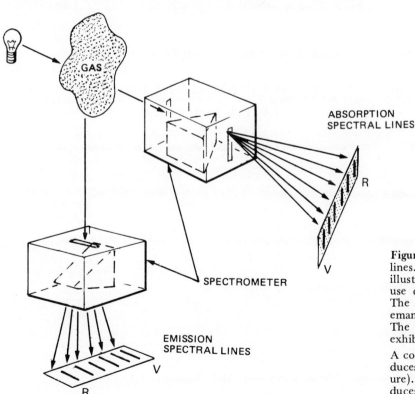

Figure 11.1. Absorption lines and emission lines. The spectrometers in this figure are illustrated schematically. Most spectrometers use diffraction gratings rather than prisms. The black body radiation indicated here is emanating from a tungsten lamp (or star). The lamp produces a continuous spectrum exhibiting all the colors of the rainbow.

A cooler gas in front of the black body produces absorption lines (as shown in the figure). If this gas is excited separately, it produces an emission spectrum (as shown).

167

bulbs) and examining the light, bright emission lines can be obtained. Dark lines appear, however, at the same wavelengths as some of the bright emission lines. What is the mechanism by which dark lines are obtained on a bright background or bright emission lines on a dark background? (Fig. 11.1.) This problem leads us quickly into the details of how the atom functions and, in fact, requires us to study the overall problem a little bit more carefully. Historically, the first to see these dark lines in the spectrum of the sun was W.H. Wollaston in 1802. In 1804, Fraunhoffer studied these in great detail and designated some of the more prominent features of the sun's spectrum. A modern spectrogram is shown in Figure 11.2. By the year 1859, the German scientists Kirchhoff and Bunsen recognized the overall significance and the chemical principles as follows: *Each chemical element in the form of a gas produces a set of characteristic bright lines which are different from one element to the next.* If white light (which has a continuous spectrum) is passed through the gas, some of the characteristic lines will be absorbed and will become visible as dark lines (Fig. 11.1). For over a hundred years, hundreds of thousands of stellar spectra have been taken, catalogued and examined and studied in all possible detail. Among the most significant features of these studies is the following: A hydrogen atom in the laboratory emits the same spectra as a hydrogen atom in any star in

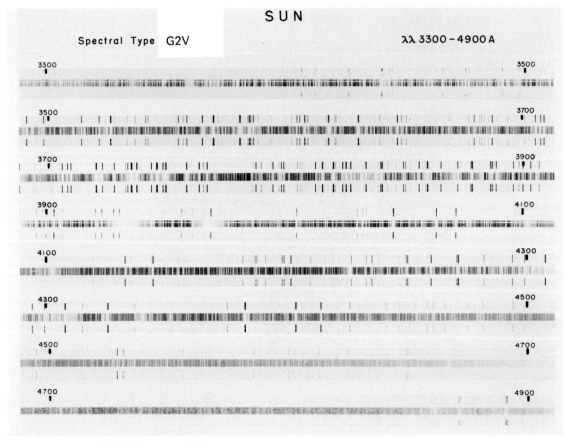

Figure 11.2. A small portion of the sun's spectrum (Hale Observatories).

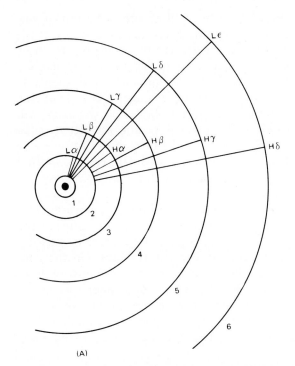

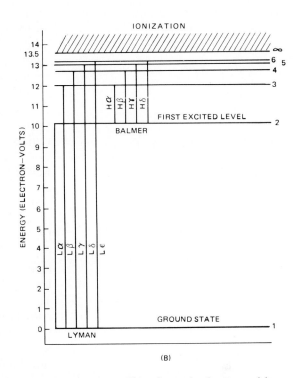

Figure 11.3. Figures A and B show the energy level scheme for the hydrogen atom. The schematic electron orbits are shown around the nucleus (not drawn to scale). The lowest level is called the ground state, designated with the quantum number 1, the next excited state is indicated by 2 and so forth. The well-known transitions in hydrogen atoms are designated by the letters shown in this diagram. The Lyman series and the Balmer series are the best known hydrogen spectral lines.

which it is observed. (The implication, of course, is that the laws of Physics are the same here on earth as they are on stars [or, we could boldly extrapolate, anywhere in the universe].)

The hydrogen atom consists of a nucleus of one proton having a positive charge +1 and one electron with a negative charge of −1, thus making it chargewise neutral. The electron can occupy various discrete orbits, as shown schematically in Figure 11.3. By exciting the atom, the electron is allowed to occupy only these very discrete orbits. As it makes transitions back to its ground state, it will emit radiation. Millions of such atoms are engaged in similar processes. Since the electron has the ability to make a large number of such transitions (jumps), as shown in Figure 11.3, we will get the song of the hydrogen atom as being composed of a series of frequencies.

In the spectrograph, these frequencies stand out as a series of bright lines (Fig. 11.2). Each time the electron makes a jump (or transition), electromagnetic energy of a specific frequency is generated (or emitted). This process however is possible only when the electron returns to its accessible lower states (to which it is allowed to return). Finally, when the electron reaches the lowest state possible, it will cease to emit light and it will stay there until it gets re-excited. That is the simple story of how emitted spectral lines are generated. The dark absorption lines come about in a rather similar process.

When continuous radiation (containing all possible frequencies) is incident on an unexcited (relatively cooler) atom, the electron in the atom will absorb radiation of specific frequencies, permitting the electron to reach one of the allowed excited states. An atom will respond only to those frequencies which correspond to its characteristic excited states. Once it gets excited, it will immediately de-excite in the time of 10^{-8} seconds on the average. Upon de-excitation, the electron jumps to a lower state, and the atom will radiate in all possible directions. Since the reemitted radiation is projected in *all* directions, the probability of receiving the radiation in the *line of sight* is very small. Hence, we find an *absence* of radiation at specific frequencies (these are called absorption lines).

A star's hot surface produces a continuous spectrum. Dark lines are produced by the relatively cooler gases outside the star (Fig. 11.1). This does not imply, however, that emission lines are never produced in stellar atmospheres. On the contrary, some of the very hot stars contain both emission lines as well as absorption lines. Even the sun, under special circumstances, has certain parts of it, namely, those areas near the sunspots, that occasionally will produce emission lines rather than absorption lines. The sun's corona has many emission lines also.

To summarize: Continuous spectrum, emission and/or absorption lines provide important clues on the nature and condition of a star's outer layer.

Contrary to public opinion, astronomers do not use their large telescopes to admire the beauty of stellar objects; rather, they are engaged, almost exclusively, in analyzing the light from cosmic objects. The spectrograph is their main auxilliary tool. They use the finest quality spectrographs and attach them to their telescopes. Or, as is more common: light from the telescope is directed by mirrors into a fixed spectrograph. The astronomer's task lies mainly in selecting celestial objects of interest. They then guide the delicate mechanisms of their telescopes, thereby ensuring that the light stays on their selected objects during the time exposure. At times, such exposures could be as long as five or more hours in duration for very faint and distant objects.

Instrumentation

Spectrographs and spectrometers used in astronomical observatories are identical in their operating procedures to similar instruments used in the physics laboratory. They consist of gratings, mirrors, and photographic plates (or photo tubes) to detect the signals. During the last two decades, astronomers began to improve on these one hundred year old techniques by attaching to the telescope electronic and photoelectric gadgetry. Stellar images can now be enhanced by the use of light intensifiers. Instead of recording the various frequencies on photographic film, sensitive photo tubes can record the images electrically, print out results on tape, or store them in a computer. The very latest in image intensification technology provides enhancement by a factor of about ten thousand in light intensity. The latest in photoelectronic equipment permits light to be examined when there is so little present that individual photons (or little bullets of light) can literally be counted. These new instruments have been installed on most of the large optical telescopes. Their use will make a considerable improvement in the range and depth by which astronomers can see the rest of the universe.

The World of the Atom

Back in the physics laboratory, a number of advances were made in understanding how the atom radiates its energy. By 1914, Niels Bohr enunciated his postulates governing radiation from the atom. These were as follows:

1. The electron may move only in certain permissible orbits. Not all sizes of orbit are allowed to the electron, but only a discrete set of sizes.
2. As long as an electron is revolving about the nucleus in one of the allowed orbits of postulate 1, it cannot radiate.
3. When the electron jumps to a larger orbit (farther away from the nucleus), it must *absorb* energy, and when it jumps to a smaller orbit (closer to the nucleus), it must *emit* energy.
4. Whenever an electron jumps from one orbit to another, it emits or absorbs energy, as the case may be, in the form of a single photon. The energy of the photon emitted or absorbed is exactly equal to the difference of the energy of the electron in the two orbits.

$$h\nu = E_f - E_i$$

where E_i = the energy in its initial orbit and E_f = the energy in its final orbit and ν = frequency of the emitted photon.

These laws led to advances in the study of spectroscopy and, no doubt, stimulated more advances in the field of astronomy. By 1926 Schrödinger, Jordan, de Broglie, Heisenberg, Born and a number of other physicists, had formulated and improved upon these laws, organizing them within a self-consistent framework, which was called Quantum Mechanics. The new laws permitted precise calculations to be made, predicting detailed properties of light emission and the electron's behavior inside the atom. The success of Quantum Mechanics has been so enormous that its laws have not been essentially superceded to this day. This new theory could predict electronic energy levels precisely, as well as the intensity of the emitted spectral lines. Only very minor modifications of this theory were discovered some thirty years later.

Stellar Zip Codes

Spectral Classification—The H.R. Diagram

There is a strong human tendency to organize. Whenever a subject is perplexing and complex, the usual first step is to classify it. Biology, zip codes and yellow pages are typical examples. The ubiquitous pigeonhole is present everywhere. People are classified by social security numbers. Stars are arranged by **spectral classes.**

A systematic effort was begun in 1885 by E.C. Pickering to group all stars by their **spectroscopic signatures.** His work was continued by Annie J. Cannon. The fruits of their enormous labor was the publication, in 1924, by Harvard College Observatory of the Henry Draper Catalogue. It contains the classification of over 250,000 stars. The basis of their classification rested on spectroscopic signatures: The intensity of certain spectral lines of specific elements (Table 11.1). Not only is it impressive that the majority of stars can be pigeonholed within six classifications, but, as H.N. Russell pointed out, there exists a continuous gradation of stars between adjacent spectral classes. The deeper significance for this continuous gradation of spectral classes is the continuous variation in stellar surface temperatures. (An analogy would be the smooth height distribution of children ages 0 to 15 years. The single most important parameter which statistically could predict a child's height would be his age.)

Stars are classified by the sequence of letters: O, B, A, F, G, K, M, and R, N, S. An O type star is the hottest, the others are successively cooler. Typical temperatures range from 40,000°K, for O to about 3,000 to 4,000°K for an M-type.

TABLE 11.1
Spectral and Other Characteristics of Stars

Spectral Class	O	B	A	F	G	K	M	Carbon Stars R	N	S
Most prominent lines	HeII HeI HI OIII NIII CIII SiIV	HeI HI CII OII NII FeIII MgIII	HI (Balmer) Ionized metals	HI CaII TiII FeII	H and K Lines of CaI, FeI, TiI, MgI Some molecular bands Balmer Lines	H and K of CaII, HI (Balmer) Molecular bands	Molecular bands of TiO, CaI	Bands of C₂ CN CH Carbon stars	Similar to R in bands. Lines like K	Bands ZrO YO, LaO Lines of Technitium
Colors	Blue-white	Blue-white	White	Creamy	Yellow	Orange	Red	Red	Red	Red
M	—6	—3.7	+0.7	+2.8	+4.6	+5.2	8.9			
T_e	35,000	21,000	10,000	7,200	6,000	4,700	3,300			
Percentage of stars in galaxy		0.03%	0.6%	0.2%	9.3%	39.1%	50.0%			
Typical examples	ζ Puppis	ζ Persei Rigel γ Lyr	Sirius Vega Deneb δ Cas	Canopus (FO) Procyon (FS) β Cas	Sun Capella β Her	Arcturus Aldebaran ε Peg	Betelgeuse Antares η Gem			

Main Sequence B8-A2

HeI4026, which is equal in intensity to K in the B8 dwarf β Per, becomes fainter at B9 and disappears at A0. In the B9 star α Peg HeI4026 = SiII4129. HeI4471 behaves similarly to HeI4026.

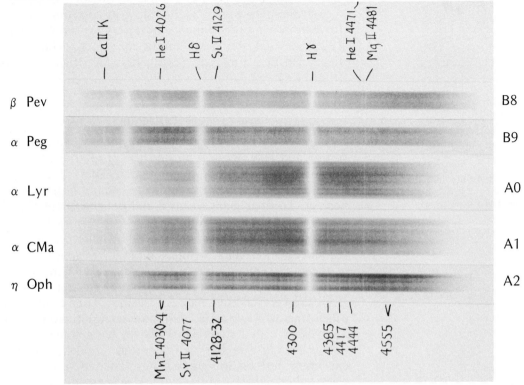

The singly ionized metallic lines are progressively stronger in α CMa and η Oph than in α Lyr. The spectral type is determined from the ratios: B8, B9: HeI4026: Ca II K, HeI4026: Si II 4129, HeI4471: MgII4481. A0-A2: MgII4481:4385, Si II 4129: MnI 4030-4.

Some comments are given on the technical terms used: K refers to a strong line in calcium. The Roman letters following the chemical symbol give the state of ionization of the atom; Viz HeI refers to neutral helium, MgII to a singly ionized atom. E.g., HeI4026 refers to the line of neutral helium at 4026Å.

Figure 11.4. (Yerkes Observatories).

A Carbon Star and a Long Period Variable

The spectrum of HD 52432 (upper) contains strong bands of C_2 and CN. Its spectral type on the R-N system is R5; this corresponds to an equivalent spectral type of around K4.

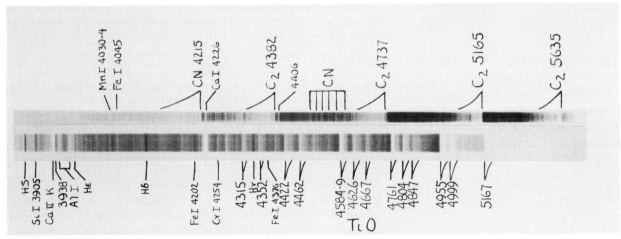

The spectrum of o Ceti (lower) has strong bands of TiO, and the ultimate lines of CaI, CrI and AlI are very strong in absorption. There are also a number of strong emission lines present, including the Balmer lines, SI 3905, and FeI 4202 and 4376. The spectrum was taken on November 8, 1940, when Mira was near the eighth magnitude, approaching light minimum.

Figure 11.5. A carbon star and a long period variable (Yerkes Observatory).

173

Figure 11.6. Astronomy and the famous mnemonic. (See text.) "Oh be a fine girl (guy), kiss me, right now sweet."

Each spectral class is divided in turn into 10 subgroups. The sequence runs as follows: B0, B1, B2, B3 . . . B9, A0, A1, A2, A3, and so on. The sun is classified as G2.

Astronomers were also not slow in adopting a mnemonic for memorizing the sequence of letters. An astronomer in the 1920s devised the now famous mnemonic which goes like this: "Oh Be a Fine Girl (Guy), Kiss Me, Right Now Sweet" (Fig. 11.6).

H-R Diagram

A major advance in astronomy resulted when Einjar Hertzsprung and H.N. Russell plotted the properties of thousands of stars on a sheet of graph paper. They plotted spectral classification (temperature) against absolute magnitude (luminosity). To their great surprise and delight, these stars fitted into a very simple pattern as shown in Figure 11.7. Ninety percent of all the stars lie along what is known as the **main sequence**. Other stars, whose temperatures are equal to those of the main sequence but whose luminosity or the amount of energy radiated is far greater, must be larger stars. These were given the very creative names of **giants**. Then there were still other stars which radiated still more energy than those giants. They were called **supergiants**. There were some other stars, not many in number but unusual enough, which were extremely hot on the surface but radiated very little. They were called **dwarfs**. As a further refinement, because they were not only hot but also white in color, they were called **white dwarfs**. Other small stars of reddish hue were appropriately called **red dwarfs**. Some odd-ball, variable stars were found to be a little off and above the main sequence. These were called **variable stars**.

An immediate side benefit of the H.R. diagram was the following: If 90% of the stars lie along the main sequence, then it is readily possible to reverse the process and obtain the distance of an unknown star just from a knowledge of its temperature or spectral class. To do this, one draws a line as shown in Figure 11.7, to the main sequence, and then projects a horizontal line to the luminosity or absolute magnitude. Then, resurrecting the equation M = m + 5 − 5log d (Chapter 10), everything is known in that formula except the distance d. The technique for getting distances for stars using this method is called **spectroscopic parallax**. It has an inherent error of about 20% and is certainly good for stars in our galaxy that can be identified spectroscopically.

The great fascination of the H-R diagram, however, is the intriguing possibility that such a graph represents some sort of evolutionary development for stars. Astrophysicists have been trying for many years to make sense out of these diagrams, showing how stars would travel one way or another and end up along the main sequence. Such attempts supposedly trace out the life cycle of a star. Where do they get born and how do they die? Surprisingly, however, like women, stars do not automatically tell their ages. They do not even start with a 21 plus X. We are left with just the X. One thing, however, is obvious—stars on the top left-hand corner are the very hottest and, because they radiate the most, must be the youngest—largely because their rate of energy dissipation is so great that they could not live very long. Rigel, one of the dominant stars in the Orion Nebula, is very prominent on this curve. The sun is an average star among the G2 classification. We know its absolute magnitude is 4.8 and its surface temperature is close to 6,000°K. We will return to one aspect of this intriguing stellar evolution problem when we discuss the evolution of the solar system, because the two problems are related.

It is worth pointing out in the Hertzsprung-Russel diagram that the very hottest stars are greatly overrepresented. In view of their enormous luminosity, they can be detected at large distances. A H-R diagram consisting of only nearby stars to the sun (none further than 30 light years) would reveal a different diagram entirely. Most nearby stars are on the main sequence below the sun, i.e., most are cooler and more reddish in color. There are no giants or supergiants nearby.

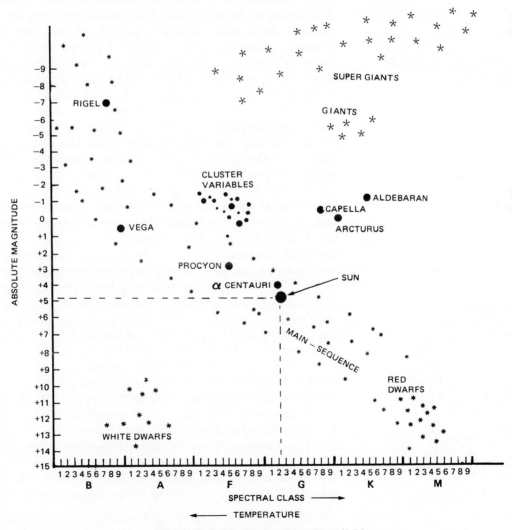

Figure 11.7. The Hertzsprung-Russell Diagram.

175

Chapter 12

THE STARS:
A HOT TRIP INTO A LIVE STAR*

Figure 12.1.

We are now ready to tackle one of the most difficult of all our journeys; the trip inside a star.

Prior to our trip, it is important to lay the ground work as best we can. Let us review, therefore, what we know about a typical star before we get there. We know the luminosity, the surface temperature, and we know its radius, mass, and chemical surface composition. What we wish to know is the density, the mass, the temperature, the chemical composition, the luminosity, and the pressure *at every point inside the star* as we proceed from the outside working our way in towards the center. This is a partial list of stellar interior properties that we seek to study. Can this be done? Well, astrophysicists have been working on this for the last thirty years or so, in terms of formulations that they thought reasonable, and this is now what we have to look at. Let us look at a typical star and ask ourselves a few questions. Will it make any difference where on the star we begin this trip? Should we start on the left side of the star or on the right side or on the top? It is apparent that it makes no difference whether we go a thousand miles starting in from the top or the bottom of the star, we should observe the same stellar properties at either end. In fact, *bottom* and *top* are meaningless quantities in this context. So, one of the first discoveries we make is the fact that the star is symmetrical, i.e., it has **spherical symmetry**. Next, we shall organize the trip in such a way that we shall proceed in giant steps. Instead of an inch at a time, let us proceed a mile at a time. What we are doing (mentally) is dividing the stars into onion shells, or steps, and, irrespective from which direction we go down into the star, as long as we keep track of the number of steps travelled, we should anticipate observing the same property at each onion shell stop. We shall designate each *change* by the symbol Δ (delta). Thus, when we go down a a distance Δr the change in mass from one shell to the next is ΔM. The change in the luminosity will be ΔL, the change in the temperature ΔT, the change in density $\Delta \rho$, and so forth. [$\rho(r)$ is the density at a distance r from the center.] Our job will be to devise a simple means whereby we can predict the properties one step at a time. Using this procedure, we shall set up four equations, each equation being a relationship between various

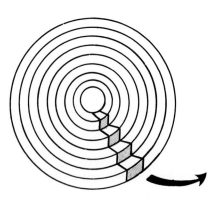

Figure 12.2. Onion shells.

*Recommendation: To be taken only if adequately prepared emotionally and algebraically.

properties. The easiest equation is just the change in the mass. The volume of this onion shell is $4\pi r^2 \Delta r$, where Δr is the thickness of the onion shell. The mass is then just volume times the density (ρ) so the mass of the onion shell ΔM is given by our first equation.

$$\Delta M = 4\pi r^2 \Delta r \cdot \rho \qquad (12.1)$$

(This was a rather simple one to derive.)

The next equation involves **energy generation**. If epsilon (ϵ) is the rate at which energy is generated per gram inside the star (per gram, mind you), then all we have to do is multiply the mass of the onion shell by ϵ, and then we have the amount of energy generated in the shell, ΔL. That immediately gives us equation 2.

$$\Delta L = 4\pi r^2 \Delta r \cdot \rho \cdot \epsilon \qquad (12.2)$$

The next thing we observe is that there is complete equilibrium in the star. The star doesn't explode or implode. There must, therefore, be some sort of buoyant equilibrium such that the change in the pressure, ΔP, forcing a certain small increment of the star (or unit cross section) up, is exactly counterbalanced by the gravitational attraction. This is expressed in equation 3.

$$\Delta P = -\frac{G\, M(r)\rho(r)\Delta r}{r^2} \qquad (12.3)$$

[Note, the shorthand convention of writing $M(r)$. This means the mass of the star within a sphere of radius r. Similarly, we shall abbreviate $L(r)$ as the luminosity of all shells up to distance r from center.] The minus sign reflects the fact that the pressure increases as we go deeper into the star. G is the universal gravitational constant.

The fourth equation is a little more subtle. Here, we are concerned with the manner in which the radiation is actually coming out of the star, since there are a number of ways by which it can come out, either by radiation, convection, or bulk transport. The fourth equation listed here involves radiation transport only:

$$\Delta T = \frac{-3\kappa\; L(r)\rho}{16\pi a \cdot c \cdot r^2 \cdot T^3} \cdot \Delta r \qquad (12.4)$$

We are not home free yet because we have to define each of the terms. a is related to the Stefan-Boltzmann constant σ (remember Chapter 10?). Actually, $a = 4\sigma/c$, where c is the speed of light. Factors such as π, 3/16, you can look up in tables. The minus sign means that it gets hotter as we step deeper into the star. So look out! *Kappa* (κ) is the opacity, the resistance against escaping radiation. It is given by another horrible looking equation. The density can be written down in terms of other factors describing the properties of the star at that point.

Finally, we have no way of knowing what the percentages of hydrogen and helium are inside the star. These have to be guessed. The way astrophysicists handle this problem is that

Figures 12.3 and 12.4. Schematic diagram: stepping carefully into the depths of a star. The star is divided into steps or shells of radius r. Each shell has a thickness of Δr.

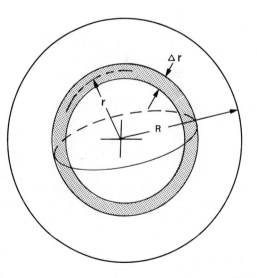

177

they guess initially at the percentage of hydrogen, x, the percentage of helium, y, and the percentage of heavy elements, z. Obviously, x plus y plus z is equal to one. They have to add up to 100%. This is the simplest of all the equations. (There has to be something simple in all this complexity!)

$$x + y + z = 1 \qquad (12.5)$$

Technical Note No. 14 summarizes all the equations.

Now, we come to the most exciting part of the problem: where does all the energy originate? How is the energy manufactured inside the star? This had intrigued astronomers for decades. In the 1920s, it was thought that gravitational contraction of the sun would be responsible for producing energy—the only mechanism known to astronomers of that period. The trouble with that hypothesis is that the sun would have to be too young, a mere few hundred million years old, since there is only a relatively small amount of energy available from gravitation. However, from the age of the earth, where rocks have been dated to be at least 3.3 billion years old and from meteorites that are 4.6 billion years old, we know that the solar contraction hypothesis leads to untenable results. The apparent solution to this dilemma was given by nuclear physicists, in particular, the discoveries by Dr. Hans Bethe.

Nuclear fusion produces energy by combining four hydrogen atoms to produce one helium atom. The sum of the four hydrogen atoms weighs more than a helium atom produced by the fusion of the four hydrogen atoms. The *mass that is destroyed* reappears *as energy*, using the famous Einstein equation, $E = mc^2$. The process of producing energy, called the **proton-proton** cycle (Table 12.1), presumably predomi-

TABLE 12.1
The Proton-Proton Cycle

$_1H^1 + {}_1H^1 \rightarrow {}_1D^2 + \beta^+ + \nu$	1.44 Mev
$_1D^2 + {}_1H^1 \rightarrow {}_2He^3 + \gamma$	5.49 Mev
$_2He^3 + {}_2He^3 \rightarrow {}_2He^4 + {}_1H^1 + {}_1H^1 + \gamma$	12.85 Mev

Note the energy generated by each step.

Note the following notation:

β^+ is a positively charged electron or positron.

ν is a neutrino. A particle of no mass, no charge (no character and no charm either).

γ is a gamma ray—a high energy photon.

The subscripts and superscripts: e.g., $_2He^3$.

2 refers to the atomic charge of the nucleus (2 protons). Superscript 3 refers to its atomic weight. It must have one neutron, to make 3 particles.

TABLE 12.2
Carbon-Nitrogen-Oxygen Cycle

$_6C^{12} + {}_1H^1 \rightarrow {}_7N^{13} + \gamma$	1.95 Mev
$_7N^{13} \rightarrow {}_6C^{13} + \beta^+ + \nu$	2.22 Mev
$_6C^{13} + {}_1H^1 \rightarrow {}_7N^{14} + \gamma$	7.54 Mev
$_7N^{14} + {}_1H^1 \rightarrow {}_8O^{15} + \gamma$	7.35 Mev
$_8O^{15} \rightarrow {}_7N^{15} + \beta^+ + \nu$	2.71 Mev
$_7N^{15} + {}_1H^1 \rightarrow {}_6C^{12} + {}_2He^4 + \gamma$	4.96 Mev

nates inside the sun. There is another more elaborate cycle, known as the carbon-nitrogen-oxygen cycle, shown in Table 12.2 which also produces helium, but which uses oxygen and nitrogen nuclei as intermediates. Of interest here is to see that the carbon (CNO) cycle is by far more temperature sensitive than the proton-proton (P-P) cycle. The curves of Figure 12.5 show the energy generation as a function of temperature, and reveal that both processes are active. However, the efficiency for the carbon cycle overtakes that of the proton cycle at higher temperatures (Fig. 12.5). Thus, at the very high temperatures only the carbon cycle is the dominant one whereas, at the lower temperatures of say a few million degrees, the proton cycle is the dominant.

The other term that has not been adequately explained is the opacity (κ) in Equation 12.4. This is a very complicated function. It includes peculiar factors such as the **gaunt factor** and the guillotine factor; it also depends on the hydrogen-helium content, density and temperature. In short, it depends on many elements and functions at each point inside the star. Basically, κ (kappa) is a measure of how readily the radiation can be transported from the inside to the outside of the star. It is also very much dependent upon temperature (Tech. Note No. 14). The interesting part of this whole complicated exercise is to show how interrelated all these quantities are, where each property of the star depends on every other property (e.g., the density depends on the temperature and location, etc.).

The solution is obtained by solving these four equations simulatneously, assuming initial values for the quantities x and y, and making some judicious assumptions on the type of model for the star; i.e., namely whether it consists of two-zones or three-zones, where each zone of the star is either a radiative or convective region. Other choices include whether energy is transported radiatively, convectively, or in lumps.

Equations 12.1 to 12.4, plus all the auxiliary equations, are solved simultaneously for different values of x, y, and z. Computers are used to grind out the numbers. The astronomer engaged in this calculation feels the task is completed as soon as self-consistent results are obtained.

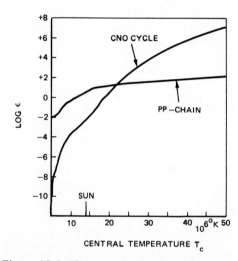

Figure 12.5. The temperature dependence of the energy generation function ϵ (epsilon) ergs/cc for the proton-proton (p-p) and the carbon (CNO) cycle. The scale is logarithmic, e.g., a change from -4 to 0 corresponds to a change of 10,000 in energy generation. Note also the point where the curves intersect. At that temperature both processes are equally efficient.

179

Stellar Rotation

One of the basic stellar properties that had not been included in the inside star trip analysis is the fact that stars rotate. This property of stars can be measured by means of their surface velocity, using the Doppler effect (Chapter 15). Table 12.3 shows the equatorial rotational velocities for stars as a function of their spectral classification. There are three columns associated with each such classification: the first one refers to giant stars, the next to the main sequence, and the third column has the listing of the maximum rotational observed velocities. There is a distinct difference between giants and main sequence stars. The most pronounced feature in the table is the sudden drop in rotational velocities for spectral classes of G and below. Note that the sun has a surface velocity of only two kilometers per second.

TABLE 12.3
Stellar Rotation*

Spectral Class	Average Equatorial Rotational Velocity (km/sec)		Maximum Rotational Velocity (km/sec)
	Giants	Main Sequence	
O5		180	400
B0	95	200	420
B5	120	230	390
A0	140	190	320
A5	160	150	250
F0	130	100	180
F5	60	30	100
G0	20	4	
K,M	<12	1	
The SUN (now)		2	

*Data from C.W. Allen *Astrophysical Quantities,* 3rd ed., Athlone Press, 1973.

The significance of this table is that young hot stars rotate extremely rapidly and that the more aged well-settled stars like the sun almost cease to rotate at all. What happened in its evolutionary development? This question also has a bearing on the evolution of the solar system. One of the present dilemmas concerns the distribution of angular momentum in the solar system. The mass of the sun constitutes 99.9% of the total mass of the solar system, yet the sun appears to have only 2% of the angular momentum of the solar system. These facts lead us to suspect that there is a deeper significance to the evolutionary development of stars connected with their rotation. It also helps us to make some predictions as to which stars might possibly have solar systems like our sun. It is apparent that only stars of classification G, K, and M, based on this rotational analysis, have any chance for solar systems.

To appreciate the surface speed of the more rapidly rotating stars, consider that 400 kilometers per second is equivalent to a speed of 900,000 miles an hour. Compare this to the rotational speed at the earth's surface of 1,000 miles an hour at the equator; or of the surface speed of the present sun of 4,500 miles per hour.

Star Clans

Like people, stars apparently prefer the company of their own kind. They don't enjoy being left alone in outer space, either. It is estimated that perhaps as many as 50% of all the stars in our galaxies are components of at least a binary system or perhaps a more complicated association of stars. Binary systems are the simplest ones to analyze and to envision. We shall, therefore, start with that system. It involves the motion of two stars revolving around each other; or, in fact, moving around a common center of mass, which is technically called the **barycenter**. Let us call two typical stars A and B and observe their motions around their common center of mass (Fig. 12.6). At every instant in their orbit, a line between A and B must pass through the barycenter. Each star will describe its own ellipse, with periods given by the now well-memorized equation of Kepler's modified third law. Astronomers have catalogued more than thirty thousand such systems and have studied them extensively. Binary systems are the only systems for which the masses of a star can be obtained unambiguously. From Kepler's third law (as modified by Newton, of course):*

$$\frac{P^2}{a^3} = \frac{4\pi^2}{G(M_1 + M_2)}$$

The equation shows that one obtains the sum of the masses $(M_1 + M_2)$, but not the individual masses.

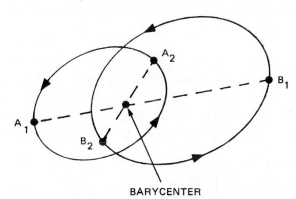

BARYCENTER

Figure 12.6. This shows the motion of two stars revolving around their common barycenter. Note that the line joining the two stars, A and B, must intersect the barycenter at all times. Since the barycenter also has a direct motion, resulting from its orbit within the galaxy, the net resulting motion is a more complicated motion than shown here, see Figure 12.10.

*In actual practice, since the orbit makes a finite angle with respect to our line of sight, allowances have to be made for the angle by substituting a sin i for a, where (90-i) is the angle of the orbital plane with respect to the line of sight.

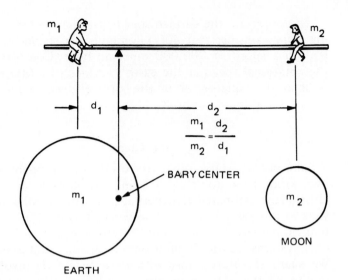

$$\frac{m_1}{m_2} = \frac{d_2}{d_1}$$

Figure 12.7. The barycenter between masses M_1 and M_2. For the earth and the moon, this barycenter is three-quarters of the way from the center of the earth.

How does one obtain the individual masses? We have two unknowns, so one obviously needs two equations. The second equation makes use of a very interesting and simple principle. All of you have observed a seesaw when you were a child. Balancing weights on a tilting seesaw, the ratio of masses m_1/m_2 is directly proportional to the ratio of d_2/d_1 (Fig. 12.7). It is technically known as taking moments about the common center of mass. This is our second equation, whereby the barycenter can be determined in space. It is not the easiest of tasks, but certainly one that is feasible for many binaries. By observing binary systems over a long enough period of time, their orbits and periods can be traced out and their individual masses determined. Table 12.4 gives examples of masses and luminosities of stars. When the two stars are so close together that one cannot optically distin-

TABLE 12.4
Masses and Luminosities as a Function of Spectral Class

Spectral Class	Mass (Solar Masses)		Luminosity (Units of Solar Luminosity) Supergiants
	Supergiants	Main Sequence	
O5	158	40	250,000
BO	50	18	63,000
B5	25	6.5	20,000
AO	16	3	10,000
A5	12.6	2	7,900
FO	12.6	1.7	6,300
F5	10	1.3	6,300
GO	10	2.5	6,300
G5	12	3.1	7,900
KO	12	4	15,800
K5	16	5	50,000
M2	20	8	

Data from C.W. Allen, *Astrophysical Quantities*, 3rd ed., p. 209. Athlone Press, 1973.

182

guish between them by means of the highest power telescope available, then indirect methods have to be invoked, such as by studying the **Doppler shifts** (Chapter 15) of the spectral lines of each individual star, since the double stars are recognized by the oscillating Doppler shifted lines associated with each star. From the periods obtained from the oscillations, rough values for their masses can be obtained. A more precise value of their masses can be calculated, or read off, from the Mass-Luminosity relationship (Fig. 12.8).

Figure 12.9 shows an example of a well-known binary system, Beta Persei (Algol). Astronomers have studied this star for many years and plotted the light output. It is readily apparent that one can interpret the sharp changes in light intensity by assuming that one of the stars eclipses the other, and that one of the stars is far brighter than its dance companion. An example of this type is known as an eclipsing binary system. The chance of seeing such systems is not as great, since the plane of stellar binary orbits are most likely randomly oriented with respect to our line of sight, and only by luck will some of these orbits lie exactly in our line of sight, such that the stars will eclipse each other periodically.

Positions A, B, and C correspond to the total intensity of the combined output of the stars. The two stars are obviously so close together that one cannot visually distinguish their positions in orbit. Their closeness can be ascertained from their very short period of seventy hours.

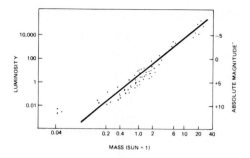

Figure 12.8. Mass-luminosity relationship.

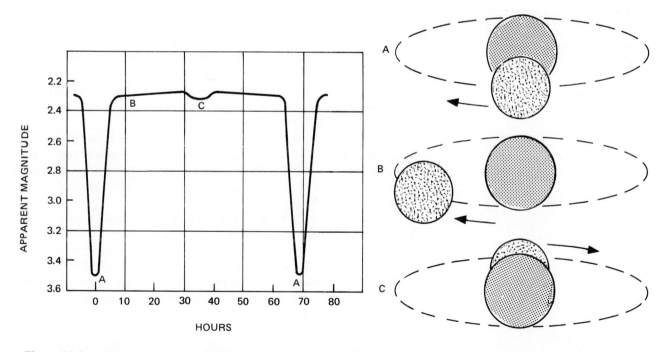

Figure 12.9. A binary star system and the resulting light curve from both stars as they alternately eclipse each other. At position A the brighter star is eclipsed by the dimmer star, consequently a deeper minimum is obtained in this manner. Position C when the two stars change roles, the minima is less pronounced. These are schematic drawings indicating many typical binary situations.

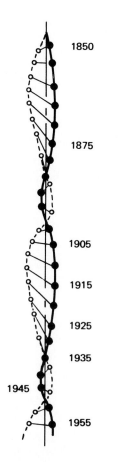

Figure 12.10. This shows the wavy motion of the star Sirius projected against the background of the sky. Also indicated is the motion of its more dimly emitting companion star.

An example of another system is shown in Figure 12.10. It shows the path of one of our nearby stars, Sirius, which has been tracked for over a hundred years. Its position was found to waver in a periodic manner. This strongly suggested the possibility that it had a companion whose light output was very low. Bessel, in 1834, made such a prediction after studying it for ten years. It was not until the advent of high quality telescopes that this previously unseen companion was discovered by A. Clark in 1862.

There are more than a hundred systems within thirty light years of our sun whose stellar motions are similar to those of Sirius. This implies that they have companions, so-called dark companions, whose light output is insufficient to be seen in our big telescopes. However, there is no question about the fact that indeed there are companions going around them. Could these be solar systems?

How would our sun look to another astronomer from another solar system associated with another star? Would our sun perform a dance like Sirius is performing? (Exercise 15.) Although Jupiter would not be seen (since it radiates insufficient energy), its gravitational pull on the sun is sufficient to make the sun perform a small wavy path whose period is about twelve years, corresponding to the orbital period of Jupiter around the sun.

The implication of this is obvious. Because there are so many dark companions around, the chances of these dark companions being either extinguished stars, or perhaps large planets, becomes moot, the difference being mainly one of semantics. Consequently, we can be reasonably sure that our solar system is not unique; that perhaps all stars sooner or later will have bodies revolving around them, such as we have.

We'll get back to this very intriguing point in the summary chapter on Cosmology, when we discuss the possibility of life in other parts of our galaxy. However, the clues that we obtained by this study clearly suggest that stars have more in their environment than meets the eye.

One other question one ought to ask is how did these binary systems come about? As we implied earlier, there are even more complicated systems around. A number of them are known where two binary systems revolve around each other; sort of two pairs, each pair performing its own dance and then dancing around the common center of mass. Since triple and quadruple systems are well known, it makes the question of how these systems came about in the first place a very acute one. Are these all chance captures? The probability of capture is too small to allow for so many of these "planetary" type systems. Consequently, one has to come up with a better explanation.

The Oddball Stars

If you've survived the inside star trip, you will be ready to explore the world of the crazy stars, the abnormal or peculiar stars, or whatever names that one can attach to stars that

184

differ from the run-of-the-mill stars. The first thing that one does with a group of stars that cannot be readily explained is to put them into categories. Just like the biologists who lump all the flying animals together as one group and all the reptiles in another, one uses the same procedure with stars. What makes these stars peculiar? Their change in intensity as a function of time. Where the sun, thank goodness, remains constant in its light output, these stars change their intensity in various periods. So the first thing that one does is to divide them into those that have long periods and those that have short periods. As one breaks them into various groups, one group of stars with very short periods seem to be of greatest interest. These are called Cepheids. There is an elaborate family tree of variable stars, which we shall not itemize. We shall consequently ignore the other periodic type stars, except for the Cepheid variables. What makes them so interesting is that their periods are constant to a very high order of precision, to a part in a million. Not only does the light intensity change, but the spectral class changes; i.e., the temperature on the star's surface changes during the course of a cycle (Fig. 12.11). Also, its expansion velocity has been measured to change in a periodic manner. The picture that one obtains is that the star progressively becomes bigger and then smaller in a periodic way. It sort of blows itself up and then contracts in a time frame of the order of days. That is a very rapid change for a large object like a star. The period is

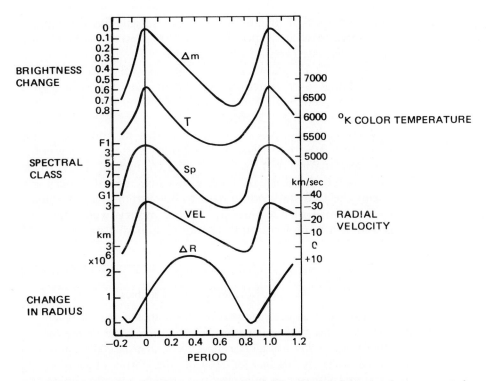

Figure 12.11. Various properties of cepheid variables. Their brightness change, spectral class changes, radial velocity and changes of radius as a function of period. (Adapted from A. Unsöld, *The New Cosmos*, Springer, N.Y., 1969.)

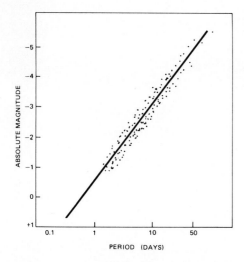

Figure 12.12. This gives the relationship between the period of cepheid variables and their absolute magnitudes. A very important criteria for distance determinations.

inversely proportional to the square root of the star's mean density or, more specifically, the period is:

$$P = \frac{k}{\sqrt{\rho}}$$

where k = constant
ρ = density

This property seems to be obeyed by most of these Cepheid stars. What makes these Cepheids so important is that if one takes hundreds of them and plots on graph paper the absolute magnitude versus the period for each one of them, one obtains an approximate straight line as shown in Figure 12.12. Why is it important? Pick any Cepheid at random; then just by knowing its period, one can deduce its absolute magnitude. One of the techniques for getting stellar distances (d) uses the absolute magnitude and apparent magnitude in the following equation:

$$M = m + 5 + 5\log p''$$
$$\text{or } M = m + 5 - 5\log d$$

where d = distance = 1/p''
M = absolute magnitude
m = apparent magnitude

This was done for stars in the small Magellanic Cloud and indeed it changed the whole astronomical distance scale of one of our neighborhood galaxies. It turned out that, by using these Cepheid variables as distance indicators, its real distance was larger than had been previously determined. The determination of distances for stars and galaxies throughout the universe is an important and ever-present problem, and will be discussed more fully in Chapter 17.

Figure 12.11 shows the intensity as well as the spectral class change as a function of time or over the course of a complete cyclic variation (period) for a typical Cepheid variable.

What causes a star to behave in this manner? An early suggestion was that it was a close binary system. This was the first explanation put forward by astronomers, only to be subsequently discarded, largely because the distances between the two stars would have to be extremely close—closer than the size of a typical star. Other models were then suggested, but none were quite satisfactory in all aspects.

Author's Note on Cepheid Variables

A model that was suggested by this author is that there are two cores inside the same star. This in turn is based on the author's assumption that all stars have cores, that the cores split or fission occurred, and that for Cepheids, the splitting of the cores was not sufficient to bring the two stars far enough apart to create a visible, spectroscopic binary system. Both cores remained inside the star revolving around each other. The image we would expect to see in this proposed model is of a typical Cepheid variable. Namely, as the cores rotate around their common center of mass, the gaseous envelope is pulled along with the cores producing an orbital extention. Consequently, it appears to us as if the star has an uneven surface, expanding or contracting as the inner cores rotate. This model would account for the high reproducibility of the period and in fact would also give a very simple explanation for the relationship between period and density, assuming that the masses of the Cepheid variable are approximately equal to that of a solar mass. One can easily deduce, using Kepler's third law, that the period would obey a $\frac{1}{\sqrt{\rho}}$ relationship. The important clues that emerged from this analysis are that (1) the stars have cores, (2) core fission is as possible as nuclear fission of the atom, and (3) if core fission is a common occurrence, one would expect to see a large number of binary systems where, unlike the Cepheids, cores have separated enough to generate visible stars that can readily be seen revolving around each other. Indeed, the question should have been, "why are there so many binary systems in the galaxy?" It appears that no other explanation is as plausible as that of stellar core fission. The binary capture hypothesis would be a rarer event and, besides, there are just too many binary systems in the galaxy to account for the rare capture of one star by another.

This takes care of the regular variable stars. Are there any irregular ones? Yes, there a lot of irregular stars with periods that are not only irregular but highly erratic. Among the most interesting ones are the novae and supernovae.

Novae

In contrast to a variable star, a star that becomes a nova undergoes a rather sudden and dramatic change in its brightness. The word *nova* is derived from the Latin meaning *new*. It reminds us that a star which could change its brightness by as much as 60,000 times may make its appearance known at a position in the sky where previously it had not even been suspected to exist (using small diameter telescopes for instance).

Novae are occasionally seen in the Andromeda nebula. The physical characteristic of a nova is its light curve: a sudden and dramatic change in the star's light output of about 12 to 13 magnitudes or about 20,000 to 60,000 times brighter over a period of hours or days (Fig. 12.13).

A typical nova was Nova Aquilae, which occurred in 1918. Prior to its outburst, it was an A type star. Then, suddenly, its magnitude changed from 5 to −8, i.e., it increased in brightness by 13 magnitudes. An example of a **recurrent nova** is that of a star called T Pyxides which went "beserk" in 1890, 1902, 1920, and 1944. Its magnitude change was from 14 to 8. There are a number of examples of O type stars which astronomers have studied in post and prenova condi-

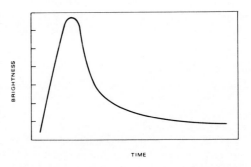

Figure 12.13. The light curve of a typical nova. Note the sudden increase in its brightness and the relatively slow decline, back to its original luminosity.

tions. Many novas occur in binary systems. This is consistent with the cosmological model outlined in Chapter 18, where it is proposed that core fission and subsequent developments are part of the normal stellar evolutionary stages (including the development of a complete solar system).

We shall leave novas temporarily and get to the next stage of apparent catastrophic events in the universe.

Supernovae

No one can stage as spectacular an event as that of the supernova! It is the most violent and the most awesome sight in the galaxy. The change in its luminosity corresponds to 10^8 or 10^9; its absolute magnitude could be as large as -19 at maximum. In fact, a supernova observed in another galaxy emits as much light as *all the stars* in that galaxy combined! A truly dramatic event. There have been seven to nine supernovas observed in our galaxy in the last eighteen hundred years. The most interesting and the most studied was the one that occurred in 1054 (Crab Nebula remnant). Tycho Brahe observed a supernova in the constellation Cassiopeia in 1572 and Kepler observed one in Ophiuchus in 1604. We shall spend some time discussing the Crab Nebula supernova (in the Constellation Taurus) because the mysteries and information which have been opened up since the identification of the remnant have led to much new information in astronomy and astrophysics. It is not an exaggeration to state that its study truly deserves the great attention that it is now getting. It turns out that the major remnant of the Crab supernova most likely is a **neutron star**, no larger than 10 to 50 miles in diameter (Tech. Note No. 19) and spinning at tremendous speeds. The story of the identification as a supernova remnant in itself is a fascinating story. The year was 1054. What records do we have in the European literature of this event which was so dramatic that the supernova could be seen in daylight?

Unfortunately there is not a single written record in the European Literature. Ancient Chinese Annals describe the event very clearly. The court astronomers of that period recorded the brightness of this new *guest star* as they called it. They also noted its position among the constellations in the sky. It was carefully observed for many months as it gradually became dimmer. Its presumed light curve was no doubt similar to that of a nova (Fig. 12.13) except that its initial steep rise in luminosity was far more dramatic. (The actual search of ancient records and the identification of the Crab Nebula as the supernova remnant came about as a result of the collaboration of a Dutch astronomer and a Chinese scholar in the 1920s.)

The absence of records in the European literature suggests that they walked around with their heads looking down, not up. It was indeed a time of the Dark Ages!

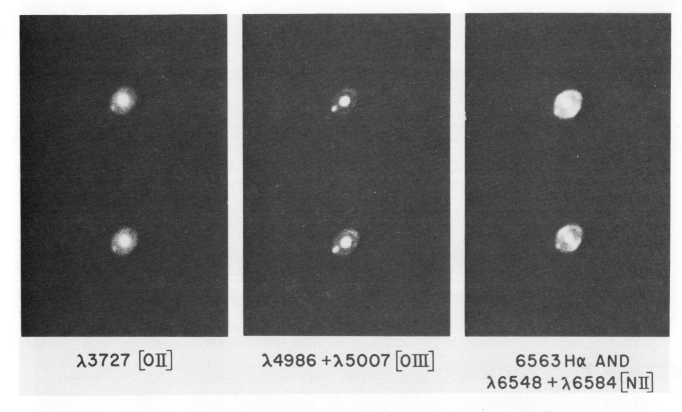

$\lambda3727$ [OII] $\lambda4986 + \lambda5007$ [OIII]   6563 Hα AND $\lambda6548 + \lambda6584$ [NII]

Figure 12.14. Nova Herculis (1934) as it appeared in 1951 (Hale Observatories).

Galactic Supernova

Supernovas are a rare occurrence in a galaxy. Or could they be rare only for a well-developed older galaxy? In any event, they are occasionally detected among other galaxies, when their sudden and dramatic brightness becomes conspicuous. Table 12.5 lists a set of supernovas whose presence were inferred from diverse and generally obscure ancient records. Except for Tycho Brahe's and Kepler's supernovas, which were carefully studied and recorded, the others "to be brought to light" (on the list) required a great deal more research.

Stephenson and Clark, in a recent popular journal article (Scientific American, June 1976), describe the fascinating search of old records for evidence of "guest stars" that are visible for periods in excess of half a year. Apparently, the best supernova signature is their longtime visibility. The shorter time light decay curves are more likely to be ordinary Novas. A few remarks on the spatial distribution (positions) of each of the supernovas listed in Table 12.5: they all seem to be close to the plane of the galaxy. That is not too surprising, because that is where the stars are located. How-

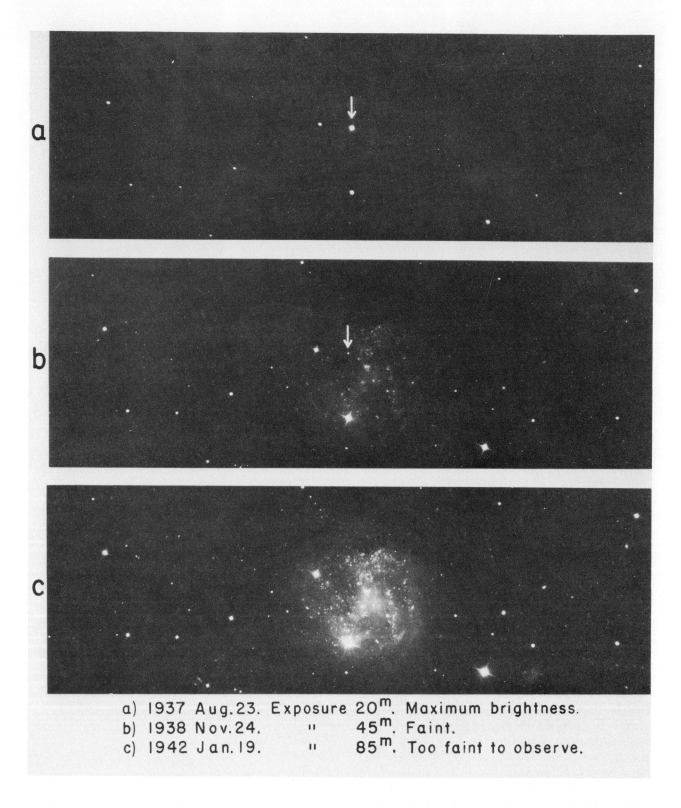

a) 1937 Aug. 23. Exposure 20^m. Maximum brightness.
b) 1938 Nov. 24.   "   45^m. Faint.
c) 1942 Jan. 19.   "   85^m. Too faint to observe.

Figure 12.15. A supernova in another galaxy IC 4182, photographed at three different times (Hale Observatories).

TABLE 12.5
Supernovas in Our Galaxy, Recorded During the Last 1,800 Years

Year (A.D.)	Constellation	Remnant Radio Source	Apparent Magnitude
185	Centaurus	G 315.4 −2.3	−8
393	Scorpius	G 348.5 +0.1 or G 348.7 +0.3	−1
1006	Lipus	G 327.6 +14.5	−8 to −10
1054	Taurus	G 184.6 −5.8 (Crab Nebula)	−5
1181	Cassiopeia	G 130.7 +3.1	0
1572	Cassiopeia	G 120.1 +1.4	(Brahe) −4
1604	Ophiuchus	G 4.5 +6.8 (Center of galaxy)	(Kepler) −2.5
1667±	Cassiopeia A	? $\ell=112, \beta=-2$	distance = 3.4 kpc
? 827	Sco	?	−10

Reference: F.R. Stephenson, and D.H. Clark, *Scientific American*, June, 1976, p. 100, and C.W. Allen, *Astrophysical Quantities*, 3rd ed., p. 221.
Note. C.W. Allen lists the 393 A.D. supernova as 396 A.D. Also, last two entries are from Allen.

ever, each observed supernova was situated in one of the galactic spiral arms, with the 1604 one being closest to the center of the galaxy.

The remnant of each supernova has essentially been identified with a galactic radio emitter. The designation of each source involves a set of numbers which are in effect their galactic coordinates (address in space). The first number is the galactic longitude, and the second number refers to galactic latitude. The plane of the galaxy is the fiduciary base line in this coordinate system, just as the horizon or equator were the coordinate systems discussed in Chapter 1. Any object that lies close to the galactic plane has a low number for its galactic latitude. Note that the radio sources corresponding to the galactic supernova all have very low galactic latitudes. The plus and minus signs specify whether the source is above or below the plane, respectively. For example, the supernova of 1006 situated in the constellation Lipus had a galactic longitude of 327.6° and a galactic latitude of +14.5; its apparent magnitude was between −8 and −10. It was as bright as about 1/4 full moon.

The Crab has been studied a great deal. The time is ripe for affirmative action among supernovas:

> **Give other remnants**
> **Equality semblance**
> **Remove the Hiatus**
> **of unequal status.**

(F.M.J.)

Chapter 13

THE INTERSTELLAR MEDIUM

Figure 13.1. Horsehead Nebula (Hale Observatories).

If you are looking up into the sky in the right direction on a clear night, away from city lights and smog, you will see the Milky Way. The Milky Way comprises billions of stars, seen from our obscure vantage point *inside* the galaxy. The region where the sky appears brightest is a view along the edge of our galaxy. If you consider each star a raisin, we are indeed inside this raisin pudding looking out. Figure 1.7 is a schematic diagram indicating the position of our sun, thirty thousand light years away from the center of the galaxy. Figure 16.4 (p. 229) would be a similar view from outside the galaxy.

We shall now discuss the material between the stars. Let us look at Figures 13.1 and 13.2, which show some of the regions of the galaxy we wish to examine. The dark areas in

Figure 13.2. NGC 1976 Great Nebula in ORION. Messier 42. 120-inch photograph (Lick Observatories).

some of these pictures were initially thought to represent an absence of stars. The bright areas are emission nebulae consisting of enormous gas clouds. It was later realized that the absence of stars was really obscuration, scattering of starlight by *dust*. We now come to the most intriguing parts of our present story. What is this so-called dust?

One of the enigmas associated with these dust clouds is the chemical and physical nature of their constituents. Unfortunately, we are no closer to the truth in this matter than astronomers were forty years ago, but there are lots of clues. The earliest clues were in the nature of the scattering (reddening) process itself: that is, the study of the scattered light. Almost everyone has noticed the reddish glow of the sun at sunset. This is due to small dust particles in the atmosphere which scatter *blue* light. The remaining unscattered light that reaches us is more reddish in appearance. Some of the reddest looking sunsets may sometimes be seen in the Los Angeles area when the particulate matter (smoke from brush fires for example) is very abundant in the atmosphere. The technical name for this scattering process is **Rayleigh Scattering**.* Its wavelength or color dependence is inversely proportional to

*Strictly speaking, Rayleigh Scattering refers to the scattering of light from centers (molecules) which are very much smaller than the wavelength of light. (This is the cause for the blue sky. However other size particles cause scattering also.)

193

(λ^4). The shorter the wavelength, the more readily does the light get scattered. This is why our sky looks blue (the moon's sky is black because there is no atmosphere on the moon). It was natural for astronomers to assume that similar processes must occur in the interstellar medium.

Suppose we were to examine a B type star which, from our previous studies (Chapter 10), has a certain bluish color. If we now examine a similar star from behind a large dust cloud, its apparent color might be reddish looking instead! By subtracting the radiation due to a reddened star from an unreddened star, we can obtain, hopefully, the intrinsic scattering of the intervening dust.

Gas atoms or small molecules do not contribute to the interstellar reddening phenomenon. The scattering process depends critically on the sizes of the particles, their chemical makeup (whether they are dielectric like ice or metallic), how much they absorb, and their shape. With such a host of variables, it seems almost hopeless to match the observed interstellar reddening unambiguously.

On top of all this, the observed astronomical reddening curve has a very characteristic color dependence. (It was initially about $1/\lambda$, but then as the infrared and UV regions became accessible, it became progressively more complicated.) It also varies in different regions of the galaxy. In addition to this reddening phenomenon, a large fraction of starlight may actually be blocked out. We may obtain as little as 1/1,000 or less of the actual emitted starlight, if the star lies behind an obscured region of space. There is a lot more that happens to starlight, but let's first trace the developments of how astronomers tackled the dust problem: both laboratory and theoretical studies were undertaken. Then, comparisons were made between theory, experiments, and astronomical observations in order to characterize the chemical nature of dust based upon such comparisons. Unfortunately, such efforts were not scientifically convincing.

In addition to investigating its chemical nature, attempts were also made to extract a size distribution of the dust based on the reddening (scattered starlight) effects. It turns out that sizes cannot be unambiguously determined either. Presumably, there exists a range of sizes. If one range of size does not fit the data, one considers a bimodal or double-sized distribution. Finally, if all these theoretical models do not correspond to the actual observations, one resorts to putting various coatings on these so-called *dust particles*. If one set of coatings does not work, one resorts to two or three different types of coatings. All this is done with a great deal of seriousness and without placing one's tongue in one's cheek. Some might come to the defense of these "dust scattering specialists," however, since it is extremely difficult and probably impossible to obtain any sort of chemical information from the meager data that is presently available. Meanwhile, starlight continues to travel across thousands of light years, interacting with and being scattered by various sorts of particles whose chemical nature so far eludes us.

How much easier it is to identify the atoms and molecules in the stellar atmosphere! Whenever one studies atoms and molecules in stars, in the intervening interstellar medium, or in a laboratory, their characteristic signatures of emission and absorption spectra are clear, unambiguous, uncluttered and easily identified. Such studies are now almost routine. Likewise, it has been possible to identify atoms and small radicals, using these same absorption studies for atoms and molecules in the interstellar medium. A list of such atoms, radicals, and molecules identified optically is shown in Table 13.1. Figure 13.3 shows a typical spectrogram in which absorption spectra are shown, using a series of hot background stars as illuminators. The sodium D lines and the calcium lines show up

TABLE 13.1
Intersteller Atoms and Molecules Detected Optically

H, He, Ca, Na, K, Ti, Fe	Atoms
CH, CH^+, CN, CO, H_2	Radicals or molecules
Mg, $C_{46}H_{30}N_6$ (Molecule χ)	Largest interstellar molecule identified to date

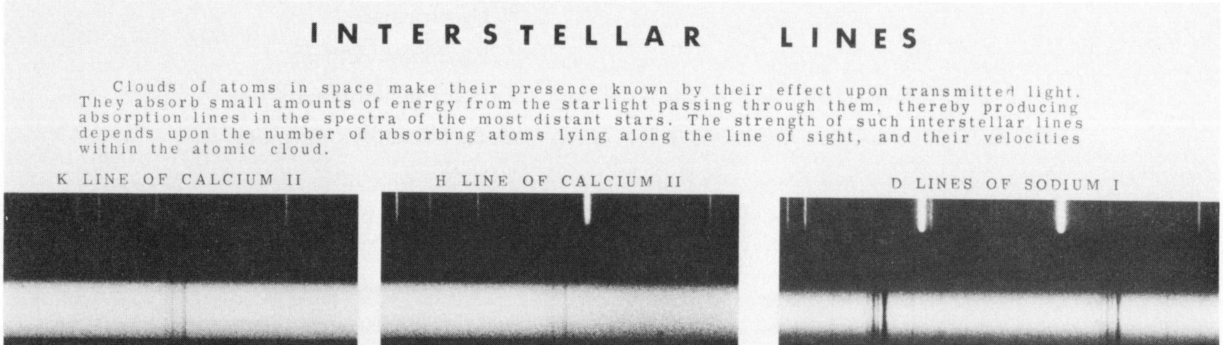

INTERSTELLAR LINES

Clouds of atoms in space make their presence known by their effect upon transmitted light. They absorb small amounts of energy from the starlight passing through them, thereby producing absorption lines in the spectra of the most distant stars. The strength of such interstellar lines depends upon the number of absorbing atoms lying along the line of sight, and their velocities within the atomic cloud.

K LINE OF CALCIUM II

Five components are visible in the interstellar H and K lines in the spectrum of Epsilon Orionis. The displace-

The star HD 172, 987 is about 20,000 light years distant, and shows in its spectrum unusually strong, complex, interstellar

The star HD 47240 shows in its spectrum three weak, highly displaced interstellar K lines. This star lies in the direction of, and beyond the gaseous nebula NGC 2237, in the constellation of Monoceros.

H LINE OF CALCIUM II

ments of these lines indicate heliocentric velocities for the five absorbing clouds of + 3.9, + 11.3, + 17.6, + 24.8, and + 27.6 kilometers per second, respectively.

calcium lines as shown above. The broad faint lines adjacent to the H line originate in the atmosphere of the star.

D LINES OF SODIUM I

Five components are also visible in each of the interstellar D lines in the spectrum of Epsilon Orionis. They yield the same radial velocities as the calcium lines.

Each D line in the spectrum of 6 Cassiopeia is made up of two groups of lines, each group arising in separate clouds of sodium atoms in two different arms of our Galaxy whose radial velocities relative to the sun differ by about 30 kilometers per second.

In the spectrum of HD 14134 is visible the same complex structure of the interstellar D lines that was shown in the spectrum of 6 Cassiopeia. This indicates that this star also lies in or beyond a second spiral arm of our Galaxy.

Figure 13.3. Interstellar lines from atomic sodium and calcium in various stars. The multiplicity of the lines indicates the Doppler shifts arising from the motions of more distant regions of our galaxy (Hale Observatories).

195

very clearly and can be used as reference markers. The next spectrogram, Figure 13.4 (kindly supplied by Dr. George H. Herbig), shows a set of diffuse interstellar lines.

Until 1940, only a limited set of interstellar diatomic molecules (radicals) and atoms were known. The situation did not change much for 23 years. An exception was the discovery in 1951 of radio signals, at a wavelength of 21 cm, emitted by excited hydrogen atoms throughout our galaxy. Since then, our entire galaxy has been carefully mapped, using the 21 cm radiation as a marker. These hydrogen radio signals clearly outlined the spiral arms of our galaxy.

The unidentified interstellar diffuse lines, however, continued to be an enigma for three decades. Meanwhile, in 1963 the list of interstellar molecules was increased by one with the discovery of the OH radical by A.H. Barrett. In 1965 and again in 1967, the author suggested the presence of complex organic molecules in the interstellar medium. A list of these suggested molecules is shown in Table 13.2. It was based on

TABLE 13.2

(1965) Proposed Organic Molecules in Interstellar Space

Compound
C_2H_3N methyl cyanide*
C_3H_8 propane
C_4H_8 dimethylethene
$C_2H_8N_2$ dimethylhydrazine
C_3H_6N dimethylcyanamid
$C_3H_5N_2$
C_3H_5N ethyl cyanide*
C_2N_2

Ref. F.M. Johnson, 1965, Conference on Interstellar Grains, NASA publ. SP 140 (page 236).

*Discovered about ten years later, see Table 13.6.

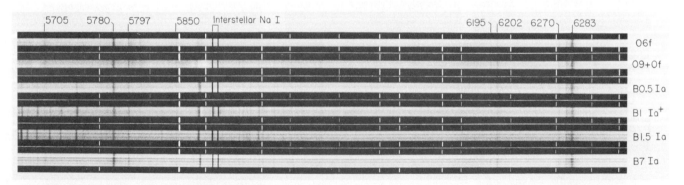

Figure 13.4. Diffuse interstellar lines. Composite photograph of 6 stars, showing these important interstellar absorption lines. Compare the interstellar sodium lines, which are very sharp in appearance, with the diffuse lines having the appearance of fuzzy edges; indicating that they have wider line widths than atomic lines (photo, G.H. Herbig, Lick Observatories).

interpretations of energy level spacings derived from the diffuse interstellar bands. In 1969, the author's experimental study culminated in the isolation of a complex organic molecule, magnesium tetrabenzporphin. Its main spectroscopic features matched within the accuracy of the experimental measurements, those of the strongest bands associated with the diffuse interstellar lines (Table 13.3).

Interstellar Molecules
(Some Clues for Start of Life?)

The historical developments deserve to be reviewed first. It is a most fascinating part in today's astronomy.

Table 13.4 shows the chronological order of the discovery of interstellar molecules. The earliest radical, CH, was accidentally discovered in a star's spectrum in 1937. To establish its interstellar rather than its stellar origin required about ten years of controversy. It was finally settled when the same optical lines associated with the CH radical were seen in a binary system. The reasoning behind this is as follows: In a binary system, a pair of revolving stars exhibit oscillating Doppler shifted lines (Chapter 15) intrinsic to the binary system; the CH spectrum, however, did not participate in this oscillation, clearly indicating that it did not belong to the background binary stars (which merely serves as an illumination of light sources for the spectra).

While CH and CH^+ were discovered in 1937, CN made its debut in 1939. Then came a long dry season, without any discoveries of interstellar molecules at all. The fact that only diatomic species or radicals were discovered was gratifying to astronomers, since stellar spectra, in general, never exhibit anything bigger than diatomic molecules.

TABLE 13.3
Matching of Spectroscopic Fingerprints
Comparison of Laboratory Data (1975)
on Molecule χ and Astronomical Data (The Diffuse
Interstellar Lines)

Wavelength of Major Astronomical Diffuse Line Å	Relative Strength of Diffuse Line	Line Width (Astronomical) Å	Laboratory Wavelengths Å (±2A)	Line Width Lab Å
4,428 (4,430)	3.4	20	4,430 (strongest line)	40
6,284	2.0	3.8	6,282	7
6,314	0.8	19	6,315	25
6,353	.06	3	6,353	6
6,376	.1	1.5	6,375	3
6,379	.16	0.86	6,378	2

See References: Fred M. Johnson, Mem. Soc. Roy. des Sciences de Liege, 6th series, Vol. III, 391-407 (1972) 1st announcement of molecule χ: 132nd meeting, Am. Astron. meeting, Boulder, Col., 1970.

TABLE 13.4
Interstellar Molecules and Radicals

No.	Year of Discovery	Spectral Region	Name of Molecule	Chemical Formula	Structure
1	1936	visible 4,428-A + 3 others	4 diffuse interstellar lines (39 lines by 1976)	See No. 10 for identification	
2	1937	visible 3,958-A	methylidyne (ionized)	CH^+	$:\overset{\oplus}{C}-H$
3	1937	visible 4,300-A	methylidyne	CH	$:\overset{\cdot}{C}-H$
4	1939	visible 3,875-A	cyanogen radical	CN	$\cdot C\equiv N:$
5	1963	radio 18.0-cm	hydroxyl radical	OH	$\cdot\overset{\cdot\cdot}{O}-H$
6	1968	radio 1.3-cm	ammonia	NH_3	$H\underset{H}{\overset{H}{\diagdown}}N-:$
7	1969	radio 1.3-cm	water vapor	H_2O	$\underset{H}{\overset{H}{\diagdown}}O:$
8	1969	radio 6.2-cm	formaldehyde	H_2CO	$\underset{H}{\overset{H}{\diagdown}}C=O:$
9	1970	radio 2.6-cm	carbon monoxide	CO	$:C=O:$
10	1970	visible Lab identification	porphyrin molecule χ (Chi)	$MgC_{46}H_{30}N_6$	See Fig. 13.5
11	1970	radio 3.4-mm	hydrogen cyanide	HCN	$H-C\equiv N:$
12	1970	radio 3.4-mm	(x-ogen) identified in 1976: formyl ion	HCO^+	
13	1970	ultraviolet 1,060-A	molecular hydrogen	H_2	$H-H$
14	1970	radio 3.3-cm	cyano-acetylene	HC_2CN	$H-C\equiv C-C\equiv N:$

TABLE 13.4 (cont.)

No.	Year of Discovery	Spectral Region	Name of Molecule	Chemical Formula	Structure
15	1970	radio 35.9-cm	methyl alcohol	CH_3OH	
16	1970	radio 18.3-cm	formic acid	HCOOH	
17	1971	radio 2.0-mm	carbon monosulfide	CS	
18	1971	radio 2.7-mm	methyl cyanide (ajanomethane)	CH_3CN	
19	1971	radio 2.5-mm	carbonyl sulfide	OCS	
20	1971	radio 2.3-mm	silicon monoxide	SiO	
21	1971	radio 3.3-mm	(?) hydrogen isocyanide	HNC	
22	1971	radio 3.5-mm	methyl acetylene	CH_3C_2H	
23	1971	radio 6.5-cm	formamide	NH_2CHO	
24	1971	radio 28.1-cm	acetaldehyde	CH_3CHO	
25	1971	radio 3.4-mm	isocyanic acid	HNCO	
26	1971	radio 9.5-cm	thioformaldehyde	H_2CS	
27	1972	radio 1.8-mm	hydrogen sulfide	H_2S	

TABLE 13.4 (cont.)

No.	Year of Discovery	Spectral Region	Name of Molecule	Chemical Formula	Structure
28	1972	radio 5.7-cm	formald- imine	CH_2NH	
29	1973	radio 99.3 GHz	sulfur monoxide	SO	
30	1974	radio 73,000 MHz	methyl- amine	CH_3NH_2	
31	1974	radio 90.9 GHz	dimethyl ether	CH_3OCH_3	

A whole generation of astronomers became accustomed to atoms and diatomic molecules in the universe. As early as 1955, however, C.H. Townes compiled a list of possible tria- tomic species which might exist in interstellar space. These molecules were to be searched for with large radio telescopes using microwave techniques. Some of his students measured, very precisely the microwave frequencies associated with the OH radical. This paid off in 1963, when Allen Barrett and associates, using modern sophisticated electronic techniques, discovered OH in the galaxy. It was the beginning of a very substantial breakthrough. In 1968 and in 1969, ammonia and water were discovered by another group led by C.H. Townes at Berkeley. The discovery of ammonia and water in the galaxy led to a great deal of excitement and to speculation of life somewhere in the galaxy. It takes more than water and ammonia to make life; however, it was a good beginning. Thus, the start was made, and the search (scramble) began for other interstellar molecules, using microwave techniques.

The Interstellar Porphyrin Discovery

Meanwhile, the author, since 1954, was engaged in an ex- tensive, now 22-year search, for a molecule which would fit the interstellar spectral signatures or fingerprints known as the (illusive) diffuse interstellar (unidentified) lines. Astrono- mers, by the early 50s, discovered a set of these diffuse inter- stellar lines for which no atomic or simple molecule could be found to match up with its spectrum (Fig. 13.4). It proved to be a formidable challenge, comparable to the search for a needle in a haystack, since, ordinarily, one has ample labora- tory spectra immediately at hand to compare with the spec- tra taken by astronomical means. (Remember that helium was discovered on the sun before it was discovered in a labo- ratory on earth.) Was one searching here for a new type of molecule? How did one know that it was a molecule rather than an atom? The clues leading to the molecular nature were the width of these diffuse lines. The designation of diffuse meant that the lines were wide, some as wide as 20 Å, whereas atomic lines are ordinarily less than 1/100 Å wide. Wide lines are usually associated with solids, liquids, or large molecules. The problem was even more baffling, since the set of diffuse lines contained relatively sharp lines in addition. These were no wider than 1 or 2 Å. Here, one had this peculiar dilemma: most solids have line widths of the order of 100 Å to 600 Å, at room temperature. How does one get both wide lines as well as narrow lines? These were the horns of the dilemma.

Since other astrophysicists engaged in similar searches had, no doubt, exhausted the study of simpler molecules, particularly molecules extending up to 12 atoms, it was decided to make a drastic jump into the realm of still larger molecules whose spectra perhaps had not been measured or catalogued or were taken under very specific conditions. All three assumptions proved to be correct. The dilemma still was, however, "the needle in-the-haystack search": to seek the correct molecule out of a total of hundreds of millions of possible compounds. It is equivalent to searching for a criminal, given only a set of fingerprints and the task of examining four billion potential candidates. Life isn't long enough for the search. Requirements for the search included: all clues had to be systematically explored, a great deal of hard work had to be done and a certain amount of luck was needed.

The author examined thousands of compounds experimentally. A search was made of every available spectral catalogue. The clue that proved to be the most valuable was the fact that one of the diffuse interstellar absorption lines at 4,430 Å is the dominant one. Also, certain regularities in the spectrum were very suggestive of vibronic spacings associated with well-known molecules. As early as 1965, the interstellar presence of a set of organic molecules (as shown in Table 13.2) was suggested, of which some have now been found by microwave techniques.

In 1967, it became apparent that **porphyrins** might possibly be potential candidates, and in 1969, one particular porphyrin (Fig. 13.5), magnesium-tetrabenzporphyrin (χ) proved to be the correct candidate. It has its strongest spectral line exactly at 4,430 Å; it had no other lines stronger than 4,430 Å, also, its line widths are comparable (within a factor of 2) of the astronomical data. Its second strongest line at 6,282 Å was also comparable in intensity and in line width (again within a factor of 2) with the astronomical data. Four other lines have, in the meantime, been found, making a total of six coincidences. (See Table 13.3 for comparison of the laboratory and astronomical data.)

The presence of a porphyrin molecule in outer space is highly significant. Porphyrins have been found in carbonaceous chondrites (Chapter 6) and more recently again confirmed by Dr. Gordon Hodgson in 1969, and others, to be present in these meteorites. Porphyrins have also been found in oil and in very ancient shale sediments, which are at least a few billion years old.

Porphyrins have many unique properties. They have thermodynamic stability, which allows them to survive over billions of years. They are important for prebiotic evolutionary theories, because porphyrins have the ability to absorb sunlight and produce free electrons. In particular, protoporphyrin IX probably constitutes one of the earliest and most significant porphyrins: it converts sunlight into another form of energy. (Fig. 6.10)

The Microwave Minimolecules

Meanwhile, from 1969 onward, the race was on for the discovery of minimolecules, using microwave techniques. Within a period of three to four years, about 30 additional molecules were discovered (Table 13.4), some having as many as nine atoms, to be contrasted with 83 atoms in the interstellar porphyrin molecule (χ). The discovery of these molecules proved fortunate, since it made it easier to accept the presence of larger organic molecules in outer space. The question which is most often asked about molecules and about the porphyrin molecule in particular, is its stability and its mode of production. First its stability—it turns out that a porphyrin molecule is more stable than 90% of the other microwave molecules. As far as production is concerned, the breakdown of the porphyrin molecule by means of electron-bombardment has led to the remarkable production of smaller species. The disintegration products of molecule χ containing C, H, and N are being discovered in space with microwave techniques. In fact, the laboratory percentages of these disintegration products is in good agreement with the observed astronomical abundances of these molecules (Table 13.5).

TABLE 13.5
The Disintegration Products of Molecule χ (Chi) by 70 e.v. Electron Bombardment—a Few Selected for Astrophysical Interest

Molecule	Abundance (Lab.) (percentage)*	Astronomical Abundance**
$H C_3 N$	11.1	2×10^{16} cm^{-2}
$C H_3 CN$	0.1	2×10^{14} cm^{-2}
$C H_3 C_2 H$	0.24	

*F.M. Johnson and D. Rosenthal Astron. J., also Astronomical Society Meeting.
**Rank, Townes and Welch, Science *174*, 1083 (1971).

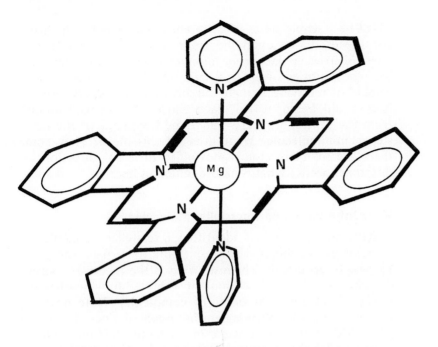

Figure 13.5. Molecule (χ), $MgC_{46}H_{30}N_6$, Magnesium Tetrabenzporphin, the largest identified interstellar molecule (discovered by F.M. Johnson in 1969).

The question of the origin of these molecules is still open. Astrophysicists concerned with interstellar molecular production are presently working on models which involve the synthesis on cold surfaces of solid grains. It is virtually impossible to generate even triatomic molecules in a cold vacuum of space, because of the rare chance of collisions, because of energy requirements, and other handicaps. If it is extremely difficult to make triatomic molecules, how would one synthesize some of the more sophisticated molecules? Hence, the present resort to interstellar solid grain surfaces as sites for chemistry.

However, if one cannot make triatomic molecules, how can one make grains which are even more complicated structures in the first place? The grains (or the dust) are also necessary to shield some of the unstable minimolecules from the disintegrating ultraviolet radiation. Meanwhile, other alleged requirements (postulated by some theoretical astronomers) on the dust are that it has to be paramagnetic, spinning, radiating in the infrared, and cold at the same time, perhaps in different regions of space, of course, the hiding place and production site for all molecules. The "dust" truly has to be a magic compound. Or to put it another way, the dust is the carpet beneath which the molecules and other dust has to be swept. We will get back to another model for the origin of molecules in the section on Cosmology.

The Motions of Interstellar Clouds

It was already apparent, from a study of the sodium D lines, that interstellar clouds were in motion. Indeed, there could be a whole series of different clouds moving at different speeds, based upon the Doppler shifts of their spectra lines. Microwave data from minimolecules showed that there were possibilities of a fairly large number of clouds, since, instead of receiving a single microwave line, a whole series of lines could be identified, each shifted by a small amount from the central arbitrary rest frame frequency of the interstellar minimolecule. What does all this mean? How come there are so many clouds moving in different directions at different speeds? What is nature telling us here?

More Information on Interstellar Molecules

With the totality of identified interstellar molecules in front of us, we might wish to examine them from the point of view of an organic chemist. What is the message? Can we decipher any of it? Let's look at Table 13.6, which has the molecules arranged in order of complexity. Note how the organic molecules outnumber the inorganic ones. There is a great deal of efficient organic molecule production going on someplace! Next, note the existence of esoteric species such as HCO^+, CCH, N_2H^+, and HNC. The presence of ionized species among this group is very significant. What does it mean? It strongly suggests nonequilibrium conditions, as well as the presence of ionizing radiation, according to a recent analysis by E. Herbst and W. Klemperer. These authors suggest that a flux of cosmic rays induces the ionization phenomena. Moreover, comparison of the abundances of organic molecules in carbonaceous chondrites and the organic radicals in comets strongly suggest a common origin: This origin must be the billions of DEBs associated with most of the stars in the galaxy. To repeat again, the DEBs seem to have all the necessary conditions and atomic ingredients to perform this nonequilibrium type chemical synthesis (Fig. 13.6). Its remoteness from the star protects it from the star's "harsh" radiation components. The DEBs internal heat source and crust are ideal for molecular synthesis as the ionized atomic species are ejected in a "plasma torch-like" fashion. The chondrite-like matrix consisting in part of MgO will certainly be an excellent catalyst for porphyrin synthesis (as was demonstrated in laboratory simulation recently).

What molecules will condense out first? The most stable ones having the lowest vapor pressure. Hence a whole host of complex, large, stable, organic compounds will undoubtedly freeze out first. In successive stages, the less stable molecules will condense out. The very light minimolecules and radicals will have sufficient velocity to escape the DEB's gravitational field; not so the heavy, stable, larger ones. Ionizing radiation from the radioactive DEBs will maintain the observed nonequilibrium situation. Some molecules will be polymerized by the radiation; others will be broken up into smaller components.

Since virtually all minimicrowave molecules are observed in emission, i.e., they emit from excited states, perhaps we

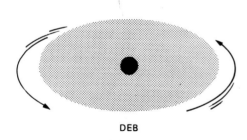

DEB

Figure 13.6. Schematic sketch of DEB. Note central, spinning, hot, radioactive core ejecting material. The resulting structure resembles Saturn's rings.

TABLE 13.6
Observed Interstellar Molecules Complete as of January 1977

Inorganic	Organic

DIATOMIC

Inorganic	Organic
H_2 hydrogen	CH methylidyne
OH hydroxyl	CH^+ methylidyne ion
SiO silicon monoxide	CN cyanogen
SiS silicon sulfide	CO carbon monoxide
NS nitrogen sulfide	CS carbon monosulfide
SO sulfur monoxide	

TRIATOMIC

Inorganic	Organic
H_2O water	CCH ethynal
N_2H^+	HCN hydrogen cyanide
H_2S hydrogen sulfide	HNC hydrogen isocyanide
SO_2 suflur dioxide	HCO^+ formyl ion
	HCO formyl
	OCS carbonyl sulfide

4-ATOMIC

Inorganic	Organic
NH_3 ammonia	H_2CO formaldehyde
	HNCO isocyanic acid
	H_2CS thioformaldehyde
	C_3N cyanoethynyl radical

5-ATOMIC

Inorganic	Organic
	H_2CNH methanimine
	H_2NCN cyanamide
	HCOOH formic acid
	HC_3N cyanoacetylene
	H_2CCO ketene

6-ATOMIC

Inorganic	Organic
	CH_3OH methanol
	CH_3CN cyanomethane
	$HCONH_2$ formamide

7-ATOMIC

Inorganic	Organic
	CH_3NH_2 methylamine
	CH_3C_2H methylacetylene
	$HCOCH_3$ acetaldehyde
	H_2CCHCN vinyl cyanide
	HC_5N cyanodiacetylene

205

TABLE 13.6 (cont.)

Inorganic	Organic
8-ATOMIC	
	HCOOCH$_3$ methyl formate
9-ATOMIC	
	(CH$_3$)$_2$O dimethyl ether
	C$_2$H$_5$OH ethanol
	CH$_3$CH$_2$CN ethyl cyanide
83-ATOMIC	
	MgC$_{46}$H$_{30}$N$_6$
	Magnesium Tetrabenzporphin
	MgTBP, or χ(chi)

are seeing molecular production in VIVO (live action)!

Once the chemical synthesis processes have ceased, a large quantity of organic and inorganic material will be frozen out on the surface of the DEB, while the remaining frozen compounds will presumably form chunks of varying sizes that revolve around the DEB core in a *Saturn Ring* like fashion, as illustrated in Figure 13.6. In old age, the DEBs, of course, are our familiar comets, whose disintegration products are very consistent with the picture outlined for the DEBs and the interstellar molecules.

Now, let's inquire which of the DEB's storehouse of molecules can be detected spectroscopically on earth either in emission or absorption. Only those molecules that are in gaseous form, of course. The molecules that are in solid form are virtually impossible to detect, except by broad-band reflection techniques (which are *not* as selective as gas spectroscopy).

A most intriguing question now arises as to why of all the large quantity of stable organic molecules, only molecule χ (chi) has so far been identified (we would certainly expect the presence of many others).

The answer involves the following considerations:

1. Abundances of the elements. C, H, N, and Mg comprise the most abundant elements.
2. Stability—Molecule χ is so stable that it can be sublimed (from solid to gas) by heating it to 450-500°C.
3. Its ability to form a very loose matrix or structure, using the pyridine ligands (Fig. 13.5) which extend perpendicular from its ring, to attach themselves to other polar or nonpolar molecules. In other words, it can form such a fluffy, loose matrix (even with water molecules as intermediaries) that the χ molecule behaves in this fashion almost like an isolated gas molecule, i.e., molecule χ has the unique ability of not freezing out into a *solid mass.*

4. The main absorption lines of molecule χ are very pronounced (i.e., strong and having relatively narrow line widths). The 4,430 Å line (called the Soret Band) for instance, has a laboratory line width of 40 Å—this is slim. Other large molecules usually have line widths in the 100-200 Å range.

It is probably the combination of these 4 unique properties which makes molecule χ stand out from its sister organic compounds.

How unique is the identification of molecule χ, could one alter it slightly and still get the same optical spectrum? NO! If one replaced just one atom of the 83 atom molecule, its spectrum is completely changed.

To summarize our extended discussion of this particular molecule: We went into more detail on it than with the others, because this molecule is probably our best clue and possible link between our solar system to the rest of the galaxy. It connects the universal origin of chemical production and the necessary source of chemical ingredients for life-forming systems.

Interstellar Polarization

We discussed how starlight can get blocked, scattered, and absorbed by atoms and molecules. There is still one other process that we briefly mentioned in Chapter 10; light can also be polarized. There is a great deal of polarized light generated right here in the solar system. Scattered sunlight becomes polarized in our atmosphere; sunlight becomes polarized on reflection from the moon, the planets, comet tails, or any dielectric surface. The extent and efficiency of this polarization phenomenon depends on the nature of the surface and on the angle of incidence, as shown in Figure 13.7.

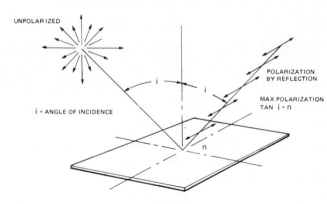

UNPOLARIZED

POLARIZATION BY REFLECTION

MAX POLARIZATION TAN i = n

i = ANGLE OF INCIDENCE

Figure 13.7. Illustrates two important physical optics principles. One, the angle of incidence (i) is equal to the angle of reflection. Two, when unpolarized light is incident on a dielectric surface, the reflected light becomes partially polarized as indicated in the figure. The maximum polarization is achieved when the angle of incidence is such that the tangent of the incident angle is equal to the refractive index (n).

Starlight has been examined for polarization during the last 25 years and a graph which shows polarization of stars throughout the galaxy is shown in Figure 13.8. Study this figure and you will also jump to the same conclusion that virtually all astronomers have done: It looks like a powder pattern of magnetic particles acted on by a huge galactic magnetic field. Hence, it was generally assumed that we must have magnetic or (quasimagnetic [paramagnetic]) nonspherical particles lined up! These elongated spinning particles then are supposed to *scatter* starlight and cause the observed polarization. It is a natural and certainly convincing explanation, but it is also very likely *wrong*. We forgot *our* solar system, as usual!

If there are enough examples of polarization by reflection in the solar system, why couldn't the whole galaxy behave in a similar manner? (Why exclude ourselves from the rest of the galaxy?) Light from *reflection nebulae* is polarized!

Most likely, the DEBs again will play the major role. Their extended Saturn-like rings provide extremely efficient reflecting surfaces, with individual frozen clumps or particles constituting the reflecting surfaces. Starlight polarization implies a preferential direction. Hence, the observed polarization implies a preferred mass distribution (via conservation of angular momentum) of DEBs within various regions of the galaxy. The deeper meaning of Figure 13.8 probably implies some evidence of the evolutionary development of our galaxy.

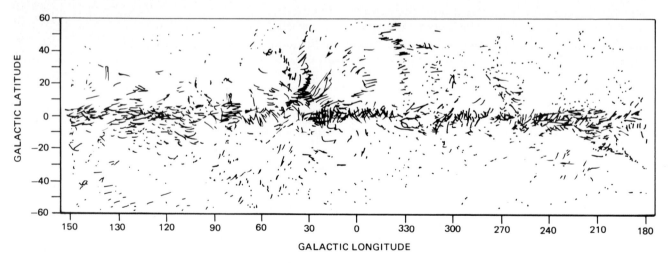

Figure 13.8. This shows the direction and strength of galactic polarization as a function of galactic coordinates. Note the symmetry of the generated pattern by plotting the polarization direction of thousands of stars. The strength of the polarization amplitude corresponds to the length of each mark on the graph. At first glance, this appears to look like iron filings in a magnetic field or paramagnetic spinning grains. See text for another possible interpretation.

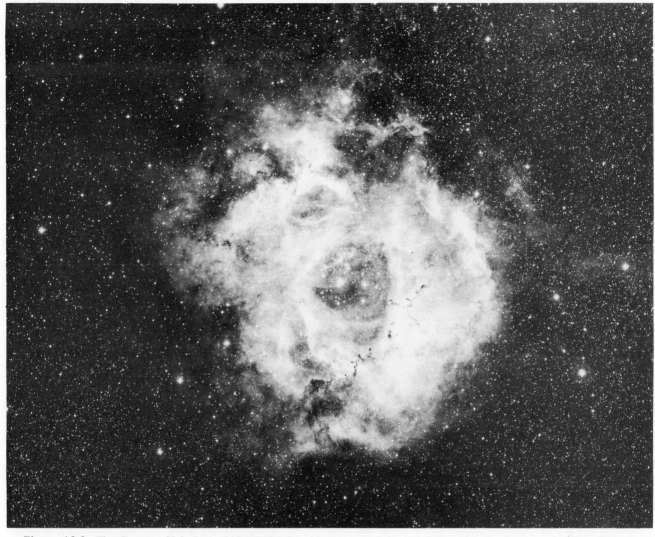

Figure 13.9. The Rosetta Nebula in MONOCEROS. Photographed in red light. 48-inch photograph (Hale Observatories).

Chapter 14

PULSARS—
THE MAGIC CRAB NEBULA

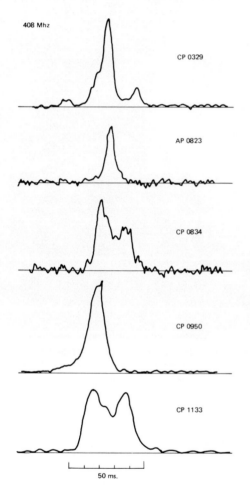

408 Mhz

CP 0329

AP 0823

CP 0834

CP 0950

CP 1133

50 ms.

Figure 14.1. This is a selection of pulse shapes for five different pulsars at 408 MHZ. Note the variety of pulse shapes.

Pulsars were discovered as recently as 1967. The discovery was purely accidental—like many great discoveries in science. The year is 1967 and you are there.

Imagine yourself as a graduate student, working away on your Ph.D. thesis, together with your fellow students and senior researchers under the direction of Anthony Hewish. Your project was to map the sky at radio wavelength in an attempt to find **quasistellar sources**. 2,048 antennae were laid out, covering a field of four and one-half acres. The data was rolling in, the sky was mapped, and you are there studying the data, when, lo and behold, you discover a peculiar signal coming in from outer space every 1.3730113 seconds. The signal came, the signal went. You think it's strange, but now being alerted, you keep your eyes open. Three months later, the signal reappears. In the meantime, of course, you will have communicated your excitement to your superior, who will then scratch his head and ponder the mystery. You have obviously discovered something very important. The excitement was high in England in 1967 among the select group of radio-astronomers, since any signal that repeated itself so precisely must have a significant story to tell. In fact, the first impulse was to suggest that these were signals sent by other intelligent civilizations. No, that was not it. There were so many clues as to the nature of the incoming signals, one simply did not give up.

The next guess as to its origin was to imagine these were pulsating stars, and, hence, they called them pulsars. But even this guess was wrong, since it quickly became obvious that for a star to be pulsing that rapidly it had to have some very unique properties.

Hewish's group quickly discovered three more pulsars. Once the news was out, the search for other pulsars began. By 1976 there were about 150 known pulsars. What are these pulsars?

Their energy was first detected in the radio regime. A pulsar emits energy for a very short time, on the order of a few thousandths of a second, and then turns off. They are off most of the time and on for a very short part of their cycle. The shape of the pulse emission is shown in Figure 14.1. Note that the various pulsars have slightly different shapes, which is not too surprising. Their pulse repetition rate is anywhere from about four seconds for the longest to

210

33/1,000 of a second for the shortest. Figure 14.2 shows a plot of the range of **pulsar frequencies**. In view of the rapidity with which these pulses are emitted and the fact that their frequency is extremely precise and can be measured to roughly twelve significant figures, it became apparent that this was not a bulk phenomenon. Also, because the frequency is so small, the emitting region has to be comparably small.

Another suggestion was that one was dealing with a **neutron star**. That is, a star whose size is between ten and thirty miles in diameter, and which is spinning extremely rapidly. Tentative theories presently under discussion by astronomers suggest that a **magnetic dipole** situated on a neturon star is responsible for beaming out the radiation as the star is spinning.

A lesson on the type of discovery that you might have made is that it always pays to have your eyes open when you are investigating physical phenomena; one never knows when your luck will enable you to hit the jackpot. The discovery was rewarded with a Nobel prize to Anthony Hewish! History tells us that many other discoveries were likewise made by men and women who were searching or stumbled onto something with their eyes open and their minds receptive.

Among all the 150 pulsars or so that were studied, there was one among them that gave scientists the best clue of all as to the nature and history of this particular enigmatic phenomenon. This was the **Crab pulsar**.* The remarkable feature about the Crab pulsar is that it is situated in the middle of the remnant of the supernova of 1054.

Astronomers immediately jumped to the conclusion that there must be a connection between a supernova and a pulsar. Furthermore, if the conjecture of a neutron star makes any sense, then all remnants of supernovae should have neutron stars at the center—is this possible? It behooves us to study the Crab nebula very carefully, because this is a good case study close at hand. It is only six thousand light years away, and it is still fairly young. In fact, it is the youngest of all the pulsars, judging from its smallness in period of pulsation. We are also fortunate to be able to study the remnant of the supernova and all the information associated with it. The only thing missing is the direct observation of the 1054 supernova with our modern instruments.

There were only three or four supernovas in our galaxy subsequent to the one in 1054, and these also occurred prior to modern astronomical techniques. A great number of supernovas can be seen in other galaxies. However, these are so far removed, that we have not yet been able to pick up the supernova remnant pulsars in other galaxies.

Let's get back to our Crab pulsar (also known by its serial number NPO532); the radiation from this pulsar has been

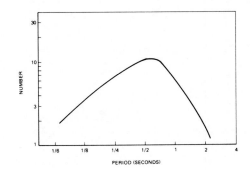

Figure 14.2. The distribution of pulsar periods, indicating their range from 1/30 seconds for the shortest to about 3 seconds for the longest.

---

*Other designations by which pulsars are known by is as a member of a catalogue compiled by a group that conducted research on them. Hence, the complete designation includes an abbreviated name followed by a sequence of numbers which usually refers to their right ascension in hours and minutes.

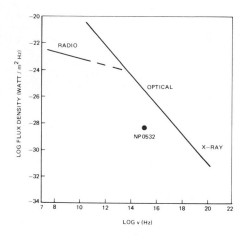

Figure 14.3. The output of the Crab Nebula as a function of frequency.

observed over the whole electromagnetic spectrum. That is all the way from the X-ray to the radio region, including, of course, the optical spectrum. Moreover, the actual pulsar has been identified with a particular star which had previously been suspected as being the remnant of a supernova in the Crab nebula. This star (Fig. 14.4) already seemed peculiar in the forties when no spectral lines could be detected in it. Now we know why! It is not a normal type of star. It is a neutron star, only 10-30 miles in diameter. It has an apparent magnitude of about 16. It emits as much energy in this pulse radiation as our sun does (Tech. Note No. 22). The nature of the energy distribution is completely different for the neutron star: Whereas the sun emits most of its energy in the visible spectrum (Fig. 8.12), the Crab pulsar emits most of its energy at other frequencies. Furthermore, unlike the sun, which emits its energy in a continuous fashion, the pulsar beams it around in space such that we receive its signals once every thirty-three thousandths of a second, or once every thirty-three milliseconds. It is on for about two milliseconds, and then it's off. In fact, most of the time the radiation is off, as far as we are concerned. The emitted pulsar beam may be likened to that of a beam from a lighthouse; it circulates about the pulsar in space and only hits us for a short fraction of the time. Consequently, the total energy emitted by the pulsar is far greater, roughly thirty times, than what is *apparently* emitted. The interval between pulses divided by the "on time" of each pulsar is about thirty (this is called the **duty cycle**).

Figure 14.4. NGC 1952 Crab Nebula in Taurus. Messier 1. Taken in red light. Remains of supernova of A.D. 1054. 200-inch photograph (Hale Observatories).

Again, the significance of this pulsar is to be found in its association with the remnant of the supernova. Do all supernovas leave neutron star pulsar remnants? The answer is probably yes. How do these pulsars get formed? What is their significance? Or, rather, how did neutron stars come about? We shall discuss these topics again in the chapter on cosmology, since they obviously must fit into the bigger picture that can only be understood when one encompasses a greater scope of astronomy (rather than examine it as an isolated peculiar event in our galaxy). A great deal of additional scientific information has been obtained during the last few years studying these hundred or so pulsars.

To obtain some sort of flavor from the data that has been received, a number of figures have been included in this chapter. They are not exhaustive, but do give some indication of the nature of the dilemmas involved in explaining the actual physical mechanism. Our rationale for stopping off at the pulsars for a little longer time in our voyage into relevant astronomy is based largely on the fact that we suspect that these pulsars do play an enormously important role and give us a set of very fine clues.

Figure 14.5 shows the Crab pulsar emission in the visible region. Note that there are two pulses, one main pulse and an interpulse between the main pulses. Interpulses are seen in

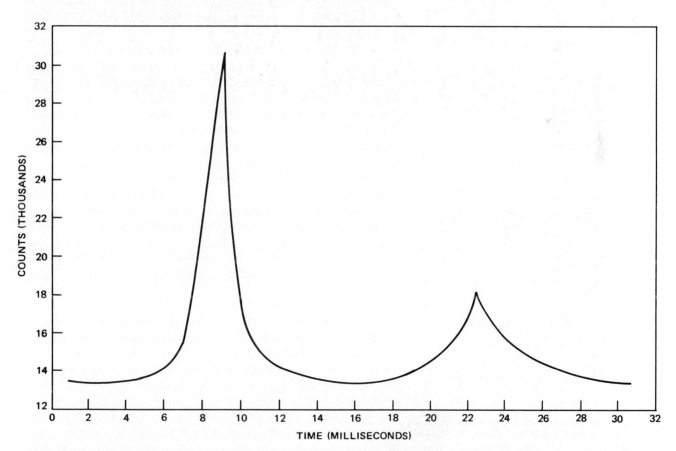

Figure 14.5. Optical light output from the Crab pulsar. Particularly noteworthy is the interpulse on the right which is not symmetric with respect to the main pulse.

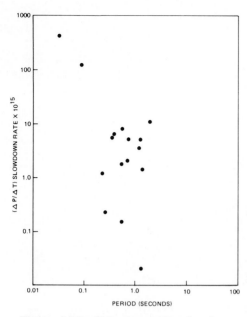

Figure 14.6. This shows the slowdown rate for a group of pulsars as a function of pulse period.

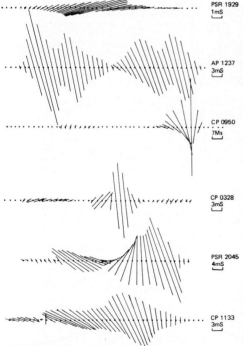

Figure 14.7. This shows the polarization of half a dozen different pulsars. Note two things: One, the direction of the polarization changes during the pulse period as well as the amplitude of the polarization vector.

quite a few pulsars. Also note that the interpulse (the small one on the right) is much less intense than the main one and is not symmetrical between pulses. The explanation for the interpulse and its assymetry is still a mystery.

A study of a distribution of pulsars suggests that their pulse width is linearly related to their pulsar period: the shorter the period, the sharper the pulse.

Using the most sophisticated electronic equipment available, the pulsar frequency could be determined with extremely high precision. (Pulsars are more accurate than most clocks.) Once the frequency was obtained, it was soon discovered that the pulsar clock is slowing down; the pulsars are coming in at slower repetition rates. The rate of slowing is indeed very small (see Figure 14.6 for a plot of slowing of 16 pulsars). The slowing rate can be understood in terms of any clock running downhill, losing energy, and, consequently, decreasing its frequency, or increasing its period.

The Crab pulsar usually leads the list in competition; in virtually all races, it is the fastest pulsar (its period being the smallest), and it also has the largest slowing rate. There is every indication, therefore, to believe that the longer period pulsars are older in age. The Crab pulsar is a good benchmark, since we know its age precisely. It is about 923 years old; consequently, we can tell how long it would take before its pulsed emission is as slow as most of the other pulsars. The Crab pulsar, being young in age, is also a far stronger emitter of radiation.

Figure 14.1 shows a variety of pulse shapes at 408 Mhz., a popular frequency at which a large number of pulsars were studied. Note the difference between pulsars. The differences in pulse shape have not yet been tackled by any theory, since the main mechanism is not even completely understood. Some of the pulse shapes are even double, and some are more widely separated. They do indeed reflect some of the intrinsic properties of the pulsar, but *what* still is a mystery.

Figure 14.3 gives the electromagnetic distribution from the Crab Nebula and the pulsar in particular. It shows that the amount of energy received at the shorter frequencies or longer wavelength is far greater than at any other wavelengths. This explains why pulsars are mainly studied in the radio region and why only two have been confirmed in the optical region (subsequent to their discovery in the radio region).

A symposium held in January, 1974, by world specialists, resulted in a summary of the observed properties of pulsars. Suggestions were made of new types of observations needed to resolve some of the dilemmas. In order to obtain more of the flavor of all the peculiar discoveries associated withe pulsars, let us enumerate a few more of them.

For one thing, whenever the beam emitted by the pulsar hits the earth, it is highly polarized (see Chapter 10 for discussion of polarized radiation and Figure 10.9 to show the difference between unpolarized and polarized radiation). Polarized electromagnetic radiation is a very strong clue as to its origin, since there are only a few ways in which electromagnetic waves can easily be polarized. One of them is by means of high energy electrons circulating in magnetic fields. Such methods of polarizing light have been observed in the laboratory using synchrotrons and cyclotrons. The mechanism is well understood; thus, a good clue is obtained regarding the nature of pulsar emission. Not only is the radiation polarized, but the direction of polarization changes as the beam sweeps by us—this is a peculiar phenomena which is not understood yet. A neutron star, as its name implies, consists essentially of neutrons. It also has a very high magnetic field associated with it (10^{10} -10^{12} gauss). It is further assumed that some of the rotational energy is transferred or presumably beamed directly into radiation.

Some pulsars have been observed whose radiation suddenly cuts off rather dramatically below 200-500 Mhz. We don't know why. Also, the radio precursor in the Crab Nebula pulsar is relatively stable, whereas the main pulse is highly modulated. Astronomers then discovered pulse *micro-structure*. That is a structure within each subpulse. Another peculiar phenomenon is drifting subpulses: these are extra tiny pulses that are drifting from one end to the other on repetitious observations.

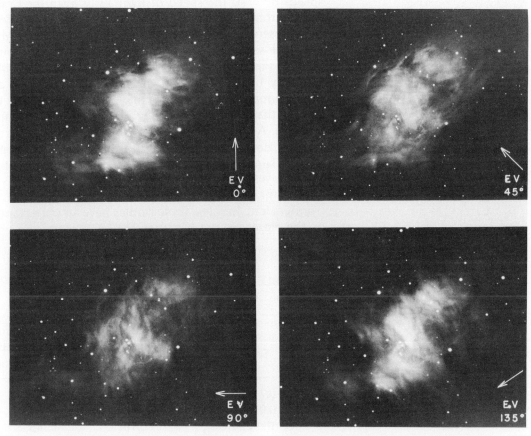

Figure 14.8. Crab Nebula. NGG 1952 the Crab Nebula in TAURUS photographed in polarized light. Directions of electric vector indicated (Hale Observatories).

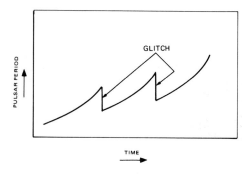

Figure 14.9.

J.M. Rankin from Arecibo Observatory and R.N. Manchester from the National Radio Observatory, West Virginia, reported on the polarization of individual pulsars, and that this polarization is related somehow to the drifting subpulsars. Subpulsars, in general, have a width from one to two percent of the period, and they are highly polarized. A maximum in the radio frequency spectrum is often observed in the pulsars, in the range from fifty to a thousand Mhz. Finally, the Crab Nebula pulsar stands out as emitting in the infrared optical X-ray and gamma ray region.

A new pulsar designated PSR 10-51, discovered by McCulloch in the Southern Hemisphere, has a period of .197 seconds and a profile remarkably similar to that of the Crab pulsar, including a strong interpulse situated approximately 40% of the period from the main component.

The pulsar frequency is extremely steady. For the Crab pulsar it is (1969) f = 30.209297624 Hz. (cycles per second). It is slowing down at the rate of $-3.857212 \times 10^{-10}$ Hz. Every two years or so, a sudden change in its frequency occurs, called a glitch. This change amounted to $-1.8 \pm 0.1 \times 10^{-14}$ Hz. See Figure 14.9 for a schematic diagram showing the slow increase in its period and the glitches. The Vela pulsar was also observed to have glitches. Some astronomers report sightings of wisps of light moving at speeds of 1/10 the speed of light away from the Crab pulsar, or neutron star. More recently, even stranger effects have been observed with pulsars. G.E. Gullahorn and J.M. Rankin reported several cases of a sudden *decrease* in pulsar frequency (antiglitches). In addition, the pulsar PSR 0823 +26 not only has antiglitched, but also has undergone a sudden phase jump: Suddenly, one day, its pulses began to arrive earlier than expected, while its frequency remained unchanged. A very peculiar pulsar indeed!

What does all this mean? No theoretical model presently can explain all the phenomena that we have been listing on these pages, and there are even more riddles. This is what makes the field of astronomy so exciting—there are still frontiers left. Besides, these riddles have an important bearing on the bigger picture (Chapter 18).

TABLE 14.1
Typical Pulsars (1969 Data)

Designation			P Seconds	Slow Down $\Delta P/\Delta t$ 10^{-15}	Pulse Width at 400 MHz 10^{-3} Seconds
	α	δ			
CP	0329	+54	0.7145187	2.05	8.7
NP	0531	+21 Crab	0.0330976	422.69	1.9
CP	0809	+74	1.2922413	0.16	45
PRS	0833	−45 Vela X	0.0892093	125.26	1.7
PSR	2045	−16	1.9615669	10.96	42

Chapter 15

DOPPLER EFFECT—
Z CRAZY QUASARS

The Doppler Effect

We must discuss a slight technicality in order to understand the next concept. By what method can we tell the velocities of objects which emit either acoustic or light energy?

As the object moves towards an observer, as shown in Figure 15.1, the number of waves per second (the frequency) changes. In general, the frequency of a wave is the number of crests that we count as the wave passes by. If the source that emits the wave is coming towards us, we would be counting more of these crests, or an increased frequency. If the source is moving away from us, we would be counting less. For example; we have all heard the fire engine bell ringing as it approaches us. Have you noticed the change in pitch as it first approaches and then recedes away from us? The pitch and/or tone changed thus: It was at a higher frequency as it approached and then at a lower frequency as it moved away. This is a vivid demonstration of the well-known **Doppler effect** with sound waves. The effect works equally well with either light or sound waves.

If the source is stationary and we were to be moving towards the source, the frequency would also increase. It is the *relative* velocity between source and receiver that counts. The relative line of sight velocity between any emitter and receiver can be determined by means of this Doppler effect.

Starting at the top of Figure 15.1, we have a stationary source emitting a single frequency or wavelength λ_o, which is always the same as long as both source and receiver remain fixed. (Recall the relationship between wavelength and frequency, wavelength X frequency = speed of wave or $\lambda \cdot \nu = c$.) Imagine that we have a hot hydrogen source with terribly excited atoms which emit their characteristic photons. A short distance away, we have set up a spectroscope that examines these photons as they make their way through the instrument. We shall note that the wavelength of one specific emission line is λ_o. We could equally well use any of the lines of hydrogen. However, once we have picked out the line of λ_o, we shall ignore all others.

Now, as the excited source (with its continuously emitting characteristic photons) moves towards the observer, the waves seem to be pushed together. We will be counting more of these waves per second. The line we were studying is now

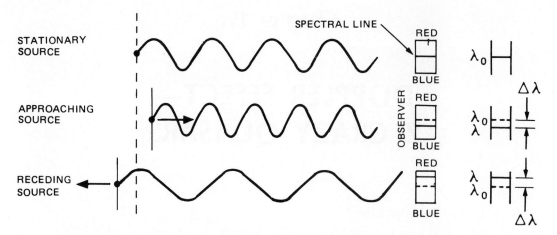

Figure 15.1. This shows the Doppler effect. Note that when both the source and the observer are fixed, the emitting line has a wavelength λ_0. When the source is approaching the observer, the line will be shifted to a shorter wavelength by an amount $\triangle\lambda$. When the object or the source is receding, the wavelength will be shifted towards the red. Similar shifts can be generated if the source is stationary and the observer is moving. Basically, it is the relative speed between source and observer that is measured.

no longer λ_0, but is shifted towards shorter wavelengths (**blue shift**) by an amount $\triangle\lambda$.

Let us repeat the same experiment, except this time, the source is made to recede from us. We would be counting less wave crests per second. The resulting wavelength has been lengthened by an amount $\triangle\lambda$ towards the red portion of the light spectrum. When scientists (usually astronomers) talk about a **red shift,** they are referring to this very phenomenon.

Now, put these qualitative concepts on a quantitative footing. We shall define a quantity z as the ratio of this Doppler shift to the unshifted wavelength λ_0, i.e., $\triangle\lambda/\lambda = z$.

The speed of the object (provided it is much slower than c) can be directly calculated once z is known. (Use equation: $v = cz$ where c = speed of light.) If the object's velocity is almost as large as c, then a special relativistic formula is needed (Tech. Note No. 17).

In the special case of low velocity ($v \ll c$), the relativistic formula reduces to the usual formula for the Doppler effect. Note that the Doppler shift is directly proportional (at the lower speed) to the relative velocity between the object and the observer ($v = c \cdot z = c\triangle\lambda/\lambda_0$). This is a very important physical phenomenon. It is one of the keys by which astronomers have unlocked nature's secrets. It enabled them to determine the relative speeds of stars with respect to the earth by merely observing the Doppler shift in the spectral lines. The sun's speed around the nucleus of our galaxy is also measured with the aid of the Doppler effect.

There is another phenomenon by which nature can create a red shift in spectral lines. This comes about if a photon is emitted from a heavy, dense, object. It loses gravitational potential energy and this, in turn, results in what is known as **gravitational red shift.** The gravitational shift is towards longer wavelengths only (Tech. Note No. 18). Ordinarily, there is no ambiguity as to whether one is dealing with a Doppler shift or a gravitational red shift.

Well-known astronomers such as J. Greenstein have studied dense objects such as white Dwarfs for many years and have verified that, indeed, the gravitational red shift is real. For moving objects, the Doppler effect is applicable. However, here comes the dilemma. Suppose an object has both effects associated with itself simultaneously! Can one disentangle these effects? Also, is it possible to construct a believable physical model of an object that would simulate the observed red shift? These are some of the questions that we shall confront as we begin our overview of the enigmatic Quasars.

z Crazy Quasars

With a z here and a z there.
The quasars are just everywhere.
Assistants, assistants, what is their distance?
Excite them not, no matter what!
Be ready for the Red Shift plot. (F.M.J.)

Quasars

To bring into context the excitement generated by the discovery of quasars in 1960, it is essential to reconstruct the state of astronomy at that time. A number of large radio telescopes were in operation, and radio emission from the sun had been detected, but was indeed very feeble. The 21-centimeter radiation throughout the galaxy had opened up the era of mapping out our galaxy (Chapter 13). Radio emission throughout the galaxy at various frequencies was being mapped. Two distinct radio sources were located and identified. These were very small sources, as could be ascertained when the source was occulted (eclipsed) by the moon, and their position was measured as carefully as possible by means of **interferometric techniques**.

By 1963, there were four such "radio stars" to worry about. By comparing the accurate radio positions of the source 3C 48 with the sky survey photographs, a fairly faint starlike object was found to coincide with the position of this radio source. The designation of 3C of a radio star refers to Cambridge's third catalogue, indicating that the 250 foot dish at Jodrell Bank near Cambridge was used in the search and that the cataloguing was done by the scientists there. The stronger of these radio sources became even more enigmatic, but also provided a very important result when Maarten Schmidt took spectra of the radio sources and discovered that they contained emission lines, corresponding to the well-known lines of the hydrogen atoms; but they were shifted very far to the red. The whole spectrum was shifted by an amount which had hitherto not been seen in stellar spectra. The starlike objects had other peculiarities. They emitted strong ultraviolet radiation and had wisps of nebulosity surrounding them. A picture of such an object looks very much like a star, hence the name quasistellar objects (QSO). QSO's are, however, not stars, but very likely galaxies in the process of birth and development.

Some of the benchmarks in the observational discoveries were:*

A. The first red shift determination of 3C 273 in 1963.

B. The determination in 1965 of a red shift as large as z = 2 (which, if it were due to a Doppler effect, would imply an enormous distance).

C. Demonstrations of fluctuations in the energy emitted by these objects both in radio and optical regimes.

D. Intensity fluctuations involving time spans of weeks or months. Hence, the objects have to be small, of the order of light months across (which would imply an exceedingly small galaxy indeed).

E. In 1966 came the first observation of absorption lines associated with the QSO's, and then

F. In 1968 the discovery of multiple red shift systems; i.e., a given quasar was found to have a number of different z's (see Table 15.1).

G. Finally, measurements in the last few years have shown exceedingly small diameters for radio sources associated with both QSO's and radio galaxies.

Table 15.1 shows a list of typical QSO's with their absorption and emission z values. This contains the best clues as to the mechanism and dynamics within the system.

Also shown in Table 15.2 is a list of the prominent atoms that are identified in Quasars. What is noteworthy, is the high state of ionization. The Roman numeral (minus one) following the species is a measure of the number of electrons missing from the atom, i.e., the state of ionization. Note that some have as many as four electrons missing, which implies a high electron temperature. Electron temperatures of the order of 20,000° Kelvin have been calculated recently.

Once these objects were discovered, it didn't take long to follow up on the clues and find a great many more. The chief clue in searching for QSO's is a blue starlike object with very large red shifts. This led to the discovery within ten years of about 300 such objects with optical techniques only. About one-third of all radio sources are presumably quasars.

For a proper perspective of the quasars, however, other types of galaxies should be discussed. These include the **Seyfert galaxies** which were discovered in 1944. They are characterized by having a very bright nucleus in the center with broad-band emission lines, which implies that they contain rapidly expanding gases. Some Seyfert galaxies are also radio emitters. Some even show strong infrared radiation from the nuclei. Seyfert galaxies are unusual in that they emit about one hundred times more radiation than a normal galaxy. More recently, X-rays have been discovered to be emitted from them.

Explosive events associated with galaxies seem to be the

*Quasistellar Objects, Geoffrey Burbidge and Margaret Burbidge, Freeman Co., 1967.

TABLE 15.1				TABLE 15.2		
Selected QSOs With Absorption Lines in Their Spectra*				Important Spectral Lines in Quasars (QSOs)		
Object	z_{em}	z_{abs}		Element	Line (Å)	Average Strength
NGC 4151	0.00327	0.00233, 0.00143, 0.00047		Hydrogen	Lα 1216	230
BSO 1	1.241	1.241			Hβ 4861	52
3C 205	1.534	1.538			Hγ 4340	26
Mk 132	1.758	1.7316, 1.3518, 1.2750		Helium	He I 5876	<1
B 194	1.864	1.8952, 1.8366			He II 1640	10
PHL 1222	1.910	1.934			He II 3204	4
0119−04	1.955	1.965		Carbon	C II 2326	10
PHL 938	1.955	1.906, 06128			C II 1335	2
PHL 5200	1.98	1.90-1.98, 1.9502, 1.8910			C III 1909	30
Ton 1530	2.046	2.0553, 1.9798, 1.9362			C IV 1549	120
1331 + 170	2.082	1.7851, 1.7754, 1.3273		Nitrogen	N IV 1488	1
0237 − 23	2.223	2.2013, 2.1758, 1.9551			N V 1240	10
		1.6737, 1.6706, 1.6564,		Oxygen	O I 1304	<1
		1.5955, 1.5566, 1.5503,			O II 3727	20
		1.5139, 1.4145, 1.3644			O III 3133	3
4C 25.05	2.360	2.3682, 2.3456, 2.3421,			O III 1663	6
		2.3004, 2.2754, 2.2432			O III 4363	10
5C 2.56	2.390	2.367			O III 5007	94
PHL 957	2.69	2.6614, 2.5504, 2.5423,			O IV 1407	4
		2.3090, 2.2250			O VI 1034	15
4C 5.34	2.877	2.8754, 2.8098, 2.7701,		Neon	Ne III 3869	20
		2.5925, 2.4739, 2.1819,			Ne IV 2439	<1
		1.7758			Ne V 2972	3
OH 471	3.398	3.343, 3.246, 3.191,			Ne V 3426	15
		3.122, 2.911		Magnesium	Mg II 2798	94
OQ 172	3.53	3.094, 3.089, 3.066,		Silicon	Si II 1817	3
		2.698, 2.691, 2.564			Si II 1533	<1
					Si IV 1397	5

*Data from E.M. Burbidge and G.R. Burbidge, Ap. J. *202*, 287 (1975).   Data from T. Tung Chan and E.M. Burbidge, Ap J. *198*, 46 (1975).

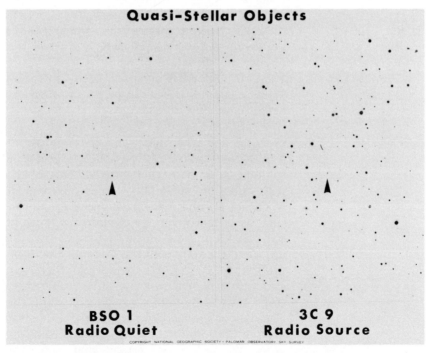

Figure 15.2. Spectacular picture of two quasistellar objects. One does not emit in the radio regime and the other does. The arrow points to these compact objects (Hale Observatories).

Figure 15.3. An unusual galaxy. It is a source of radio emission as well (Hale Observatories).

order of the day. A plot of the radio emission from a radio galaxy shows that it has a perfectly symmetrical form about the optical counterpart of the center. It looks very much like the evolution of a galaxy, which involves the ejection of materials in a symmetrical manner. Radio sources are typically 100,000 light years on either side of the center of the galaxy. Many examples of this type of symmetrical structure have been found (Fig. 17.8).

What is the "young" galaxy doing? By what procedure is it evolving, and where does this radio emission come from? We believe that radio emission arises from high energy electrons spinning around magnetic fields. This is known as **synchrotron radiation**; such radiation is observed in the laboratory whenever energetic electrons move rapidly in magnetic fields such as synchrotrons, or cyclotrons. If we now list the various puzzles and dilemmas that these discoveries have opened up, we might start with the origin of the magnetic field—what maintains it? Isn't it possible that there is some underlying structure which is not optically visible, because these electrons have to be fed energy continually if they are radiating? There is a similar problem in the Crab Nebula, where the average lifetime of these high energy electrons is about thirty years. We know for certain, that, since the advent of the supernova explosion in 1054, electrons had to be resupplied with energy, but from where and how? In both cases, it is

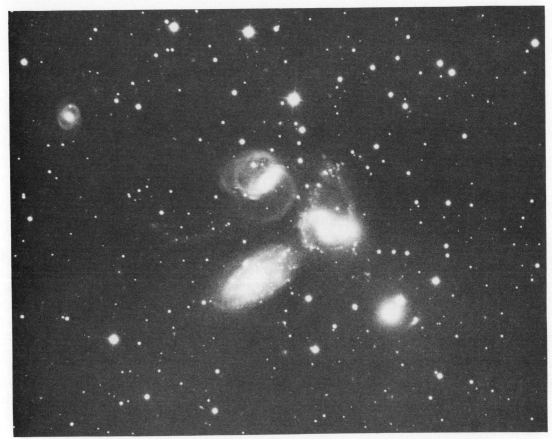

Figure 15.4. Stephan Quintet: Note the gas bridges which suggest that these galaxies belong to a local group. One of them has a low z value, whereas the other four have higher z values, suggesting possible discordant red shifts if there is no accidental overlap.

strongly suggested that there must be some underlying structure which is not visible.

The dilemma which causes some astronomers to be at loggerheads is whether the indicated z values are cosmological Doppler shifts (Tech. Note No. 17) or some other mechanism. At the present state of knowledge of physics, we know only of two mechanisms that could give red shifts in the spectrum: the Doppler effect and the gravitational red shift. If one were to take a democratic vote on the state of the controversy at this moment, the cosmological faction has the numerical advantage. However, there is a growing number of astronomers who point out certain inconsistencies in this *accepted* model.

1. Let us examine quasars, whose z values are greater than two. If QSOs are at cosmological distances, the amount of energy emitted by the quasars is enormously large. This is far greater than any mechanism that we now know of, including that of annihilation of matter with antimatter. We know of no mechanism that can create more energy than matter being completely destroyed by antimatter, and even this process cannot account for the amount of energy from QSO's if they are supposed to be so far away (billions of light years).

2. The z values from absorption lines require an explanation.

3. The rapid variability implies a small source.

4. Also, no blue shifts in absorption have been found. This also requires an explanation. The basic problem seems to be one of constructing the correct physical model of what is going on within a quasar.

More recently, H. Arp has pointed out a number of examples in the sky where a strong association between galaxies exists as if they were linked by connecting bridges. One interesting example is the Stephan quintet (Fig. 15.4), which consists of five (possibly) interconnected galaxies of which four have similar z values, but one has a very discordant small z value. How is it possible, if they are presumably all at the same distance, that one of them has a different z value? This would argue very strongly against the cosmological explanation.

The counter argument given by the opposing side is that this is an accidental coincidence. However, at least a half dozen similar examples have been found, but these, too, are being contested. It is very possible (and presumably this would be the most likely explanation) that a combination of causes gives rise to the observed z values: a combination of gravitational red shift plus cosmological distance plus an internal motion, due to the expansion and rotation of the structure itself within the galaxy. One of the objections that was raised for internal motions giving rise to high velocities is the fact that these high z values correspond to velocities not far removed from the speed of light. It seemed highly unlikely that a gas cloud traveling at that speed would have all the atoms traveling with the same velocity. The dilemma here arises from the fact that the absorption and emission lines are *very sharp*. If it were a gas with random velocities, these lines would be very broad. The observed sharp lines were used as an argument against high velocity motion.

What was neglected by this argument, however, was that it is possible to have gas associated with a moving solid body. The missing link, presumably, is underlying solid structure within the gas. There has to be some solid material underlying the gas to keep it gravitationally closely bound. Of course, we only see the gas because that is what is emitting or absorbing the radiation. The underlying structure may be composed of neutron stars of various sizes which emit no spectral lines of their own; but, instead, they emit high energy nuclear particles and electromagnetic energy favoring the very high energy end of its spectrum.

Most astronomers would agree that there is a continuity of observed physical characteristics going from quasars successively through compact galaxies, N galaxies, Seyfert objects, peculiar galaxies to normal galaxies. We shall examine some of these galaxies in the next chapter. The name dropping of various morphological galactic types is done merely to reinforce the concept of cosmic evolution. Each galactic type is but a stage in its molting like development.

Now, back to the major controversy: How does one come to grips with the large z values and how does one integrate the quasars into the larger family of above-mentioned galactic objects, including the radio galaxies? These are the horns of the dilemma. If the z's correspond to cosmological distances only, then their extreme distance implies impossibly large (unknown) sources for its power supply.

If, on the other hand it is not Doppler shifted, then some other mechanism must be found to account for its large z values. The gravitational red shift was looked at by quite a number of great minds, but, so far, no model has been accepted. Proposals for new physics are looked at even more suspiciously.

Given these choices, it is understandable why a large number of astronomers would rather hold on to the well-understood Doppler effect (and let the devil take care of the energy problem!). There are some brave astronomers, like H. Arp, who constantly come up with examples of discordant red shifts between closely-related galaxies.*

A very important statistical analysis of the quasar z values was undertaken by M.B. Bell and David N. Fort. These authors assumed that the quasars are located somewhere in between the two extreme the "cosmological" and "local" hypotheses. They utilized the apparent magnitude and the Hubble relation (Chapter 17). From their analysis, they found that the absolute magnitude, M, of a Quasar can be expressed as follows:

$$M = -20.4 + 1.6z_x$$

where z_x is an intrinsic red shift of the quasar. The cosmological Doppler shift z_c, and z_x are related to the measured z value by the relation

$$(1 + z) = (1 + z_c)(1 + z_x)$$

Bell and Fort succeeded in separating the cosmological (z_c) and the intrinsic (z_x) components. Having done this, one can now examine the distribution of intrinsic (z_x) values (Fig. 15.5). Note the peaks towards lower z values and the sparsity of high z values.

Another important plot by these authors is illustrated in Figure 15.6. This figure contains all the quasars and radio galaxies whose data was available. Note how the quasars apparently form a continuous link with the radio galaxies once their intrinsic z_x values have decreased to zero. Also, note how the quasars become progressively brighter as their z_x values decrease. The faintest quasars have $z_x \cong 2$. Quasars of $z_x = 0$ are about 1 magnitude fainter than a radio galaxy.

With this analysis, quasars are no longer superbright but instead have luminosities similar to a supernova at maximum brightness. The following evolutionary scenario is consistant with Bell and Fort's analysis.

Compact, faint quasars with large intrinsic red shifts evolve into radio galaxies. As they evolve, they increase in size, be-

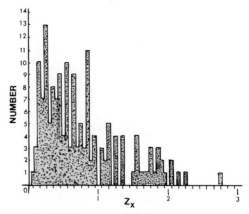

Figure 15.5. The distribution of intrinsic z values (z_x) for radio quasars. This is called z Histogram. Note very few quasars have z values greater than 2. Presumably the larger z values are associated with younger quasars. The bulk seems to lie in the 0 to 1 range. As quasars age, they loose their z_x! (From M.B. Bell and D.N. Fort.)

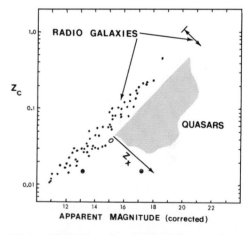

Figure 15.6. Plot of cosmological, z_c, values versus apparent magnitude (K-corrected). The shaded portion comprises the quasars. The dots are radio galaxies. Note the following: (1) Quasars are fainter than radio galaxies. (2) As they age and mature, their z_x decreases. (3) They seem to connect to radio galaxies once their z has vanished. Open circles are quasar stragglers that could not be included within the shaded region.

---

*"The Redshift Controversy" by G.B. Field, H. Arp and J.N. Bahcall, Benjamin, Inc. Publ., 1973.

come more luminous and their intrinsic red shift component decreases. In the process, an increasing percentage of their luminosity is transferred, through some method of ejection or expansion, to a surrounding nebular structure which eventually becomes visible, even in the presence of the bright nucleus. At this stage they are called N galaxies and have little or no intrinsic red shift component.*

Anticlimax

With the heavy controversy about z, we almost but not quite neglected the chemical aspect of quasars. Table 15.3 lists the atomic elements so far identified. The most important life forming and also the most cosmologically abundant elements are represented in the quasars. This is an important point, easily overlooked. If quasars are young and evolving, the key atomic elements are already there. At least these elements do not necessarily have to await subsequent recycling and regurgitation via alleged stellar life cycles.

TABLE 15.3

Elements Identified in QSOs (Quasars)

H, He, C, N, O, Ne, Mg, Si, Ar, Fe, S

Summary

To summarize this fascinating area of astronomy, the last word has not yet been spoken. These quasars must play a very important role in the evolutionary development of galaxies; perhaps what we are seeing are galaxies at the very initial stages of their development.

To confirm these conclusions, here is the latest news on discordant red shifts: Dr. Halton Arp pointed out recently** that all 12 certain companion galaxies of M31 and M81 show *greater* red shifts (from +60 to +230 km/sec) than the central, dominant galaxy! The implication of these results is that intrinsic red shifts are not restricted to quasars and that indeed an evolutionary development is indicated.

*M.B. Bell and D.N. Fort, Ap. J. *186*, 1 (1973).
**I.A.U. Colloguium No. 37, Paris, Sept. 1976.

Chapter 16

VOYAGE TO OTHER GALAXIES

We are now ready to venture into deep space by leaving the confines of our own galaxy, the abode of some 100 billion odd stars, give or take a few billion. The sun is a rather average insignificant star among this galactic multitude of stars. It is only after we have traveled a few hundred thousand light years away from our galaxy and have taken a final look back, that we can clearly ascertain the structure of our galaxy. It is made up of spiral arms, flattened, with the sun situated on one such arm some 30,000 light years from the center. At this distance, it is almost impossible to isolate the sun among the billions of stars. An even more frightening thought is the prospect that once this far away from home base, it will be impossible to find our way back at all. It is hopeless to send distress messages to earth, for they would take twice 200,000 years for the round trip, traveling at the fastest speed we presently know—at the speed of light. However, not only are *we* moving in this intergalactic space trip, but *everything* in the universe is moving as well. The galaxy is rotating in such a manner that every star, outside the inner core of the galaxy, obeys Kepler's laws. This means that the period for each star in its revolution around the central hub of the galaxy is directly related to its distance from the center. The inner stars revolve much more rapidly than the outer ones. The sun takes about 270 million years for one complete revolution around the center. The central region is composed of stars that are much more closely spaced to each other than stars in the solar neighborhood. At the distance of 300,000 light years from our galaxy, we see the whole structure, which in appearance is very similar to another typical galaxy, M-31 (Fig. 18.20). We now have to increase our speed, since galaxies are, on the average, millions of light years away from each other. We note that galaxies, like stars, often occur in groups or clusters and that their appearances are not uniformly alike. Within a distance of 3 million light years, there is a local group of about 20 galaxies, of which our own galaxy is a member.

As we were leaving our galaxy, we passed a globular cluster (Fig. 16.2). It contains about 10^5 stars, containing virtually no dust nor gas. Each galaxy seems to be surrounded by hundreds of such clusters, constituting a spherical shell about the whole galaxy. The orbits of these clusters are highly elliptical and at large angles with respect to the plane of the

Figure 16.1. The start of our intergalactic flight, visits to other galaxies and solar systems.

Figure 16.2. NGC 5272 Globular star cluster in *Canes Venatici*. Messier 3. 200-inch photograph (Mount Wilson and Palomar Observatories).

galaxy. Their role and function may be analogous to the comets (DEBs) in the solar system.

Next, on the way out to inspect a few oddball galaxies, we encounter an enormous amount of electromagnetic radiation in the radio region. A really odd looking galaxy comes into view (Fig. 16.3).

This galaxy is indeed an odd one. So let us pass on.

We next encounter a very beautifully shaped galaxy edge-on (Fig. 16.4). This galaxy exhibits one of the features of our own galaxy. It is a flattened pancake shaped disc with a high concentration of stars at its center. The core of this (as are most others) galaxy is far more luminous than the rest. Also note the dark obscuring material in the plane of the galaxy. This dark material is called *dust* but, in reality, it indicates the presence of well-developed stellar systems, their planets and their DEBs.

Another galaxy (Fig. 16.5) comes into view, almost edge-on as well. This one has a far larger central core and an almost circular dark ring surrounding it.

Next, we encounter a spectacular group of galaxies floating

228

Figure 16.3. NGC 5128 Galaxy, unusual type in CENTAURUS. A source of radio noise. 200-inch photograph (Hale Observatories).

Figure 16.4. NGC 4565 Spiral galaxy in COMA BERENCIES, seen edge on. Photographed on an unfiltered red sensitive plate. 200-inch photograph (Hale Observatories).

229

Figure 16.5. NGC 4594 Spiral galaxy in VIRGO, seen edge on. Messier 104. 200-inch photograph (Hale Observatories).

in space (Fig. 16.6). Someone remarks: "If you have seen one galaxy, you've seen them all." This is not quite true. There is a large variety of galaxies in the universe. In order to appreciate and study this variety at your leisure, a dozen representative galaxies are assembled in Figures 16.7 and 16.8. Their shapes range all the way from spherical to a variety of spiral-shaped ones. Figure 16.8 exhibits a rather interesting variety of so-called barred spiral galaxies. Noty the luminous crossbar stretching along the center of the galaxy. Another noteworthy feature of these galaxies is their symmetric structure about the center-line bar.

The symmetry of these galaxies and the double feature symmetry of the radio galaxies about a center strongly suggest an evolutionary pattern originating from explosive developments from the core of the galaxy. These pictures might, therefore, be considered as snapshots of a variety of galaxies in various stages of development.

This was one of our more distant voyages into space. As we try to grope our way back to our own galaxy, we observe that the space between galaxies is devoid of all matter.

Galaxies, galaxies everywhere, but not an atom in between
Galaxies, galaxies everywhere, their end cannot be seen.
Where's our own, where's our own, fellow students groan.
Hang on tight, with the speed of light, our ship will soon be home.
(F.M.J.)

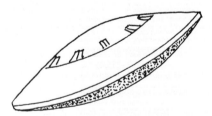

Our ship is coming home.

Figure 16.6. Cluster of galaxies in HERCULES. 200-inch photograph (Hale Observatories).

231

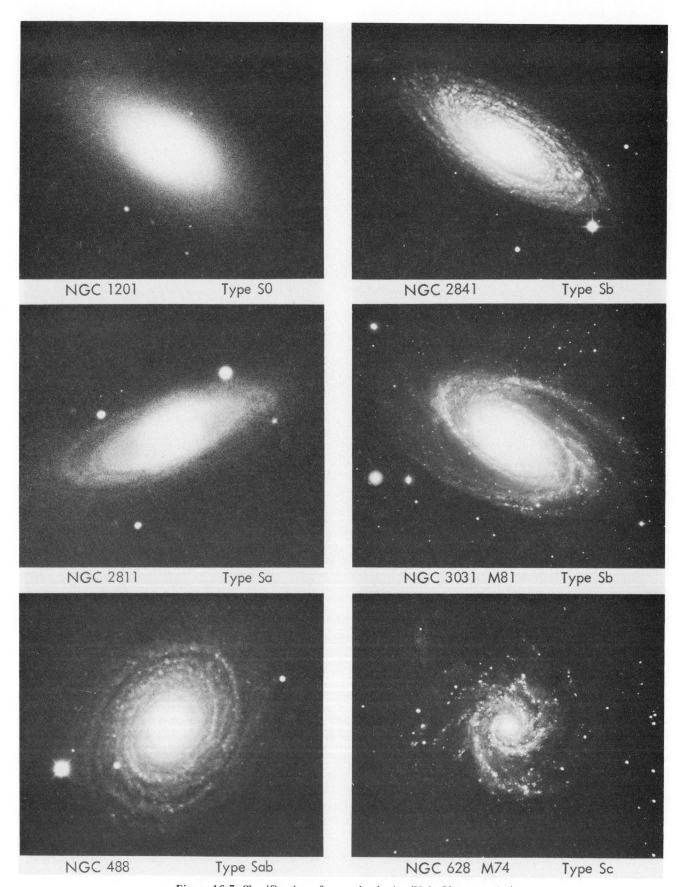

NGC 1201   Type S0

NGC 2841   Type Sb

NGC 2811   Type Sa

NGC 3031 M81   Type Sb

NGC 488   Type Sab

NGC 628 M74   Type Sc

Figure 16.7. Classification of normal galaxies (Hale Observatories).

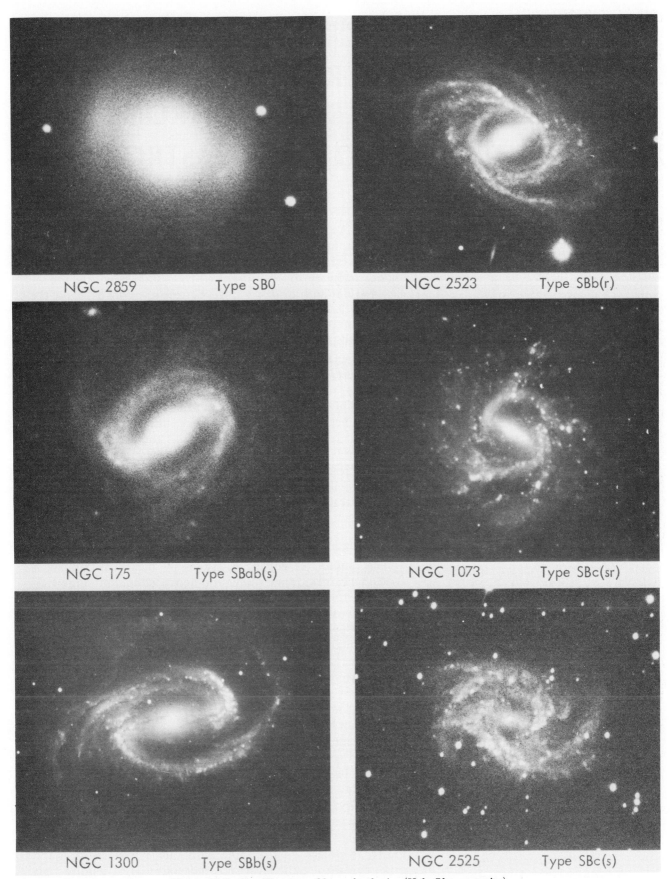

NGC 2859   Type SB0

NGC 2523   Type SBb(r)

NGC 175   Type SBab(s)

NGC 1073   Type SBc(sr)

NGC 1300   Type SBb(s)

NGC 2525   Type SBc(s)

Figure 16.8. Classification of barred galaxies (Hale Observatories).

233

Chapter 17

UNIVERSAL DISTANCES, RED HOT TOPICS SUCH AS I.R. ASTRONOMY, RADIO ASTRONOMY, X-RAYS, NEUTRINOS, TOOLS OF ASTRONOMY

Universal Distances

Astronomers have always worried about distances in the universe. Tycho Brahe's sixteenth century cosmological model was very much influenced by distances within the solar system and nearby stars. Erroneous concepts of the ancients can be excused on the basis of the fact that distances to any of the objects they could see with their naked eyes were completely unknown, with the exception of some crude attempts made to get relative distances of the moon and the sun. These early philosophers used simple geometric concepts, for instance, to obtain some idea of the distance to the moon. While this was a very modest beginning, there were some ancients who had the correct idea that stars are very much further removed from us than the sun is, but these were merely intuitive feelings. It was not until the nineteenth century, that the first measurement was made of the distance to one of the sun's neighboring stars. The method used was that of **parallax**.

No. 1 Trigonometric Parallax

The method of getting distances by means of parallax is used in a camera range finder and hence, should be somewhat familiar. Let's do a simple experiment. Hold your finger in front of your face, about six inches from your nose, and then close one eye, keeping one eye open, and then close the other eye, again keeping the other one open. What do you see? You will note that your finger apparently shifted in position with respect to the *background*. It is the *apparent shift* of the position of your finger that should be apparent. If there were no background, this method, of course, would not work. This works well for nearby distances. In fact, the baseline should be comparable to the distances you wish to measure in order to obtain good precision in the measurement. The technique becomes less and less accurate as the distances increase relative to the baseline. This gives the brain its **depth perception**. People who are unfortunate enough to have only one eye, miss this particular advantage. You can simulate this handicap by placing your eyes at the edge of a table and trying to locate an object on the table with one eye closed and the other eye at the table level. You will find you have quite a bit of difficulty trying to locate an object anywhere on the table. Nature had good reason for giving animals that are hunters the ability to have two eyes that look forward, and presumably a stereoscopic brain function to match.

The depth perception is lacking in two-dimensional television; however there one obtains an idea of depth by the relative sizes of the objects, as well as by motion relative to the background. Our eyes are trained to recognize depth by secondary means. Hollywood movie makers take advantage of this knowledge. A great deal of trick photography is done where an object, with whose size you are familiar, is placed in a different location, relative to the size of an object that you may wish to examine (the trick photography of a very small man on an egg cup, or vice-versa). But this is getting too far afield from our stars.

Now, how would you arrive at the distance of a nearby star? Imagine you are a giant with eye separation corresponding to the positions of the earth at the extremeties of its orbit; say, position 1 and position 2 (Fig. 17.1). Examine a nearby star first with one eye, then with the other. This difficult task is now simulated by actually taking the star's picture when the earth is in position 1 and then, with the same equipment, taking the identical picture of the same object when the earth is in position 2. There is a half-year time delay in this photography, but the results are the same. You will then integrate the results by combining both pictures. Lo and behold, the star has moved! It appeared to have moved with respect to the background stars. It is from this data that we can determine the star's distance. Note the angle that is subtended at the star between the sun and the earth. This angle is known as the parallax. We defined the parallax then by simple geometric considerations (Fig. 17.1). The distance (d) is defined as being inversely proportional to the

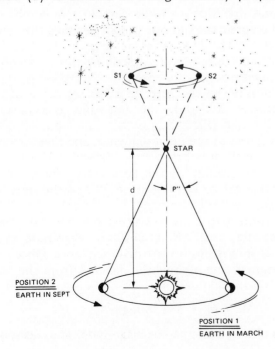

Figure 17.1. Measurement of stellar distance by trigonometric parallax. The parallax of a nearby star as shown from position 1 and position 2 during the earth's orbit around the sun. Note the apparent projected movement of the nearby star during the earth's motion.

235

parallax (Tech. Note No. 13). To simplify the problem, we now define a new unit called *parsec*, which is that distance, measured from the sun to a star, where the parallax is exactly equal to 1 second of arc. The formula looks like this:

$$d = 1/p''$$
(p'' is measured in seconds of arc) d in parsecs

Incidentally, the term light years and parsec both measure distances, the conversion factor is: one parsec = 3.26 light years. Astronomers use both terms interchangeably.

It so happens that one of the next nearest stars is Alpha Centauri, is four and one-half light years away. Therefore, the parallax is just under a second of arc, a very small angle indeed. Now we have the explanation of why the ancients and the astronomers of the Middle Ages, like Tycho Brahe, had all failed in detecting this; because the angle was smaller than their best instruments could ever possibly measure. The best instruments of Tycho Brahe could not measure better than one-minute of arc. His logic was fine, but the instrument precision of his equipment was not adequate for the task. What is the ultimate capability of the earth-based equipment at the moment? The error in a measurement of parallax is presently ±.005 seconds. For example, if you were to measure a star at a distance of 200 parsecs (corresponding to a parallax of .005 seconds) the error would be ±100%. Hence, this technique is only good for stars that are at distances somewhat less than that. It works best for stars up to, say, 30 parsecs (50 at the most), i.e., our nearby stars! Our galaxy, however, is at least 100,000 light years in diameter and other galaxies are millions of light years away. For these longer distances other techniques must be used.

No. 2 Spectroscopic Parallax

This technique makes use of the fact that hundreds of thousands of measured stars in our galaxy lie along the main sequence branch of the H-R diagram (Fig. 17.2). This involves a special procedure. Before describing this technique, let's review the background:

It is always possible to characterize a star by virtue of its spectral classification. Let's take the sun, which is a G2 star. From the H-R diagram (Fig. 17.2) draw a line from its spectral class to the center of the main sequence, and then extend this line to the coordinate of the vertical branch and read off directly absolute magnitude or the luminosity. We are now dealing with statistical corelations since 90% of the stars lie along this branch.

All one has to do is to know the star's spectral class. One can then immediately read off its absolute magnitude, provided that one is sure it lies on the main sequence. Once the magnitude is known, one obtains the distance from the formula:

$$M = m + 5 + 5 \log p''$$

One can always obtain the apparent magnitude. Thus, as soon

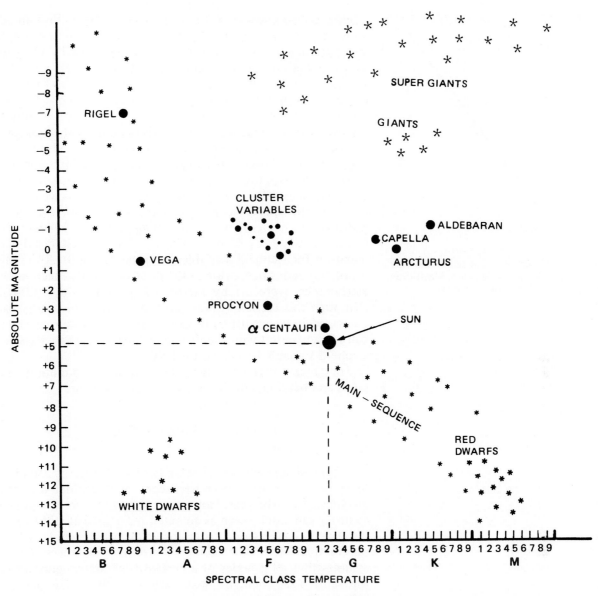

Figure 17.2. Spectral class temperature.

as one obtains the absolute magnitude, the parallax p″ or distance d becomes known (Tech. Note No. 13). The precision of this technique is no better than about 20%.

No. 3 Cepheid Variables

· The discovery of **Cepheid Variables** and their statistical analysis proved invaluable in determining distances to nearby galaxies. The technique involves the following:

By plotting hundreds of Cepheid Variables on a plot of period versus absolute magnitude, it was discovered that there is a very simple relationship between them such that as soon as one knows that one is dealing with a Cepheid Variable of a certain type, one can go to this table and pick off the absolute magnitude of the star (Fig. 17.3).

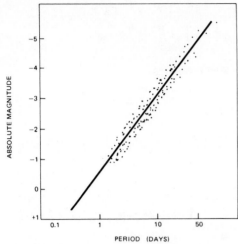

Figure 17.3. Schematic diagram showing relationship between Absolute Magnitude and period of Cepheid Variables.

How do we know that it is a Cepheid Variable? First of all, its light intensity varies in a periodic manner. For an example of a typical star's light deviations, see Figure 12.11. One can study its periodic spectral and radius shifts as well. Once the star is clearly identified as this particular variable, then one can use this particular curve with confidence (Fig. 17.3). To repeat, once the period is placed on this curve, one can read off the absolute magnitude. One always knows the star's apparent magnitude: hence, once the apparent and absolute magnitude are known, the distances are immediately arrived at by using equation 10.3 ($M = m + 5 - 5 \log d$ where d = distance). The error in this determination, as well as the error in the spectroscopic parallax, arises from the finite width of the curve. If the curve is wide, the error is large; if it is narrow, the error is small. The error in the distance determination for Cepheid Variables is probably about 20%. This is not too bad, since, prior to the discovery of this technique, astronomers were off by factors of ten (errors of 1,000%). Although this technique was carefully studied in nearby galaxies and in stars within our galaxy, it is useful so long as one can recognize individual stars and as long as one can discern a Cepheid Variable in a distant galaxy.

For objects that are still farther out, say 100 million light years and beyond, another technique is called for.

Galaxies or Clusters of Galaxies

No. 4 Sizes of Objects

A typical star whose diameter is of the order of a million miles or so can no longer be "seen" as a distinct disc at a distance of a light year. However, a group of stars comprising a cluster can still be seen as an extended source at still further distances. Galaxies or clusters of galaxies as a whole will be our next crude yardstick for determining distances. If one assumes that all galaxies of a certain type are roughly about the same size, then, by just measuring their size or their brightness, one can get a rough idea of their distance. This technique is getting back to basics and simple fundamentals. It takes us out to the realm of enormous distances of intergalactic space (Fig. 17.4). It fails completely for Quasars, however. Compare the sizes of galaxies in various clusters with the distance scale adjacent to the diagram.

On the right of the diagram is the subject of the next technique, namely the red shift of the spectral lines.

No. 5 Red Shift—Hubble Law

Note the arrow in Figure 17.4 which points to H and K, which are two well-known absorption lines in calcium atoms seen in the stars as well as in galaxies as a whole. What we are seeing is the totality of all the stars, plus the gas in the galaxy, having these spectral properties. Note that this pair of H and K lines moves to the right as the galaxies get farther

RELATION BETWEEN RED-SHIFT AND DISTANCE FOR EXTRAGALACTIC NEBULAE

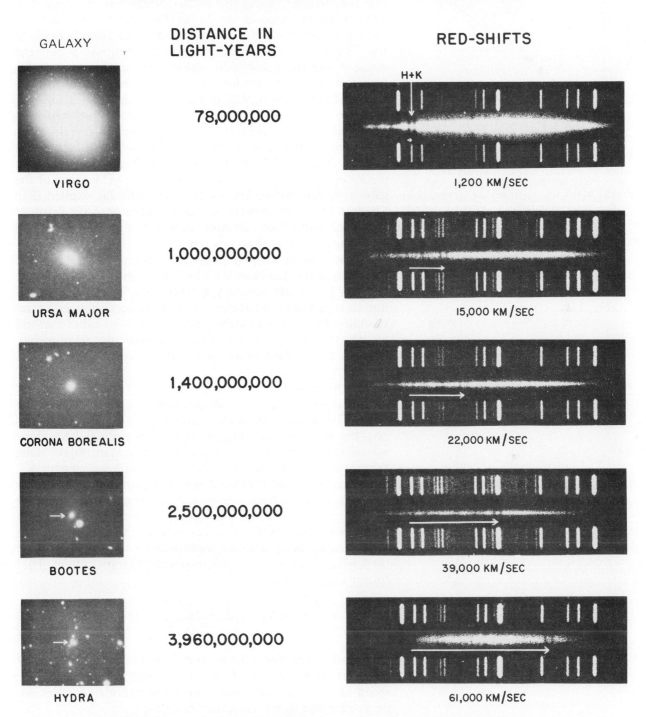

GALAXY	DISTANCE IN LIGHT-YEARS	RED-SHIFTS
VIRGO	78,000,000	H+K ... 1,200 KM/SEC
URSA MAJOR	1,000,000,000	15,000 KM/SEC
CORONA BOREALIS	1,400,000,000	22,000 KM/SEC
BOOTES	2,500,000,000	39,000 KM/SEC
HYDRA	3,960,000,000	61,000 KM/SEC

Red-shifts are expressed as velocities, $c\,d\lambda/\lambda$. Arrows indicate shift for calcium lines H and K. One light-year equals about 9.5 trillion kilometers, or 9.5×10^{12} kilometers.

Distances are based on an expansion rate of 50 km/sec per million parsecs.

Figure 17.4. Relation between red-shift and distance for extragalactic nebulae (Hale Observatories).

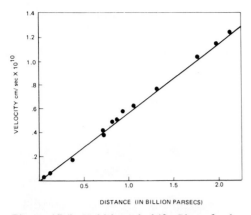

Figure 17.5. Hubble red shift. Plot of velocities of distant galaxies versus their distance. Note the linear relationship. This diagram also of course has tremendous cosmological significance, since it implies that the whole universe is expanding.

and farther removed from *our* galaxy. The motion, as indicated by the Doppler shift, can also be seen by the length of the arrow pointing to these absorption lines. At a distance of one billion light years, the arrow corresponds to a speed of 15,000 km per second, or 33,000,000 miles per hour. It is 1/20 the speed of light. The discovery that Hubble made in the 1920s was that there is a linear relationship between distance and the speed with which these objects are receding from us. This relationship certainly seems to hold for distances of 500 million years or maybe even farther.

The basis of this distance-measuring technique involves a determination of the shift of spectral lines (in certain types of galaxies) from their normal positions when the atoms are at rest. Figure 17.5 shows the direct relationship between distance and speed of recession of galaxies. The speed of the galaxy is determined by its Doppler shift (as explained in Chapter 15). One projects the galaxy speed onto the graph of Figure 17.5 and then can immediately read off its distance on the bottom scale.

There is some overlap with this technique and number three, using the Cepheid Variables in nearby galaxies. But, at least for the nearby galaxies, this technique has been checked out very carefully. At the enormously larger distances, corresponding to billions of light years, there is no other method by which one can readily check this particular relationship. At 5-10 billion light years, one is at the limit of our abilities to determine distances.

For those who are more ambitious, see Technical Note No. 17 and Chapter 15 for a description of the Doppler equations. The actual shift is measured as follows: One measures $\Delta\lambda$, the shift in wavelength, from the normal laboratory wavelength λ_0 to what is measured in the distant galaxy. One then takes $\Delta\lambda$, divides it by the laboratory wavelength λ_0, which is $\Delta\lambda/\lambda_0$ and is defined as z. The Hubble relationship is given by: $H \times d = c \times z = v$ = speed of recession, where H is Hubble's constant, d is distance, and c is the speed of light. Once the speeds become so large that they approach the speed of light, a more sophisticated formula has to be used which makes use of the relativistic Doppler effect. That formula is as follows:

$$\frac{\Delta\lambda}{\lambda} = \frac{1 + v/c}{(1 - v^2/c^2)^{\frac{1}{2}}} - 1$$

It looks very formidable, but it reduces to the simpler equation when the speed becomes small compared to the speed of light. Do we really need these expressions? Yes, we do as we come to the subject of Quasars.

Figure 17.6 is a composite diagram showing all distance measuring techniques now in use and their useful range of applicability. Note the range of overlap of some of them, facilitating our reach into successively farther distances by a sort of "boot-strap" technique.

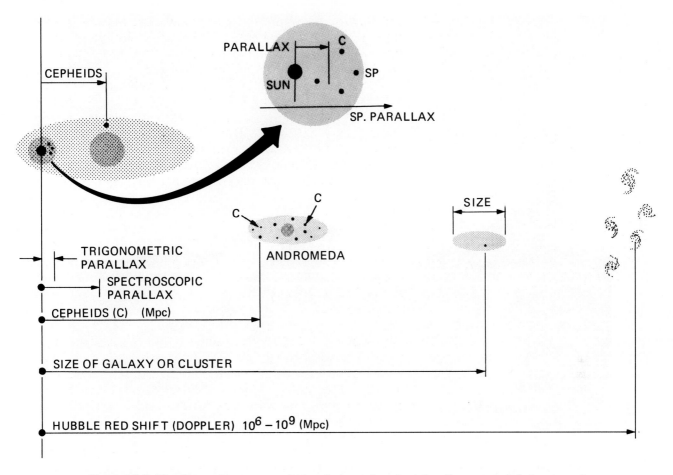

Figure 17.6. The five major astronomical techniques for obtaining distances and their range of applicability:
1. Trigonometric parallax.
2. Spectroscopic parallax.
3. Cepheids—period—luminosity.
4. Angular apparent sizes (also brightness).
5. Hubble Doppler red shift.

Note the overlap of each technique.

Radio Astronomy

A large number of galaxies are shown in this book (Chapter 16). These were pictures taken in the optical region using the largest available telescopes. Radio Telescopes, such as in Figure 17.7, can perform the same mission at much longer wavelengths. Recently, a group of scientists at the Radio-Astronomy Institute at Stanford, California, mapped out 19 extra-galactic radio sources. To acquire "pictures" in the radio region is not quite as easy as just exposing a photographic plate. This difficult task was accomplished by means of a technique that goes under the sophisticated name of **aperture synthesis radio-astronomy**. In this particular case, it involves the use of five radio telescopes simultaneously, each examining the same region in the sky, extracting electrical signals, analyzing and synthesizing these signals by means of complicated computer processing, then, finally, mapping it

Figure 17.7. Radio telescopes are playing a successively more important role in astronomy. Picture shown is a pair of 80 ft. radio telescopes at Owens Valley Radio Observatory operated by Cal. Tech. (Photo by Alan T. Moffet.)

out point by point. The results are summarized in Figure 17.8, which consists of four examples representative of the type of evolutionary sequence and the development of radio galaxies. Picture 1 would represent a very compact source, such as a quasar. Picture 2 is represented by a typical example of a radio galaxy, 3C66B. It shows a central object and an elongated halo attached to it. The next stage in the development would be typified by Example #3, the source being 3C111. It exhibits three roughly equal components.

Finally, in stage number 4, the central object has disappeared and only two strong radio-emitting source regions are seen on either side of what once had a visible central core. The fact that the central core is not seen in the radio region does not imply that there is nothing there. It only means that the central core emits insufficient radio energy to be picked up at the earth. A picture in the photographic region would presumably show the presence of a galaxy.

The interest and importance of these radio pictures lie in the clues they give us on the possible evolutionary sequences that a galaxy might go through in developing from a compact quasar to a normal spiral galaxy like our own (Chapter 16).

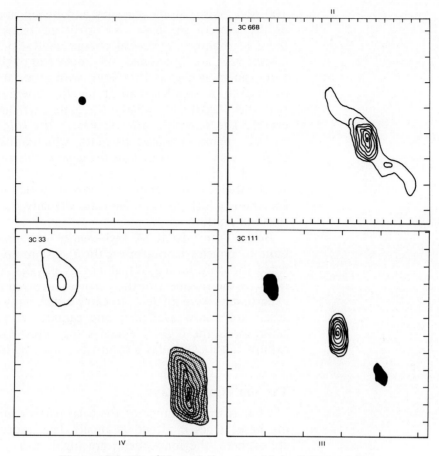

Figure 17.8. The (life cycle?) sequential development of galactic radio emitters using various sources as typifying stages in their evolution.

    I. Compact source (e.g., Quasar).
   II. Typical radio source such 3 C 66B.
  III. Radio source 3 C 111. Note the 3 components. Presumably the outer components were ejected from the central region.
  IV. Radio source 3 C 33. The outer radio sources have developed and increased in size. The inner region has ceased to ˙emit electromagnetic radiation (or is below detectibility).

Why does a galaxy in its development have to go through these stages? What does this tell us about the evolution of a galaxy?

Astronomers feel that they understand the mechanism for the production of radio signals: high-energy electrons revolving in magnetic fields, the synchotron radiation. This, in turn, implies the need for high-energy electron- and proton-emitting sources. It also requires the presence of magnetic fields. There are examples of such sources on a smaller scale in our own galaxy, e.g., the Crab Nebula. Does nature repeat itself on a grander scale by using the same techniques that it used on a smaller scale?

Cosmic Rays

The cosmic ray flux averages about four particles per square centimeters per second whose proton energies exceed

243

100 Mev. Also, alpha particles and heavy nuclei are isotropically present in space. As usual, electrons must also be there to maintain electrical charge neutrality. As far as the cosmic rays are concerned, the upper end of the energy spectrum can go as high as 10^{16} Mev, with a flux that is 22 orders of magnitude smaller than at the low energies. This means that these extremely highly energetic particles are very rare events. The scientific interest lies in the origin of these extremely highly energetic particles, which apparently are isotropically spaced throughout the galaxy. Where do they come from? In what furnace were they cooked? How were they accelerated to such enormous speeds, which gives them this enormously high energy? They are virtually traveling with the speed of light.

Before the advent of high-energy accelerating machines built in physics laboratories, these cosmic ray particles provided the only source of high-energy physics. The cosmic ray flux (or the number) of the particles involved is so small that experiments were difficult to carry out. Even with the biggest accelerators now available, one cannot yet produce in the laboratories the highest energies that these cosmic particles exhibit—although today's scientists are trying hard.

The Sun's Cosmic Rays

What is the relevance of the solar particle emissions to our life here? Does it affect us at all? The upper layers of the atmosphere, the ionosphere, are highly ionized. During daytime, as a result of the sun's ultraviolet radiation, the ionosphere becomes "activated"; it is different at nighttime. The impact of charged particles from the sun disrupts these layers in the upper atmosphere, such that long-range radio communication, which relies on these ionized layers reflecting the radio transmission, becomes disturbed sufficiently to cause disruption in service. These solar-charged particles are also responsible for the aurora, popularly known as the Northern or Southern Lights. This phenomena comes about because high-energy particles hitting the atoms in the upper atmosphere excite them sufficiently to cause them to reradiate; i.e., atoms get excited to high levels of excitation and then radiate energy as the electrons cascade back to their respective ground states. Such a cascade can be a long chain of excited states, at each stop it is possible for them to emit visible radiation. The height from which these auroras are seen, extending up to about 100 miles, was used as an early indication of the density of the atmosphere in these upper regions. It is an indirect method of evaluating the density and composition of the upper atmosphere.

3°K Background Radiation

In the 1960s and 1970s, there were other discoveries that captured the imagination and attention of astronomers and astrophysicists. Let us enumerate some of the discoveries that were made in this period.

The advent of more sophisticated and sensitive electronic instrumentation enabled scientists to detect elusive and weak radiation from outer space at 2-3 cm and even shorter wavelengths. This is the so-called three-degree blackbody radiation which is isotropic and *supposedly* the remnant of the big-bang cosmic explosion. There is still a great deal more data to be obtained, particularly at one-millimeter wavelength and shorter. This will be needed in order to unambiguously plot out the alleged blackbody radiation curve for that temperature regime (Fig. 10.5). Only half the curve has so far been fitted, hence, judgment on its origin should be deferred.

X-ray Sources

With the advent of a special orbiting satellite built to detect X-rays, a large number of discrete X-ray sources have recently been discovered and followed with great excitement. Some of these X-ray sources show pulsations and sudden bursts. Other X-ray sources have long periods indicating that they are part of a binary system.

Black Holes?

Excitement close to fever pitch is presently raging among some astronomers who are anxious to postulate the existence of a black hole associated with one component of an X-ray binary system. Since black holes, by definition, are invisible, judgment concerning their alleged existence should be delayed until more substantive data can be obtained. One should reserve judgment on such scanty data. There are sufficient numbers of binaries in our own galaxy whose companions are invisible because they are probably either dead stars or very heavy planets.

The discovery of new X-ray sources has reached a stage similar to when radio stars or quasars were discovered during its last decade. As we have mentioned previously, every time a new technology develops, it opens up a floodgate of new astronomical discoveries. Sound advice on these (almost daily) newspaper and radio announcements is to stay cool and let the cosmic dust settle for a while before advocating wholesale jumping into the dark, alluring bottomless pits of men's imaginative minds.

The Solar Neutrinos Dilemma

According to present-day theoretical analysis by astrophysicists, as discussed in Chapter 12, the sun produces prodigious amounts of neutrinos (about 3% of its total energy) during its proton-proton energy production activities (Chapter 12). Neutrinos have no mass or charge, hence, they are very difficult to detect. Physicists have been able to devise extremely clever schemes to capture these highly elusive particles: They use enormous size liquid tanks of cleaning fluid containing tetrachloroethylene (C_2Cl_4). Occasionally, a chlorine nucleus will capture a neutrino and transform into an argon 37 atom plus an electron. The argon nucleus is radioactive. So, by flushing out the argon atoms from the fluid and measuring their radioactivity, it is possible to detect these very rare, isolated neutrino events. It takes a lot of cleaning fluid to get a single neutrino to come clean!! Whereas there may be 10^{30} chlorine atoms, the radioactivity technique is sensitive enough to detect a single isolated event! The overall technique has been carefully checked out many times and is, in fact, calibrated in the vicinity of high power nuclear reactors, which also generate prodigious amounts of neutrinos.

In short, the elusive neutrinos can be captured and their presence detected.

Now, why all this long preamble about measuring neutrinos? In our discussion of the inside star trip (Chapter 12), there were many assumptions that had to be made. "Stellar astrophysicists" feel fairly comfortable with their computer-generated results. As long as their solutions were internally self-consistent and all the correct physics was used, there was no one to challenge their results. It's an ideal situation. Until recently, nothing could be checked observationally, other than stellar luminosity and total mass. Now, all of a sudden, there are small waves of creeping panic. Here is what has been unfolding for the last ten years.

Prominent and respected physicists, like Raymond Davis Jr. and colleagues, have searched for the expected neutrinos from the sun by constructing an enormous size neutrino detector 1 mile below ground level in South Dakota (the low level was required to shield from spurious radioactivity, whereas solar neutrinos have no trouble penetrating the whole thickness of the earth).

The results are coming in. They do not confirm the expected neutrino counts by an order of magnitude! There is something "fishy" someplace. Davis's experiments are being checked and rechecked. Maybe there is something wrong with the assumption of the sun's energy production via the proton-proton cycle? Remember that the theory, as outlined in Chapter 12, cannot account for some of the most obvious features of our sun, as discussed in Chapter 8: for example, the solar sun spot cycle and associated phenomena including the 10^6 °K corona. So, maybe we should entertain another careful examination of the initial assumptions.

These dilemmas are what make science so exciting—there is always the possibility of unexpected surprises and a complete revision of previous thinking.

We shall outline such a new trend of thought in Chapter 18.

I.R. (Infrared) Astronomy

During the last decade a number of star-like objects were discovered in the galaxy whose sizes were comparable to that of a solar system and whose energy output exceeded that of the sun by over 10,000 times. The sources of this energy have an equivalent temperature of 300 to 500°K, hence they are invisible in the optical region but are very luminous in the infrared region. They are too hot to touch but too cool to provide visible light. What are they? The solution to the riddle is given in the next chapter.

The sources of the I.R. are the DEBs, which are relatively young in these sources. We are most likely witnessing the birth of solar systems!

The Operation of the Telescope

Both the optical and the radio telescopes operate on the same basic principle: To gather in as much of the incoming electromagnetic waves with as large a mirror as is practicable and then concentrate this radiation into a small region so as to facilitate its examination. The principle is based on amplification of dilute radiation into a more concentrated bundle. The early refracting telescopes concentrated the light by means of a converging lens (e.g., Galileo's telescope). Isaac Newton (Fig. 17.9A) used a reflecting mirror to focus the incoming radiation. In the Newtonian version, the reflected concentrated beam is deflected first by a small mirror and then examined with another eyepiece (not shown). Another variation of this reflecting telescope design is to reflect the light back through a hole in the collecting mirror as shown in Figure 17.9B. This is called a Cassegrainian telescope. All major telescopes built today are some variation of these reflecting mirror designs.

Optical wavelengths are of the order of 10^{-5} cm, hence, telescope mirror surfaces and geometry require a high order of perfection comparable to the wavelength of light. In the case of radio waves, operating in the 1/2 to 20 cm region, the metal-reflecting surfaces obviously do not require a similar degree of alignment and polish as the optical surfaces. Consequently, it was readily possible to construct radio telescopes of 200-300 ft. dimensions.

Optical earth-based telescopes have almost reached their practical limits. First, because of the difficulty of casting huge slabs of glass; secondly, the earth's atmospheric turbulence causes blurring of images, such that the best theoretical performance possible has already been reached with a 200-inch mirror.

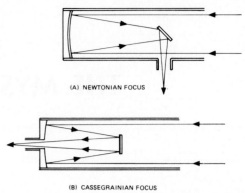

(A) NEWTONIAN FOCUS

(B) CASSEGRAINIAN FOCUS

Figure 17.9. (A) The Newtonian telescope design. (B) The Cassegrainian modification, whereby the collector beam is reflected and then sent back through a hole in the main reflecting mirror.

Chapter 18

THE MYSTERIOUS COSMOS

Cosmology

In this chapter we wish to undertake a rather ambitious task: (1) To sketch the developments in physics which had a profound effect on cosmology, and (2) to contemplate on the vastness of the universe, on its parts, its past, its development, its construction, and its possible future. It is generally associated with world outlook, perspective, philosophy, and even religion. In all religions this is implicit and sometimes even explicitly expressed: A picture of the universe and its workings and ultimately its relationship to men.

One of the many dilemmas that plague mankind is the solution of the mystery of how we fit into this vast scheme of things. Although man initially thought he was supreme and at the center, deep down he must have always felt insecure, his existence precarious and at the mercy of his immediate environment. Life was never easy for anyone. It is a constantly changing scene. Some of this is reflected on a larger scale, of course. Whereas most men not only lead lives of quiet desperation, in the subconscious mind is the ever present fear of the unknown—not expressed explicitly—the fear of our ultimate fate. Death is an obscene word to everyone but the undertakers.

But then, each of us is just a collection of organic molecules which, as we pointed out previously, are recycled; the atoms are not really destroyed. (A collection of organized molecules communicates with another set of molecules, what a strange phenomenon!) But there must be more. There must be a deeper significance to life as we know it. That is another search which takes us beyond the subject matter of this book. We are, however, concerned with the larger picture. As much as we try, we cannot exclude our own existence from this. One of the blind alleys that scientists have gotten themselves into recently was that they ignored the presence of man entirely. The universe is viewed as if it exists completely without the earth and what's on it; an interesting contrast to the Middle Ages when man was central and supreme and everything revolved around the earth. Recent cosmology has almost excluded the earth from the rest of the universe, which is understandable when one considers the study of many recently discovered fascinating objects such as quasars, pulsars, peculiar galaxies, pulsed X-ray sources, and even black holes (which may not even be real).

In order to obtain a rational overall description of the processes which are allegedly going on in the universe, one has to lean very heavily on our present state of knowledge of physics, and on our interpretations of what we see with our earth-based instruments, or with our very limited instruments sent out into space. Such interpretations, as we will discover, are strongly tainted and influenced by our previous prejudices and philosophies, and by the education which we receive in universities. Consequently, new ideas and thoughts come about very slowly indeed. New observations about the universe are generally fitted into old and antiquated pigeonholes in our minds. Facts are generally twisted and construed to fit our prejudices rather than analyzing the facts as they are and fitting a scheme of things around them. In the light of past experience, this type of approach appears almost inevitable. It is also wasteful of our resources, and often leads into blind alleys. In order to obtain a proper historical perspective, we need an "unbiased and uncluttered" presentation. We shall perhaps be guilty ourselves of adding extra clutter, or propagating old biases, as soon as we review ancient ideas and hypotheses. So how does one get around this dilemma? It is important to be cognizant of what went on in men's minds before us, without, however, falling into the trap of taking the ideas too seriously. Remember that initially even the Ptolemaic idea of epicycles was to some extent considered a mathematical device, and only in subsequent centuries taken as representing the actual motion of the planets.

By the time we come to the Age of Metal, the Neolithic Age, man's conception had advanced to a great extent. One of the best examples of his ingenuity and advanced state of knowledge can be observed from examples of Stonehenge, four to five thousand years ago (Chapter 1).

Observatories were built in England over 4,000 years ago! The position of the sun and moon were studied meticulously. A great deal of observation, commerce, meeting places, and some sort of religious practices were combined at sites such as Stonehenge. They left us a legacy of a very advanced observatory. Even today, men who have gotten absorbed on the steady diet of television would be hard-pressed to duplicate this feat which required observations of the sun and moon over many years and resulted ultimately in their ability to locate the seasons, eclipses and other phenomena, with great precision.

The cosmology as perceived by the Hindus is shown in Figure 18.2. It generally speaks for itself. Study it carefully, and you will get a fairly good idea of how they conceived the universe. You will note, among other things, that it required a series of layers to support it. This is a clever device, because you can always substitute deeper layers of support. The earth is supported by a tortoise and elephants. Elephants support a hemisphere. The turtle is standing on a serpent, the emblem of eternity. All very symbolic, of course, and full of hidden meanings! The upper region was the residence of the gods,

Figure 18.1. Ancient astronomer on his way to work, or possibly attending a meeting. Subtle persuasion, of course, is used as always to make his point.

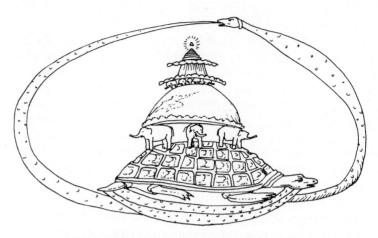

Figure 18.2. The Hindu concept of the universe.

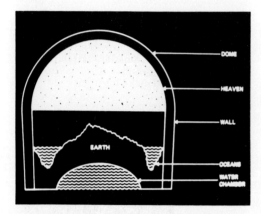

Figure 18.3. Babylonian cosmology.

the lower one infernal and the middle one—the earth. A symbolic triangle is on top. The really clever aspect of this cosmology is in having the animal closing up on itself.

The Babylonian concept is shown in Figure 18.3. Note the subterranean water chamber below the earth; they obviously had water on their minds. Also, recall the flood story in the Bible to appreciate occasional problems in that part of the world.

The Egyptian philosophy is illustrated in Figure 18.4. Note its anthropomorphic orientation. Hopefully, you will also appreciate that woman (Egyptian goddess Nert) was considered important. The goddess was on top of the whole situation! The earth represented as man was at the bottom! There are other clues that one can gather from this picture found in the tomb of Rameses VI about 1000 B.C. The Nile, of course, played an important role in their worldly affairs, hence, the ships rising and setting represented the sun's motion. The child is supposed to be air. These pictures may not do them justice. It is possible, but not likely, that their cosmology was more complex than this, perhaps even more profound, but certainly not more correct. Later cosmology represented the universe in the form of a box with Egypt at the bottom. Pictures like these are worth a thousand words, if not more. Hence, we shall stop describing their philosophy right here.

Next, we will briefly mention some of the great minds that lived in the Ancient Greek world: Pythagores, Philolaus, Heraclides, Plato, Anaximander, Aristotle, Aristarchus, Eratosthenes, Hipparchus. These men left an extremely rich legacy of sharp thinking and an approach to cosmology at which one can only marvel.

The Greeks simplified the earth support problem a little. Instead of having a great number of layers, their earlier popular anthropomorphic ideas had Atlas holding up the earth all by himself (Fig. 18.6). They presumably believed in brute force, and no one at that time seemed to have questioned what Atlas was standing on. (Perhaps if they had, Atlas would have dropped the ball.) Anaximander's view of the universe is shown in Figure 18.7.

250

Figure 18.4. The Egyptian concept of the universe. Note the rising and the setting of the sun as depicted by boats on the Nile, the sky by a somewhat oversized woman, the air by a child. The man at the bottom probably represents the earth. (Early woman's liberation cosmological concept?)

Of the great Greek thinkers whose works we know about, Aristotle held the greatest attention for the longest time. Consequently, we will just briefly mention his conception of the universe. Aristotle established the earth at the center and then, with increasing distances he had (54) transparent concentric spheres to which the planets were fixed (Fig. 18.8). The sphere closest to the earth had the moon attached to it; then Mercury, Venus, the sun, Mars, Jupiter, and Saturn in that order. Finally, on the outside sphere, "the prime mover" supposedly, rested himself, and he made all the other spheres rotate, the earth being motionless at the center of the universe. To Aristotle, man was furthest removed from "the

Figure 18.5. Greek scholar contemplating early concepts of the universe.

251

Figure 18.6. Atlas supporting the world. Popular early Greek view of cosmology.

prime mover" and at the lowest possible level. According to Aristotle, the materials that made up the regions were as shown in Figure 18.9: earth, fire, water, and air, together with opposites of cold, heat, dryness, and wetness—an idea not unlike an early Chinese concept.

We should now mention the brilliant thinker, Aristarchus, born 310 B.C., just twelve years after Aristotle's death. Incredible as it seems, Aristarchus discovered the Copernican concept seventeen centuries before it was finally accepted.

We know that Aristarchus regarded the sun and not the earth as being at the center of the system. With hindsight, one may now inquire why such a brilliant thinker's ideas were overlooked for so long. The answer presumably lies in the fact that when one has many conflicting conceptions, none of which are based on solid observation, then the one that carries the day is the one that speaks the loudest, publishes the most, has the largest audience and is the most erudite in his exposition.

Beginning of the Scientific Era

Let's take a giant leap from that era to the Middle Ages (Fig. 18.10). In the sixteenth century, there were Copernicus, Tycho Brahe, Galileo, Kepler, Descartes, and then the crowning light of the seventeenth century, Isaac Newton. Their accomplishments and contributions to astronomy have been enumerated in Chapter 3.

The heritage left from Newton's monumental work was a picture of the universe compared to a clock running precisely and predictably, once the positions of all its parts could be determined. A deterministic, precise, well-understood universe was largely the conception from the seventeenth to the twentieth centuries. Our planetary system was the main preoccupation. Stars were examined also, to be sure, during that period. Telescopes were built on a larger scale, particularly by the grand telescope builder, Herschel. Additional planets belonging to our solar system were discovered. In fact, the main preoccupation of some seems to have been the study of the planets and the comets. Other astronomers in the nineteenth century mapped the sky and extensive catalogues were prepared. Confidence in Newton's Laws were increased when his laws were used to predict the return of comets to a higher precision and to aid in the discovery of Uranus, Neptune, and Pluto in succession. Each discovery was motivated by the fact that planets did not quite move the way they should, implying the suggestion, which was made each time correctly, that another planet further out was influencing its orbit. These influences are officially called pertubations. Thus, Uranus was discovered, then Neptune, and finally, in this century, in 1930, Tombaugh discovered Pluto. Pluto is the most distant planet, while at the extremities of the solar system are the comets (perhaps as many as 3×10^{11}, according to Oort).

The nineteenth century also saw the development of optics and the physics of practical spectroscopy, which, when

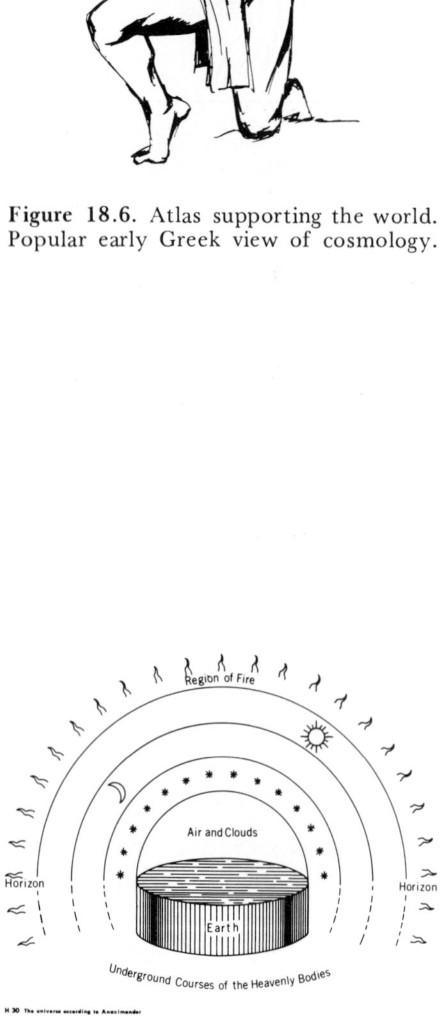

Figure 18.7. The universe according to Anaximander. Note the *Underground* courses of the heavenly bodies. (Modern astronomy courses are now completely *above* ground or at least above board.) (Yerkes Observatories.)

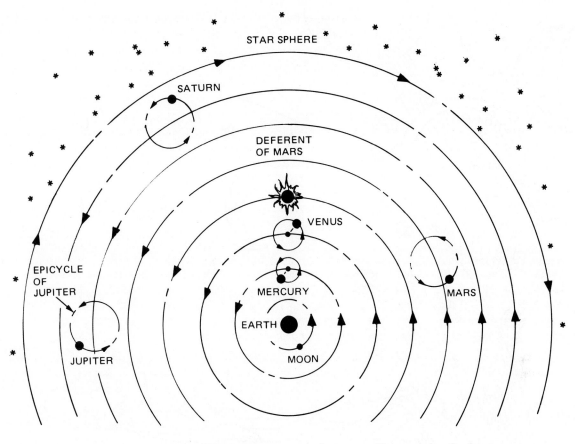

Figure 18.8. The early concept of Greek cosmology according to Aristotle. It was later refined and tabulated by Ptolemy.

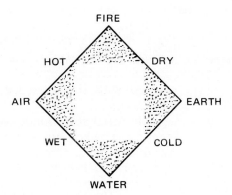

Figure 18.9. Aristotle's concept of the four basic elements; air, earth, fire, and water. See text.

253

Figure 18.10. A medieval concept of the universe. The illustration is often said to be a sixteenth-century German woodcut; according to Owen Gingerich of Harvard University, it is more likely a piece of art nouveau that was apparently published for the first time in 1907 in *Weltall and Menschheit*, edited by Hans Kraemer.

coupled with the telescope, yielded a whole new class of information.

With this background, we shall now approach the nineteenth and twentieth centuries. Physics and Cosmology—the Age of Einstein.

The Nineteenth and Twentieth Centuries

We are 7/8 of the way through these two centuries and have an accurate perspective as to what happened to astronomy during the last two hundred years or so. There was, indeed, a turning point in physics around the beginning of the twentieth century. There weren't many scientists in the field of physics at that time. The field was small enough so that each physicist knew almost everyone else and no doubt

254

corresponded with many of them. It was a small family circle, as it were. Making a living in this endeavor, however, was not easy, and high-caliber training and proficiency was necessary in order to obtain the few available positions which were generally, as they were at the time of Kepler, at a university. Industry had not yet developed to absorb the large number of physicists which were ultimately produced in the twentieth century. Also, physics, by and large, was practiced mainly in Europe, which was the "center of gravity" for physics research. There were exceptions, of course. The United States had Gibbs, for instance. It also had great inventors like Edison and the entrepreneurs and industrialists that capitalized on the inventions.

The turning point, as will be discussed later, actually came in 1895. It is ironic that about this time some pompous physicist was supposed to have made this remark at a meeting: "All we have to do now is work a little harder to get the next decimal point in the physical measurements that we are engaged in." This statement gives a very good reflection on the state of physics at the time. However, one should not forget that the nineteenth century had many other significant advances which perhaps were not sufficiently appreciated at that time. They included the work of Faraday—electromagnetic induction (our electric motors and generators); Hertz and Maxwell—electromagnetic theory, propagation of electromagnetic waves; as well as American physicists Michelson and Morley, who, in their classical experiment, attempted to measure the motion of the Earth with respect to the ether, obtaining a negative result. (This led to Einstein's relativity.) There were also very impressive advances in thermodynamics, the field which deals with the manner in which atoms behave. The concept of the atom was fairly well inferred in the early nineteenth century by Dalton. The periodic table was established by Mendeleev; chemistry was making strides. The period is generally summed up as the *classical period* in physics.

One should also not ignore the fact that the nineteenth century saw the work of Charles Darwin in the establishment of *biological* evolution on a firm basis. Since chemistry, biology, physics, and even geology had parted company as separate disciplines in universities, it is not surprising that little cross-fertilization occurred, if at all, between these disciplines.

The year is now 1905. This was the time when Albert Einstein (Fig. 18.11) introduced a number of concepts which changed physics in a most dramatic manner, to say nothing of the discovery that was made in 1895 when radioactivity was discovered by Becquerel, leading subsequently to the isolation of uranium, radium, thorium, and other radioactive elements. Also, X-rays and electrons were discovered—all about this time. As if these discoveries were not enough, the discovery by Einstein in 1905 changed physics in a spectacular manner; for he had challenged and restructured our concepts of the laws of physics to involve principles of space-

Figure 18.11. Albert Einstein (1879-1955) (Yerkes Observatory).

time, generally referred to as **special relativity.** (These concepts are summarized in Tech. Note No. 16.)

The net consequences of his theory were that there is energy associated with mass given by the celebrated equation $E = mc^2$.

Also, mass can be increased relative to a stationary observer if its speed approaches that of the speed of light. The speed of light was given a very important part in this theory and no information content can be transmitted faster than the speed of light. This hypothesis, coupled with the concept that no reference system is better than any other, required the laws of physics to be formulated in such a way that they are independent of the reference system in which they are observed. This led to his theory of special relativity. Some examples of the consequence are given in Tech. Note No. 16. The most spectacular of them is the energy-mass conversion equation whose impact was not appreciated at the time it was formulated, but whose dramatic presence was felt by about the year 1951, when it was demonstrated experimentally (which is the ultimate test of any theory). Indeed one can transform mass into energy—catastrophically (Fig. 9.12). The fission bomb is the trigger to obtain the required high temperatures for the **fusion bomb.** In the fusion bomb, mass is transformed into energy. The bulk of the energy from fission, however, is derived from the release of electrostatic binding energy of charged particles within the nucleus and its conversion to the kinetic energy of the disintegration products. There is, fortunately, also a peaceful use for fission. Nuclear reactors (Fig. 9.13) and power plants are usually operated without the sudden release of such huge amounts of energy, first demonstrated in 1942 by a group of physicists led by Enrico Fermi.

The fusion process, in which astrophysicists believe the stars participate, has unfortunately not been duplicated yet in a peaceful manner in the laboratory.

Lest one gets the erroneous impression that Einstein was a maker of atom bombs—far from it. He had an enormous compassion for mankind and corresponded with world leaders throughout most of his lifetime, attempting to improve the lot of mankind; a fighter for liberty and freedom. Among Einstein's other scientific contributions which have made enormous impact, was his discovery in 1919 of stimulated emission of atoms: an atom once excited with radiation to which it is ordinarily resonant, can be induced to emit that same radiation from its excited state. Such reradiation preserves the "memory" of the photons that had stimulated it. It will reemit this photon in the same direction and with the same phase as the incident radiation. This discovery didn't make too much of an impact at the time either, but a brilliant physicist, Charles H. Townes, utilized this principle to invent the maser in 1954, which ultimately became the laser in 1961.

Another discovery by Einstein, in 1905, was that light can be thought of as a bullet or photon rather than a continuous wave. It was this conception of the photon point of view which was applied as his explanation of the photoelectric effect; that is, when a photon of light hits a surface, it emits an electron. This particular phenomena is utilized in phototubes, photoreceivers that are extremely sensitive and multiply very weak light signals. Such instruments are now utilized in virtually all large telescopes to enhance astronomers' light-gathering abilities.

What else has Einstein done—since we think of this as the Age of Einstein? He extended his ideas of relativity to general relativity, which includes considerations of gravity. Basically, his description is a geometrical interpretation of the laws of gravity rather than considering forces at a distance, as formulated by Newton. By means of general relativity, Einstein went one important step beyond Newton's laws.

There were three discrepancies which could not be accounted for, using Newtons' formulations. These small corrections can indeed be explained by means of general relativity. It should be mentioned that such radical changes in our conception of the universe and the laws of physics did not go unnoticed, nor unchallenged by physicists of his time, and even today. Many attempts have been made to show

Einstein's work wrong, all without success.

We shall now take leave of Einstein and return to other advances in physics which also enormously changed man's conception of the universe. These are concerned with the nature of the atom and the nucleus. In fact, the latter part of the nineteenth and the rest of the twentieth century were largely concerned with studies of this type. They began initially with the study of blackbody radiation (Chapter 10), where scientists had been unable to theoretically predict the shape of the spectral intensity distribution curve (Fig. 10.6). It was only when Planck hit upon the concept of "quantizing," that is, splitting radiation into tiny little pellets of radiation called photons, that he was able to derive the exact expression which reproduced the experimental blackbody curve precisely.

Meanwhile (focusing attention briefly on the later part of the nineteenth century), spectroscopists had analyzed a great number of atoms and plotted their spectra (Chapter 11). The name of the game at that time (until the early twentieth century) was to try and find a physical basis for some of the regularities in the spectral lines. Ritz had discovered such regularities and so had others, but physicists were looking for the deeper meaning. (There is a good lesson here, namely that regularities are never there quite by chance, as we will soon discover when we reexamine Bode-Titius' Law, which had been around since 1772.) These Ritz combination lines were known for about fifty years. The man who did finally crack the code was Niels Bohr, a Danish physicist who, in 1914, showed that these lines can be explained by considering negative electrons going in orbits surrounding a positively charged nucleus and held in by an electrostatic force, just like the planets going around the sun are held in by gravitational forces. His formulation is slightly similar to Newton's with the exception that Bohr was dealing with electric charges whose attractive forces also obey an inverse square law, but are far more powerful. Bohr also had to invoke quantum concepts: only certain orbits are allowed, so the idea of quantization, as it is called, became established. To recapitulate: electron *orbits are not continuous.* (Planets, too, are not all over the place, but at discrete orbits going around the sun. At the very outer extremities of an atom, electrons, too, can be all over the place, analogous to the outer comets.)

Bohr made a momentous discovery. Experimentalists and theoreticians examined as many spectra as they could put their hands on to test out Bohr's ideas. There were still some discrepancies he could not explain. But this had to wait until 1925 and 1926 to be rectified.

Let's examine our concept of the atom. It, too, changed dramatically at the beginning of the twentieth century. In the nineteenth century, the atom was considered as a hard sphere just like a billiard ball by some. The Thompson atom had electric and positive charges intermingled, in a cloudlike fashion. Then the discovery was made that the atom had a very tiny, tight, very small nucleus, of size 10^{-12} cm; the electron cloud surrounding it had a size of 10^{-8} cm. This, too, was a major change in the oncept of the atom. The nucleus has a positive charge, electrons a negative charge, thus constituting a neutral atom. This dramatic change in concept was concurrent with, and followed by, the discovery of an enormously complicated electron orbit structure inside the atom. It was but one of many new discoveries which followed. The atom was not like a spread out raisin pudding, but all the raisins of one type having positive charges were inside the nucleus and the rest, the negative charges, the electrons, were outside traveling in predetermined orbits. Thus, Bohr, in 1914, developed a new picture of the atom and formulated the laws governing the orbits of the electrons within it. The immediate result was a far clearer picture of the origin of the spectral lines of the elements. Then came the important contributions of DeBroglie and Sommerfeld (there is a wavelength associated with every particle).

By 1926, mathematical physicists Schroedinger and Heisenberg had formulated these new concepts in an integrated, consistent, sophisticated manner called **quantum mechanics**, using differential equations and/or matrices. It gave descriptions of how more precise methods can be used to obtain the necessary energy levels of the electrons in the atom and how all the atomic properties measured by experiments can be theoretically predicted, at least in principle. One takes laboratory data and compares with the theoretical predictions. The success of the new "quantum theory" has been enormous and, with only minor modifications, stands to this very day. The modifications included quantum electrodynamics, which rested on discoveries made in the fifties. Proceeding on with the great discoveries, the early 1930s saw the discovery of the neutron, the **positron**, and then, in 1938, nuclear fission. The latter discovery resulted when a slow neutron was added to the nucleus of uranium isotope 235, causing it to split and release a great deal of energy. This discovery was made by Otto Hahn and Lise Meitner. The subsequent research was transferred to the United States, where it resulted in a new age, the age of the atom.

During World War II, other significant discoveries and advances were made in electronic technology, particularly radar. New devices were produced which could generate electromagnetic waves at very short wavelengths. Also, very sensitive receivers were developed. All this had a direct impact on astronomy and astrophysics. Our reason for mentioning some of these discoveries is that every time a discovery is made in physics, its impact on astrophysics and astronomy is not too far behind, and usually results in the uncovering and discovery of new and unusual sources.

We will not dwell too much on the subsequent impressive advances that were made in the study of the nucleus of the atom. A plethora of new particles were discovered by using new machines that are able to accelerate fundamental particles like the electron, protons, deuterons and helium nuclei to enormous speeds, and then having these particles hit other nuclei. By this technique, a large number of new species were discovered, resulting in a picture of complexity which seemed to unfold within the nucleus of the atom, a world as complicated as the world of the atom before the 1920s. In fact, physicists today are faced with the dilemma of a bottomless pit in the discovery of more and more particles or excited states of these particles. It is like fleas having smaller fleas having smaller fleas; there seems to be no end in sight. The dilemma of nuclear physicists and theoreticians in this field is to find a scheme that would put everything together. The "Niels Bohr" of that field may be on the horizon, there are great minds at work, but the picture is not as clear yet as it was for the atomic physicist of the 1930s.

The year 1951 saw the discovery of "radio" radiation throughout the galaxy at a wavelength of 21 centimeters. This 21 cm radiation is emitted when a proton flips over inside a hydrogen atom. The radiation from a single hydrogen atom is very weak. From a galaxy, it is strong enough to be easily detected. Its discovery was of great excitement to the astronomers, since it enables them to plot out the shape of the spiral arms of the galaxy, with the hydrogen atoms as "road markers."

The ability to obtain electromagnetic waves in general from the galaxy, other than the optical region was discovered by Karl Jansky at Bell laboratories in 1931. He demonstrated that there is "radio" (or long wavelength-microwave) radiation emanating from the galaxy! It opened up a completely new field of radioastronomy, which is now burgeoning and expanding at a very rapid rate and has many workers in it.

Large radio telescopes were constructed all over the world (Fig. 17.7). Radio astronomers are now kept busy studying our and other galaxies, picking up radiation wherever it can be found. The most fascinating of all the most recent discoveries was a result of the combination of the optical and radio disciplines working together. First, the microwave techniques had to be refined to obtain more precise position measurements for their sources. Then "optical astronomers" obtained more precise position measurements (i.e., right ascension and declination). They could, in turn, aim their telescopes at these sources and photograph them carefully and study them by optical spectroscopic means. Thus, the combination of these two techniques resulted in such discoveries as quasars, pulsars, and many other novel objects. More recently, these radio telescopes are used in the discovery of the so-called microwave minimolecules. These three latter discoveries are what astronomers were most excited about in the early 1970s.

The subjects of quasars and pulsars have been described in previous chapters and so have the microwave molecules. So what is left? What is required now is to bring it all together— the cosmological pictures; the origin of the solar system; the origin of the galaxy; the evolution of the universe.

We shall now summarize the historical developments from ancient times on. Then we shall examine cosmology from a different perspective and develop a new theoretical model.

Historical Summary

IONIAN PHILOSOPHERS—sixth century B.C. Age of Reason and Logic, Inventors of rational mechanistic cosmologies.

Thales—born 640 B.C. in Miletus. Head of Ionian school. Taught that stars were made of fire. Moon received its light from the sun. The earth was round and at the center of the universe. He knew of the ecliptic and the equator. According to Herodotus, he predicted the famous eclipse which ended the war between the Medes and the Lydians. He was succeeded by

Anaximander—invented the Gnomon which was erected in Lacedaemon to observe solstices and equinoxes. His cosmology is depicted in Figure 18.7.

Pythagoras of Croton—born in Samos about 560 B.C. "Father of science, believed in correspondence between numbers and the mechanism of nature. Whole numbers seemed to be capable of expressing the whole of nature's order and equilibrium." Earth, a sphere—not a disc. He believed in definite order in natural phenomena. Mercury, Venus, Mars, Jupiter, and Saturn revolved around earth in concentric circles, each of which was fixed to a sphere or a wheel. Beyond this was the sphere of the stars. Their school also believed in the emanicipation of women, to the alarm of the local politicians. (Has anything changed in 2,500 years?) **Pythagorean precept**: "All celestial bodies must move in circular orbits because a circle is the perfect curve and celestial bodies, which are divine, cannot move in anything but a perfect way." This axiom was good until sixteenth century A.D.

Philolaus—middle fifth century B.C. He questioned validity of theory that earth is at center of world system. He believed in central fire at center around which earth, sun, and planets revolved.

Heraclides of Pontus—540-470 B.C.—suggested earth rotates on its axis, Mercury and Venus move around the sun rather than earth.

Eudoxus of Cnidus—409-356 B.C.—inventor of homocentric (27) spheres to describe motions of planets and stars.

Aristotle—384-322 B.C.—his system: Earth at center surrounded by (54) concentric transparent spheres to which planets were attached in this order from earth: Moon, Mercury, Venus, Sun, Mars, Jupiter, Saturn, stars. He spoke of a prime mover as fixed and making the others rotate. Aristotle introduced four elements and opposites. See Figure 18.9. Fifth element is "Quintessence," which comprises celestial bodies and space.

Aristarchus—310 B.C.—in 275 B.C. suggested in his youth that *all* planets including earth might revolve around sun—**Heliocentric Theory**. He made important astronomical observations.

Eratosthenes—276-194 B.C.—measured radius of earth to 10% (Chapter 3).

Apollonius of Perga—an Alexandrian mathematician who lived in the latter half of the third century B.C. Proposed theories based on **epicycles** to explain motions of planets. It was a complicated geometrical construction with the earth as center, having planets move on epicycles with arbitrary radii and velocities about fictitious moving points in the sky. This theoretical model was invented by a mathematician! It did successfully represent the anomalies of planetary motions. However, it was not a true representation of reality. There is an important historical lesson here. In our era, a great number of astrophysical theories (disguised sometimes by pseudonyms such as *models*) are propounded. Very few of them will stand the test of time. Caution has to be displayed, lest some of these modern theories are taken too seriously, too soon.

Apollonius' epicycles were readily accepted by his contemporary mathematicians. It replaced the theory of homocentric spheres, which was inadequate to explain the observed phenomena. (Analogy: Newly exchanged merchandise, philosophies, personnel, or mates are initially considered superior to the original. Their potential flaws are usually neglected in the euphoria of the exchange.)

Hipparchus—born about 180 B.C. in Nicaea in Bithynia was one of the greatest ancient astronomers. He founded an observatory in Rhodes. Hipparchus made many astronomical observations. He determined the distance and size of the moon. He observed the angular diameter of the shadow of the earth projected on the moon during lunar eclipse. He then compared the angular diameter of the sun and moon. He concluded that the moon was at a distance of 59 earth radii from the earth. This was an incredible result. His value for the sun's distance, however, was 19 times too small. He compiled a catalogue of over 1,000 stars and compared their position with a catalogue by Timocaris and Aristyllus compiled 150 years earlier. From this data, he deduced the precession of the equinoxes, i.e., the difference between the tropical and sidereal year (Fig. 4.2). He was able to predict lunar eclipses to within 1-2 hours. (He is also credited with the invention of trigonometry.)

Claudius Ptolemy—127-151 A.D.—he wrote the *Almagest,* a treatise on astronomy which became the basic text of astronomy throughout the Middle Ages and a source of our knowledge of Greek astronomy. Ptolemy made many observations and improved on the earlier work of Hipparchus. He used the concept of epicycles; introduced small oscillations in the lunar epicycles called nutations. He also introduced the "equant." In all, he required 39 epicycles to explain all motions.

ROMAN PERIOD—the contributions of the great Roman Empire to Astronomy: nothing.

MEDIEVAL ASTRONOMY (400-1500)—no consequential discoveries. Some interesting developments include:

Albatenius—born in Battan in W. Mesopotamia. Excellent astronomical observations 877-918 A.D.; published text which improved greatly on observations of Ptolemy.

Abul Wafa—last astronomer of Bagdad; wrote a treatise on astronomy also called *Almagest* (not the same as Ptolemy's).

Nassir Eddin (born 1201)—founded a large observatory in Meragah in NW part of Persia. Established more accurate value of precession.

Ulugh Begh (1420)—Samarkand in Turkestan, built observatory, published tables, and catalogues of stars and planets. For the first time, stellar coordinates, celestial latitude and longitude, were given in degrees and *minutes* (not degrees only as previously).

George Purbach (about 1450)—professor of astronomy and mathematics at the University of Vienna. Published manual of astronomy and revised Alfonsine tables. His student, Johann Muller (Regiomontanus), collaborated. Included methods of obtaining fix at sea. These tables were known to Christopher Columbus and employed by A. Vespucci on his voyages to America.

Nicolaus Copernicus—1473-1543 A.D.—proposed Heliocentric Theory—planets move in circles. Published book *The Revolutions of the Celestial Bodies*, in 1543. Overall scheme: sun at center followed by correct order of Mercury, Venus, Earth, Mars, Jupiter, and Saturn. Moon revolves about earth and earth rotates on its axis.

The contributions of the following "greats" were discussed more fully elsewhere in this book. Hence only brief summaries are given here. In any event, the length of each entry is not necessarily related to the importance of the contributor.

Giordano Bruno (died 1600)—espoused Copernicus' Theory. Lectured extensively. Believed that life (inferior or superior to earth's) existed on other bodies in space. 400 years ahead of his time!! Stellar distances are enormous compared to distances within solar system. He extended concept of infinite universe. Burned at the stake in Rome, in 1600 by the Inquisition for heresy.

Tycho Brahe—1546-1601—greatest and last astronomer to work without telescopes (naked eye observer). Established observatory on the Island of Hveen near Copenhagen. Compiled planetary data which was essential for next step. This data passed on to Kepler.

Johannes Kepler—1571-1630—using Brahe's data, developed 3 laws of planetary motion (Chapter 3).

Galileo Galilei—1564-1642—invented refracting telescope and made important observations of planets and moon, sunspots, 4 moons of Jupiter, phases of Venus. 1632 published "Dialogue Concerning the Two Chief World Systems." This book was placed on forbidden list until 1835. Galileo tried by Inquisition (Fig. 3.6) and found guilty of heresy. He made important discoveries in physics, subsequently, using *quantitative experimental methods*, one of the great contributions to science.

Sir Isaac Newton—1642-1727—invented and constructed first reflecting telescope (1668). Invented calculus, formulated 3 laws of motion, Law of Gravity, discovered laws of optics, published his findings in two important books: *Principia* and *Optiks.* At the age of 26, became Lucasian Professor Mathematics at Trinity College.

Albert Einstein—1879-1955—formulated special Theory of **relativity** at age 26. General Relativity-1916. His theories predict new laws of motion and of gravitation. New physical principles and insight. Changed view of matter, energy, space, and time. New cosmology.

Some Great Moments in the Recent History of Astronomy

	1687	Isaac Newton published *Principia.*
	1705	Isaac Newton published *Opticks.*
	1781	William Herschel discovered Uranus—now there were 7 planets.
	1802	William Herschel discovered Binary star systems—stars had company.
	1814	Fraunhofer showed sun produces an absorption spectrum.
	1838	Bessel made first measurement of stellar distance of 61 Cygni—parallax technique. Distance was 500,000 AU, 2 1/2 parses, or 7.9 light years or 5×10^{13} miles. Earth-man discovered that stellar distances are big!
	1842	Christian Doppler demonstrated Doppler effect—important consequences in Astronomy.
	1846	Galle discovered Neptune, based on theoretical prediction by Leverrier. Now there were 8 planets!
Mid	1850s	Kirchhoff showed stars are composed of same chemical elements as found on earth.
	1868	Sir William Huggins measured radial velocity of 50 km/sec. for Sirius using Doppler principle.
	1905	Albert Einstein published the theory of special relativity.
	1908	Henrietta S. Leavitt discovered Period-Luminosity relation for Cepheid Variables.
	1912	V.M. Slipher of Lowell Observatory demonstrated from spectra of Andromeda nebula that it was approaching us with velocity of 200 km/sec.
	1915	H. Shapley dethroned sun from center of galaxy.
	1917	Slipher discovered 13 out of 15 galaxies are *receding* from us. Mean velocity was 600 km/sec., i.e., 25 times greater than mean velocity within our galaxy.
	1919	Eddington and co-workers, using solar eclipse, confirmed Albert Einstein's predicted bending of starlight by sun from general relativity.
	1924	Hubble discovered faint galaxies are very remote and that spiral galaxies were separate systems—the universe was getting larger!

1930   Hubble law discovered. Distance of galaxy is
       proportional to velocity of recession.
1930   Clyde Tombaugh discovers Pluto—now there
       were 9 planets!

Summary of Cosmology as Perceived by Present Astrophysicists

The following is a very brief summary of the present state of cosmology.*

It can be almost summarized by means of a single scheme (Fig. 18.12). It is postulated to have proceeded as follows. Initially, everything was in the form of radiation at temperatures of about 10^{11} °K. The "big bang" proceeded with radiation escaping in all directions. The radiation was homogeneous and isotropic. Ultimately, it resulted in the production of hydrogen and some helium as matter and radiation separated. The initial temperatures were so hot that all energy and mass distribution had to be completely isotropic. It is this isotropic aspect that causes certain problems in this

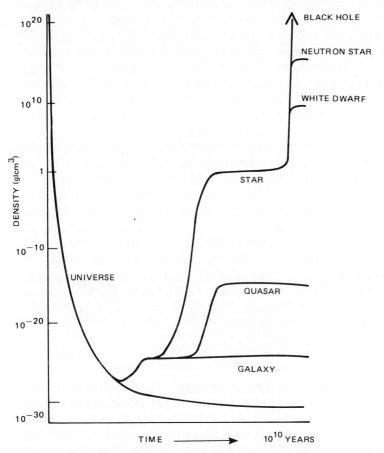

Figure 18.12. The cosmology of the 1970s.

*For those who wish to study "present" cosmology in a more leisurely context, I recommend *The Universe, Its Beginning and End* by Lloyd Motz, 1975. It is a highly readable, well-written book.

cosmological picture. (A uniform gas distribution *cannot* result in galaxy formation!!) Initial densities were exceedingly high. Then, as matter and radiation parted company and became dispersed throughout the universe, galaxies allegedly were to start to form in various regions of the universe! A subbranch shown in Figure 18.12 includes quasars. Within each galaxy, giant clouds of hydrogen and helium are supposedly moving and slowly rotating. Stars eventually formed, maybe a few isolated solar systems in the process of star formation also formed. The stars in their development stages go through various tracks on the H-R diagram (Fig. 11.7). These theoretical tracks are not shown. They allegedly depend on the initial mass of the contracting cloud. The processes are postulated to proceed along complicated "tracks" onto and off the main sequence branch of the H-R diagram. Meantime, some stars which have exhausted their fuel become white dwarfs, others, through explosive catastrophic events, collapse into neutron stars, while others, some astrophysicists hope, end up as black holes.

The scenario can be summarized more succinctly as initial chaos leading to diversity and order, i.e., starting with an initial chaotic and homogeneous mixture of the three elements: radiation, hydrogen, and helium. One is supposed to believe that this would end with, for example, our solar system, the earth and life on it. Or, to rephrase this cosmology another way: one starts off with a very compact and heavy body comprising all energy and matter in the universe, which disperses at very high speeds, and then, for reasons no one has been able to explain, some parts of the expanding cloud decide to stop expanding (some giant clouds are supposed to collide with each other, however, 40% of all galaxies are loners!) or conglomerate to form the galaxies and then within each galaxy, stars. Notice that the processes involve expansion followed by contraction or collapse. Note the ever-present concept of "collapsing": from large clouds, the size of a galaxy, to the smaller size clouds which are light years in size. Disorganized, randomly oriented gas clouds are supposed eventually to produce highly organized compact bodies, such as complex stars and planets. Stars are also allegedly recycled (many times?) to account for the cosmic abundances of the elements.

The Origin of the Solar System

According to present cosmology, the solar system is supposed to have formed as a result of the gravitational collapse of a large, slowly spinning gas and dust cloud. Laplace suggested this idea in the nineteenth century and it is still with us today (Fig. 18.13). Qualitatively, the idea sounds very convincing but, quantitatively, it is contrary to observations. First of all, according to the well believed principle of conservation of angular momentum (Chapter 3) the sun, after its formation, should have been spinning hundreds of times more rapidly than it does at present (Table 12.3). When a

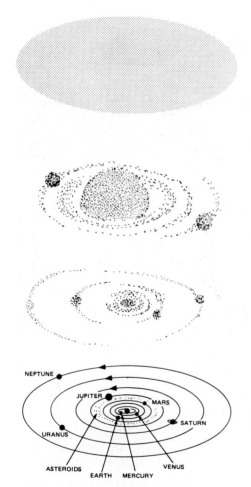

Figure 18.13. Laplace's nebula hypothesis. The evolution and development of a solar system from a nebula cloud.

266

rotating object or cloud shrinks, its massive center portion, having the bulk of the matter, should also have the bulk of the angular momentum. A simple demonstration was shown in Figure 3.17.

The sun spins very slowly now, and the major portion of the angular momentum is actually associated with the planets Jupiter and Saturn. How does one explain that by Laplace's theory? By 1944, Weizsäcker suggested a more elaborate type of collapsing gas cloud (Fig. 18.14) in order to explain the planetary orbits. Finally, in 1951, G. Kuiper attempted to patch up the model further. The dynamical problems are formidable. Does this type of approach not remind us of epicycles? The Bode-Titius law cannot be derived at all. Present cosmology has a great many other problems.

Where do the atomic elements come from, especially since some of the radioactive ones have clocks ticking? The customary answer is that (1) they were ejected from a supernova, (2) formed a cloud, (3) met another cloud, (4) then slowed down to form the presolar gas cloud, (5) and then this gas cloud collapses.

What power man has to believe
With blindness or selective sieve:
The universe must fit his mind
Put facts and figures far behind.
                    F.M. Johnson
                    May 1976

Figure 18.14. The Weizsäcker model. Supposedly, a more sophisticated concept than Laplace's, consisting of eddys within eddys (epicycles within epicycles).

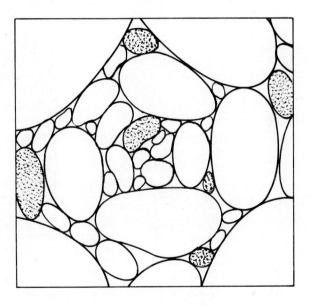

Figure 18.15. Kuiper's improvement on this. Or is it an improvement?

A New Cosmology—The Origin of the Solar System (A Different Hypothesis)*

Whereas present cosmologists consider the origin of stars and solar systems as arising from a callapsing dust and gas cloud, the model that will be considered here is a slight departure from those concepts. This new model involves the following assumptions:

1. It is assumed that the original sun developed from a small, massive, neutron-star-type-core, whose mass was approximately a hundred times the present solar mass. It will be shown that this initial mass can be deduced from information about the planets. The message of how the solar system originated is written in Bode's Law.

The neutron core surface would emit neutrons which would become, via the well-known neutron decay mechanism, protons, electrons, and neutrinos, and build up a gas cloud around a massive, fast rotating core. The radius of the protosun would roughly correspond to the span of Mercury's orbit. From afar, the sun would appear as a supergiant whose luminosity would be slightly more than a million times the present luminosity of the sun. This protosun would now proceed to develop in stages. All the stages that the sun would go through are exhibited by some of the many phenomena that we discussed in previous chapters. These include a variable star, recurrent nova, and, finally the sun would end up as a G2 spectral class on the Main Sequence. Its initial spectral class could presumably be all the way in the top lefthand corner of the H-R diagram. Stars in that region of the H-R diagram are presently recognized as O type or Wolf-Rayet stars, which are rare stars, for reasons which we are now beginning to understand. These hot stars also have very high rotational speeds, as exhibited by broadened Doppler lines originating from their surface atoms. The initial protosun was certainly spinning very rapidly. The rapid outside surface rotation is a strong indication of the inner-neutron star core spinning at an enormously high speed. Figure 18.16 shows possible stages in the development of the core; namely its fission, then the breakup of one of the fission components due to the very strong tidal interaction, and the formation of possibly a multi-ring type structure composed of very tiny components. Each component, or DEB, is tightly bound and also spinning, being stable enough to survive as its own entity. We shall call each of these tiny spinning objects a DEB, which is an acronym for developing bodies. We presume that there are millions of these DEBs rotating about the stellar core. These DEBs have densities corresponding to nuclear matter. They, too, have opportunities to develop. During this phase of the core development, one larger DEB would spin out and spiral toward the surface of the protosun. There are two possible mechanisms for this spin out. One is a

*Fred M. Johnson, Preliminary results of the following discussion are published in: Mem. Soc. Roy des Sciences de Liége, 6th series, Vol. III, p. 609-627 (1972).

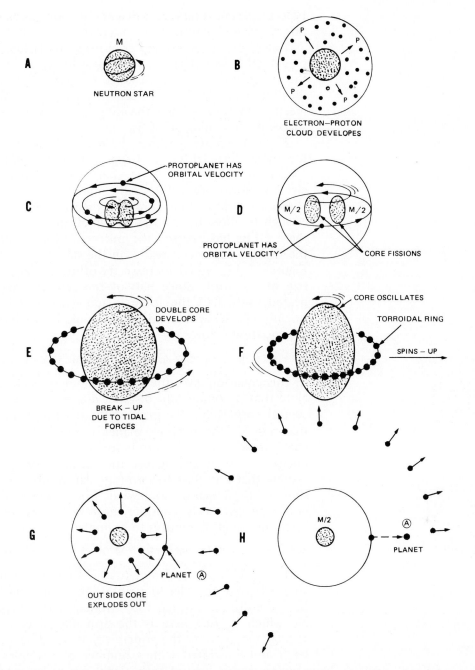

Figure 18.16. This idealized schematic diagram shows the steps involved in the launching of a planet, and the evolution of the protosun. (A) Neutron star, compact and spinning rapidly. (B) The evolution of a gas cloud consisting of electrons and protons. Its overall extent brings it to the size of the orbit of Mercury, 0.4 A.U. (C) Development of a central core. The ejection of a protoplanet and its achievement of orbital velocity at the distance of 0.4 A.U. Meantime, the core develops in a series of steps, shown in C, D, E, and F. The core fissions into two parts, one part will continue to break up into smaller and smaller components called DEBs. These DEBs, perhaps a billion of them, revolve very rapidly around the remaining core. They achieve enormous speeds eventually, via successive fission processes. All DEBs are ejected suddenly, presumably because of their enormous speeds (their effective mass could increase if they had achieved relativistic speeds). In any event, an explosion occurs (nova) with DEBs leaving the region of the star. The DEBs pass the protoplanet, on their way out into space. As soon as they do, the protoplanet's orbit doubles. The planet A is now held in by half the previous gravitational attraction. In view of the conservation of angular momentum, it will double its previous distance corresponding to the mass loss of the core (Fig. H).

type of plasma interaction that can be duplicated in the laboratory. These plasma type interactions result from proton and electron emissions and core magnetic fields. This protoplanet DEB would achieve orbital velocity at the surface of the protosun; i.e., at a distance of about 0.4 A.U. This is illustrated in Figure 18.16 schematically. The other spinout mechanism results from the kinetic energy released by the successive fissioning of DEBs.

2. Next, comes a rather dramatic development whereby the inner core DEBs revolving around the central core no longer maintain stability in their orbits and are suddenly ejected (Nova). We will have to come back to the process that allows them to do this, however, their speeds have to be high enough to allow them to escape in all directions. As soon as these DEBs have passed the outer surface of the protosun, the first protoplanet already on the surface, designated A in Figure 18.17, would increase its orbit, actually double the size of its orbit. Since half of the central mass has disappeared, only half the force is acting to hold it in gravitationally. To see why the distance would be doubled, consider the equation below:

$$J = m \cdot \sqrt{G(M + m) \cdot d \cdot (1 - e^2)}$$

This equation gives the angular momentum of the system. Note that it contains the distance d as well as the mass of the central core M and the mass of the orbiting planet m. Since the mass of the orbiting planet is much smaller than the core's mass, one can ignore it for present purposes. For simplicity, we shall also ignore the eccentricity factor, e, and assume that e is close to zero (circular motion), which would simplify the equation somewhat. For purposes of completeness, one can easily consider those factors as well, later on. Then the equation reduces to a simpler form:

$$J = (constant) \sqrt{M \times d} = Constant$$

It now becomes apparent that as soon as the mass of the core is halved, in order to maintain the same angular momentum, the distance, d, has to be doubled. The physical principle which is used here is the principle of conservation of angular momentum; the principle that was discussed in Chapter 3 and illustrated with a number of examples. Since the angular momentum of each planet has to be conserved, one can readily see that, by successively changing the mass of the core, the distances of each planet will increase in stages in proportion to the fractional change in stellar mass.

3. So far, the discussion demonstrated the launching of one typical planet. Figure 18.17 shows the complete sequence of planet launchings from beginning to end. At every intermediate resting stage of the core, a protoplanet leaves the core region and spirals out, achieving orbital velocity on the protosun surface. This is followed by the fission (division) of the stellar core and its subsequent explosion in a process very similar to the one described for the first explosion. The nova explosion comprises the leaving of hundreds

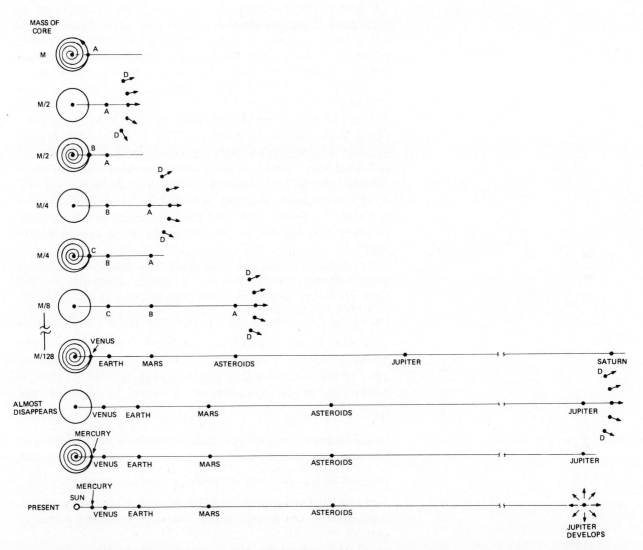

Figure 18.17. The development of the solar system. Successive stages in the NOVA like ejection of DEBs and the associated launchings of planets into appropriate orbits is shown schematically. The various steps involved are discussed in the text.

of millions of DEBs from the sun. When the DEBs pass the orbital position of each planet, their distances increase from the core in proportion to the fractional change in stellar mass. Let's postulate that the core fissioned and divided exactly in two equal parts, so that one-half the mass is lost at each nova explosion. The corresponding planetary distances are approximately doubled, correspondingly, subsequent to each nova. This process also implies that when three planets are already in various orbits, the distances for all these 3 planets are doubled as soon as the DEBs pass the farthest planet. In actual practice, each planet begins to move out as soon as the swarm of DEBs have passed the planet's position in orbit.

The overall process is controlled of course, by the gravitational attraction of the protosun. The motion of the planets in orbit is governed by the total stellar mass *inside* the planet's orbit. Any mass that is outside their orbit does not gravitationally effect the planets anymore, and can be ignored.

This is the basic principle by which, in successive stages, all the planets were launched and also, in successive stages, made to move out into more distant orbits, as shown in Figure 18.17.

To illustrate this launching process in detail, let's observe what happened when Venus was about to emerge. At the time when Venus is ready in orbital velocity at 0.4 A.U., the remaining core mass is only $\frac{1}{128}$ of the original stellar core's mass $\overline{M}o$. Proto- Venus had spiraled to the surface of the protosun. At this point, we shall postulate that substantially most of the remaining core will disappear. Incidently, there is never an exact doubling of distance because of the $(M/n + 1)$ factor, $\left(1 + \frac{M_o}{128}\right)$ for the case of Venus. The 1 in the factor is proportional to the remaining mass of the sun, including its gaseous envelope. Each planetary distance subsequent to Venus' Nova increased in proportion of $\left(1 + \frac{M_o}{128}\right)$ to 1, which corresponds to 1.75. To repeat, distances at each explosion do not double, but for Venus increased by a factor of 1.75.

Finally, when the last remaining protoplanet, Mercury, spiraled onto protosun surface, there were no more nova explosions necessary (or possible). Mercury launched itself at the protosun surface. That's all.

Since the main core now had essentially disappeared (only a vestigal core remained) and the temperature that was generated from the inside nuclear core was no longer sufficiently hot to maintain the giant size stellar radius, the protosun stellar orbit shrank to its present size of the sun. Mercury, however, remained in orbit. There may be other mechanisms for the protosun to have maintained this large initial orbit.

One of the proofs for this theory would be that of the inclination of Mercury's orbit. It is $7°\ 0'$; the inclination of the sun's equator to the ecliptic is $7°\ 15'$. This result is to be expected if there was no explosive event (Nova) for Mercury's launching, which would have slightly altered the orbital plane of the planet. Orbital planes of the planets can be easily altered as a result of an unsymmetric type of explosion or if a sufficient number of DEBs were to hit a planet to alter its path. With the exception of Pluto, all planet orbits are indeed almost in the same plane. The fact that Mercury's orbit and the sun's equatorial plane are coplanar is good evidence for the (Johnson) hypothesis.

Table 18.1 shows the results of applying the above analysis (equations) in a systematic fashion (Tech. Note No. 27).

TABLE 18.1

Assumed Protoplanet Mass m	Actual Distance	Calcul. Distance	% Error
Pluto	39.44	38.1	+3.3
Uranus	19.18	19.2	0
Saturn	9.54	9.8	−2.7
Jupiter (0.2)	5.20	5.2	0
Ceres	2.77	2.75	0.6
Mars (0.1 return)	1.523	1.52	0.2
Earth	1.00	1.00	0
Venus	0.723	0.73	−1
Mercury	0.387	0.393	−1.5

Note that Bode's Law can be obtained easily from this theory. Table 18.1 also lists the actual planetary distances. The theoretical analysis requires the following assumptions: (1) There were eight nova explosions, (2) the protosun maintained its initial giant radius at 0.4 A.U. during all the nova phases, and (3) the protoplanets achieved orbital velocity prior to each nova. This provides eight equations with only two unknowns, namely the initial size of the orbit and the initial protosun's core mass. There are, therefore, 8 overdetermined equations. Consequently (in principle), one can extract much more information from them. The final results are that the sun's original mass was 96 times the present mass; its initial radius was essentially that as given by the present orbit of Mercury.

The cause for the large number of meteor craters becomes apparent. See the planets for which pictures are available: the moon, Mercury, and, to a lesser extent, Mars. Mars and the Earth, however, have been substantially altered by weathering effects, not so the moon or Mercury.

Cratering would have occurred by the outgoing DEBs, as well as by those DEBs that never quite "made it" and eventually came back. "Those that made it," refer to the DEBs that actually left the solar system entirely, or achieved orbital velocity at distances between 50,000 to 100,000 A.U. from the sun.

Let's follow the life story of the DEBs a little further. Each planetary object launched in orbit, as well as each of the DEBs, proceeds with its own life and its own development phase. There may be as many as a billion DEBs. Each ejects gases, atoms, and molecules. It develops, eventually ending up as an object that we recognize as a comet.

Jupiter, Saturn, Neptune, and Uranus require further discussion. Jupiter, prior to its evolution, actually had sufficient mass to be characterized as a star. Its mass was roughly 2/10 (to 4/10) of a solar mass. The sun, at that point, was in fact, a multiple system, particularly if one includes Saturn, Uranus, and Neptune prior to their development. The other outmost protoplanets were not as brilliant in their stellar radiation as Jupiter undoubtedly was. In the meantime, Saturn, Jupiter, etc., went through development stages similar to those of the protosun. They each, also, ejected their own DEBs, and launched a complete satellite system. These satellites can be used to reconstruct (backwards in time) the original mass of the sun, as well as Jupiter. Indeed, using the initial masses of Jupiter and Saturn, one can reexamine the original equations which were used to describe the angular momentun of the planets associated with the protosun. The next refinement involved the mass of the core plus the mass of the planet. It turns out that the mass of some of the protoplanets, particularly Jupiter, was not inconsequential in comparison with the original core mass (about 0.2 M.). Consequently, we can improve on the precision of predicting distances. Once this is done, one achieves good agreement with the positions of all the planetary orbits!! A very convincing argument in favor of this theory is shown in Table 18.1.

The Satellite Systems of Jupiter, Saturn, and Uranus

As was pointed out long ago by Alfven, the satellites have to be explained just as well as are the planets, and, indeed, it can be done. What is more intriguing is that the core of each of these planets did not behave in exactly the same manner as the sun did, except for Jupiter, which in its first explosion did divide its core mass by a factor of two, based upon the spacings of the outer satellites. However, subsequently, the break-up occurred in a more complex pattern. The set of 4 satellites imply a break-up into quarters of the inner core. The signatures of the internal break-up of the satellites' core is indelibly outlined in the position of the satellites' orbits.

Another important enigma, related to the planet Uranus, can now be cleared up. The satellites of Uranus revolve about the planet in the plane of its equator, while the planet orbits the sun. The peculiar aspect is related to the fact that Uranus' axis of rotation lies almost in the plane of its orbital revolution. This anomalous satellite configuration is inexplicable in the older theory.

In this new theory, it is natural for a satellite system to develop *after* the protoplanet is in orbit. The planet's rotation plane is evidence of its inner core rotation. Hence, the satellites launched from such a developing planet would undoubtedly lie in the same plane as the protoplanet's inner core rotation plane.

The Galilean Satellite Surprises

Examine Table 18.2 and compare the four outermost satellites with the next set of four further inward (Nos. 6, 7, 10, and 13). There is a very close relationship between these eight satellites. The fifth column in Table 18.2 has the distances of Satellites 6, 7, 10, and 13 doubled. Note that within a few percent, the outermost four are double the distance to the next inner four.

This strongly suggests that Jupiter's core underwent nova-like development similar to the protosun. Furthermore, the inclinations of all eight satellites are roughly in the same ball park and completely distinct from the innermost five, which are in the plane of Jupiter's equator. Also, satellites Nos. 7 and 11 have identical eccentricities. Nos. 8 and 11 have eccentricities in almost a 2:1 ratio.

Now come the recent surprises regarding the Galilean satellites obtained from the NASA Pioneer 10 and 11 space missions: There is a vast hydrogen cloud in the vicinity of Io's orbit; as well as clouds of potassium and ionized sulphur. Io also emits enormous quantities of sodium from its surface (about 10^7 atoms per second per sq. cm), which spread out

TABLE 18.2

Jupiter's Satellite System

Name	$d \times 10^3$ km Mean Distance	Inclination	Eccentricity	$(2d \times 10^3)$km
V	181	0	0.003	
Io	422	0	0.000	
Europa	671	1	0.000	
Ganymede	1,070	0	0.001	
Callisto	1,883	0	0.007	
6	11,476	28	0.158	22,952
7	11,737	26	0.207	23,474
10	11,700	29	0.12	23,400
13	11,010	26.7	0.147	22,020
8	23,500	R 33	0.40	
9	23,600	R 24	0.275	
11	22,600	R 17	0.207	
12	21,200	R 33	0.169	
14	?			

Satellites 13 and 14 were discovered recently by Charles Kowal of Cal Tech. The data for No. 14 is not yet sufficient to derive the orbital elements.

R means retrograde motion.

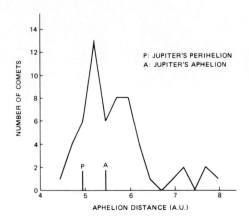

Figure 18.18. Distribution of comets around Jupiter's orbit. Note that the double-humped peak, one corresponding to the medium distance of Jupiter's orbit, the other slightly further out.

in a cloud along Io's orbit. The sodium emission from Io was discovered in 1972 from ground-based observations. Thus, Io has a complex ionosphere. Whereas the sodium cloud extends in a ring along Io's orbit, the larger hydrogen cloud extends for only 1/3 of its orbit, trailing the satellite. What does all of this mean?

It means that Jupiter and its satellites show a great deal of activity. Therefore, there has to be a *lot more energy* associated with Jupiter's interior and its satellites than present theories predict.

They are not dead, "cold" planets! We are observing another minisolar system in *action*.

Note in Table 18.3 the sizes of the 4 largest of the Jovian satellites, as well as the unexpectedly high density of Io and Europa.

There is a well-known distribution of cometary orbits around Jupiter (Fig. 18.18). This double humped curve could reflect Jupiter's early development. Perhaps Jupiter was a Cepheid variable star for a brief time while it had a double inner core. Each inner core might have developed separately, creating two distinct groups of DEBs (Comets)???

TABLE 18.3

Inner Jovian Satellites*

	Mass $\times 10^{26}$ Gram	Diameter km	Density
Io	0.8919	3,640	3.53
Europa	0.4871	3,050	3.27
Ganymede	1.490	5,270	1.94
Callisto	1.064	4,900	1.72

Note particularly the densities compared to the moon's average density of 3.3.

*Data from NASA Pioneer 10, Pioneer 11.

Jupiter: Planet or Star?

The usual distinction that is made between planets and stars is that the planets shine by reflected light, whereas stars generate their own energy. This distinction, however, need no longer be accurate. Based on recent results from the Pioneer X and XI Space Missions, we have the exciting results that Jupiter radiates about twice as much energy as it receives from the sun. Jupiter has a magnetic field associated with it, whose strength at its surface is between 11 and 14 gauss. It has high-energy protons, about 2 Jupiter radii away from its surface, whose total flux is about 10^7 protons per square centimeter per second, a very respectable quantity of protons. The sun is capable of performing in a similar manner.

TABLE 18.4

	L (watts)	M (grams)	M^2	M^2/L	Density (average)
Sun	3.8×10^{26}	2×10^{33}	4×10^{66}	1.0×10^{40}	1.41
Jupiter	6.6×10^{18}	1.9×10^{30}	3.6×10^{60}	5.5×10^{41}	1.34
Earth's core	3×10^{13}	2×10^{27}	4×10^{54}	1.3×10^{41}	
Moon	3.8×10^{11}	7.35×10^{25}	5.4×10^{51}	1.4×10^{40}	

Let us examine Jupiter further in comparison with the sun. A number of features are very similar: The mean densities of the sun (1.41) and Jupiter (1.34) are not far apart. However, the most interesting comparison is when one compares the masses and luminosities of the sun, Jupiter, the earth and the moon (Table 18.4). The earth is included in this comparison, since measurements on the earth's surface indicated that heat energy is being transported from inside the earth out to its surface. This energy, integrated over the total earth's surface, represents its luminosity (similarly for the moon). The radiation from the earth is not, of course, in the visible region, it is entirely in the infrared. Nevertheless, it is still electromagnetic radiation. In analyzing this comparison further, it was decided to list only the mass of the earth's core, since it is the core which must be responsible for the present generation of its heat. In order to compare these four objects, the square of each mass was divided by the luminosity to see whether there is a mass-luminosity relationship. Such a relationship exists among stars. However, amongst stars it is postulated to be to the 3.5 power. That is, the (mass)$^{3.5}$ is supposedly proportional to the luminosity. Such a power law, however, for stars, is valid only over a very small range of values of stellar masses. The comparison shown in Table 18.4 has a far wider range, involving 15 orders of magnitude range for luminosities, and 7 orders of magnitude change for mass. Consequently, it would constitute a far more stringent test. The results shown in the table indicate that there is a rough correlation between the luminosities of all four objects. A graphical plot, which includes these objects as well as stars gave a $M^{2.3}$ power law. This gives a very strong indication that the four objects are indeed related; the relationship that one wishes to establish is a "maternity suit." All the planets do, in fact, originate from the sun. They still retain active central cores whose energy output is proportional to their (masses)$^{2.3}$. Similar results are expected for the other superior planets, Saturn, Uranus, and Neptune.

Also shown on Table 18.4 is a comparison of densities. The earth's mean density (5.5) is far greater than the sun's or that of Jupiter. However, this is a very deceptive quantity, since it does not include the fact that both the sun and Jupiter presumably have dense cores and a large gaseous atmosphere, which the earth does not have. The densities represent average quantities over the whole object and are, consequently, exceedingly misleading. They are applicable in comparing the sun and Jupiter, because both have cores and a large gaseous envelope. The comparison of luminosities may be independent of the detailed structure, since it is assumed that the energy is generated from within and will get out eventually. Therefore, one has a measure of the total internal energy from the object in question.

A heat sensor attached to the Viking lander on Mars would also be able to take measurements of the heat emanating from Mars and provide another checkpoint for this hypothesis.

There is also evidence from Saturn that it radiates more energy than it receives, based on earth-based measurements of the infrared energy from Saturn. Since the Pioneer Spacecraft will rendezvous with Saturn in 1979, hopefully, we will have a better measurement from that important planet as well.

A Missing Link—The Planet-Star Connection

Examine Figure 18.19 carefully, and you will discover the line which connects the stars with the planets, and even the moon. This connection is brought about by plotting their luminosity against their mass. Actually, we've plotted the fractional luminosity versus the fractional mass, compared to the sun, on a logarithmic scale, which allows one to examine these objects over an enormously wide range of luminosities and masses. The luminosities range over twenty orders of magnitude and the masses vary over eight orders of magnitude!! It is incredible to discover that the stars and the planets follow the same line. Note that the moon, earth, Jupiter, the sun, and some of the stars (those not much more massive than the sun) lie on the same straight line. One can draw the heavier stars on another continuation of this line with a slightly different slope; the slope being 3.2, whereas the planet-star connection has a slope of about two as discussed previously. Apparently, for the heavier stars, the efficiency of their energy reproduction mechanism increases more rapidly as their mass is increased. Stars like the sun though are *directly connected* by the identical mass luminosity relationship to the planets. The fact that the lunar core lies slightly below the curve, is what one would expect if the moon had a catastrophe early in its development and presumably lost some of its nuclear core.

Some Remarks About Energy Sources

It is remarkable that fission of heavy nuclei produces about 10 times more energy per event than fusion. Of course, the energy generated per nucleon still is more efficient for fusion, since 4 protons converted to 1 helium nucleus produces $\frac{20}{4}$ = 5 Mev per nucleon. Whereas, in fission of a heavy

278

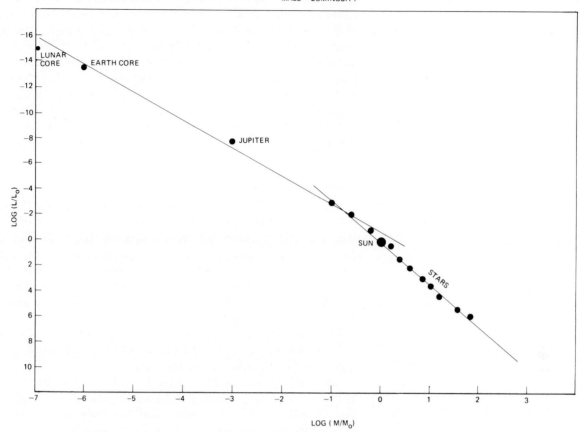

Figure 18.19. The universal mass-luminosity relationship. Note the straight line connection between the planets and the stars. The slope of the connection is such that the luminosity is roughly proportional to M^2. The slope increases for the heavier stars.

particle, about $\frac{200}{240} \simeq 1$ Mev per nucleon is generated.

In any event, however, since *large scale* fission processes seem to occur within stars to create the DEBs, it is tempting to speculate on the possibility that perhaps the energy within stars is generated (at least in part) by nuclear fission. The M^2 dependence is consistent with the concept of fission. The energy produced from nuclear fission results from the release of electrostatic energy associated with the closely bound nuclear charged particles. (This is about 200 Mev of energy released per fission event. It is the primary energy source of the atomic bomb and the nuclear reactors.) If this is the case, then, would not these energy sources inside the planets (Fig. 18.19) also imply that the cores of planets have a similar energy source?

The energy dependence being related to mass by a quadratic relation (i.e., proportional to M^2) is consistent with the energy source arising from electrostatic forces. The higher dependence ($M^{3.5}$) for the heavier stars might be due to the larger available surface areas. This would suggest that the giant and supergiant stars might perhaps have an enormously large number of circulating DEBs inside their supposedly large gaseous envelopes. This would account for their larger sizes and also for their more efficient energy production (i.e., a large number of energy sources spread throughout the star). This would also account for the peculiar emission line phenomenon of some giant Be type stars: The DEBs could be circulating close to the surface and exhibit their potentially higher effective temperatures resulting from their nuclear particle emissions (solar wind analogy). The sun spots, on a small scale, perform the same function, except that on the sun, the number of DEBs (sun spots) near the surface is very small at any one time.

Natural Fission Reactor on Earth*

During the last few years, scientists were literally flabbergasted when they discovered that nature (not man) had operated the first uranium fission reactors on the earth. The discovery was made at the Oklo open pit uranium mine in the Gabon Republic, near the coast of West Africa. Based on chemical and isotopic analysis of certain areas of the rich uranium veins, a fairly good reconstruction of these ancient fission reactors was possible.

These natural reactors were operating 1.8 billion years ago in Precambrian rock, producing enormous quantities of energy, just like the man-made reactors.

Six such natural reactors have been located in the region. The reactor identification is based on uranium 235 depletion (as a result of nuclear fission) and the presence of tell-tale U235 fission fragments, in the same proportion as observed with man-made reactors.

Now here comes the speculation:

There is little reason to doubt that rich uranium veins on the earth's surface are a result of bulk extrusion from deeper regions within the earth. Is it possible that the earth's interior, at an earlier epoch operated extensive fission type reactors? If this were the case, it could account for the apparently, high, inferred, central core, effective temperatures, as discussed in Chapter 7.

If the present luminosity of the earth (3×10^{20} ergs/second) is a lower bound, we can calculate the minimum amount of U235 necessary to provide this hypothetical earth energy source.

It requires about 400 grams of U235 per second, or about 5×10^{19} grams, since 4 1/2 billion years ago. This quantity of uranium represents about 10^{-8} of the earth's core mass. The quantity of uranium required is consistent with the extrapolated cosmic abundance.** It should also be mentioned that the density of uranium oxide is 10.9 (and that of pure uranium 18.7). The earth's inferred present central density is between 10 and 13. Perhaps it does not consist totally of iron-nickel as is presently speculated?

*Reference: George A. Cowan, Scientific American, July, 1976.
**Table 7.2, p. 109.

The Pluto Mystery

Pluto is not only the farthest planet out in the solar system, but also the one about which the least is known. Even its mass and radius are uncertain. If one takes the listed mass for Pluto as 0.17 (earth masses) and brackets the range of its estimated radius as between 3,200 and 1,750 km, then one obtains an astounding result for its average density: between 7.3 and 44. These densities are so great that astronomers are unwilling to even write them down. All astrophysical tables leave a blank space for Pluto's density!! The reason for the reluctance to face the facts of Pluto's high density is that it is completely inconsistent with present models of the solar system's origin. These theories require the condensation of light elements at the extremities of the solar system. Pluto just does not fit into this scheme. Hence, data such as Pluto's density gets ignored. After all, one can always point to uncertainties in Pluto's radius. True, but even the lower limit of its possible density is worth noting—it is large! Why could Pluto's density be large in the Johnson hypothesis? Because Pluto does not have a substantial atmosphere, its diameter would represent a solid core. It has a solid frozen surface, consisting in part of methane (according to reports by Cruikshank, Morrison, and Pilcher). The other superior planets, Jupiter, Saturn, Uranus, and Neptune, all still have a substantial gaseous atmosphere outside their respective solid cores, thus giving the misleading impression of a low average density for the whole planet. The quoted densities of these superior planets represent merely the average density of the planet's core *plus* its atmosphere. A high density for Pluto is consistent with its origin from within the sun and its subsequent development, just like that of the earth. Note the higher densities inside the earth and the still higher extrapolated densities of the earth at earlier epochs (Tech. Note No. 24).

The *average* earth's density over 4 billion years ago was about 36. The earth now has an inner solid core of average density 13.0.

The Pluto-Neptune Connection and Its Interloper

We now wish to examine some of the known facts about the present orbits of these two far-out planets. From this, we hope to gain some insight into the distant past, when these two might have had a more intimate relationship. We shall keep in mind the conservation laws of physics.

The beauty of the laws of physics is that we have absolute confidence in their universality and permanence. The main problem is concerned with their proper application in reconstructing the past.

Examine Table 18.5 carefully, and you will note that the perihelion distance of these two planets is almost identical. The perihelion distance is the closest distance of a planet to the sun. The difference in their *present* perihelion distance is only 0.22 A.U. Thus, prior to the orbit expansion resulting

TABLE 18.5

	Perihelion Distance	Orbit Inclination to Ecliptic	a Semimajor Axis	
Neptune	29.80	1°46′	30	
				Mean value 34.72
Pluto	29.58	17°10′	39.44	
Difference	0.22			
Halley's Comet	0.59	18° R	17.8	
				2a= 35.6

from the protosun development, these two planets could have been as close as 0.22/96 or about 0.0022 A.U. Or perhaps they were once together!

Now we come to the mysterious interloper, whose significance can only be speculated. Note this interloper, Halley's comet, has about the same inclination to the ecliptic as Pluto, except it moves in the opposite direction: it retrogrades. Halley's comet has a perihelion distance of 0.59, i.e., only 0.20 A.U. distance from the protosun's original orbit. (Also keep in mind the perihelion distance differences of 0.22 A.U. between Pluto and Neptune.) Furthermore, at Halley's comet extreme distance (aphelion) away from the sun, it is about in the middle of Pluto and Neptune's mean distance from the sun. What does this all mean?

It suggests some possible connection, but the details of such a scenario still have to be worked out. It is one more of the many unsolved cosmic mysteries.

A Stillborn Planet

Did all the processes associated with the protosun proceed in a smooth manner? We have one probable example where it didn't. The asteroids bear testimony to the fact that one planet, as it achieved orbital velocity, presumably "never made it" (either lost its core by ejection or was fatally bombarded or both). Or, another way to look at it, the planet which should have occupied the asteroid position ejected material from its own dense core (while near the protosun surface), some of which achieved orbital velocity. The mortally wounded planet might have worked its way back into the sun again, and would ordinarily have been lost, if it hadn't been captured by one of the other protoplanets on its way out. It was the earth that had the dubious privilege of capturing this almost "dead" planet. Such a capture process has a far better chance of coming about *within* the protostellar radius than outside in a vacuum, as some scientists have postulated. Consequently, when the earth was launched, it presumably rescued the moon with it. If this were indeed the case, it would make a very romantic and beautiful love story. It is hard to explain, though, why it was left to the earth to rescue the moon rather than Mars, which would have had first shot at it. Consequently, this last discussion on the moon is very speculative and deserves further study and analysis.

The two satellites of Mars, however, were probably captured when Mars was still on the protostellar surface. Deimos and Phobos look as if they had been bombarded by other meteorites. Their surfaces are heavily cratered. They could very likely be asteroid-type bodies. Maybe Mars just picked up these asteroids and missed the moon!!

What other evidence do we have to substantiate this model?

Sunspots

The sun, at the present time may still be in some kind of elemental process of creating protoplanets which unfortunately are stillborn. They do not achieve orbital velocity; their speed does not exceed two kilometers per second as they appear on the surface. Orbital velocity on the sun's surface must now be at least 434 km/sec. They make one or two orbits and then go back inside from whence they came. This indicates that there is still a vestigial core left within the sun, far different from what it was initially. However, the same physical processes apparently are still at work to allow protoplanets to be born. The sun's core must have a sufficient magnetic field to influence the spin-up of these so-called sunspots, which incidentally are of denser type material than the solar gas cloud. The *apparent* temperature of these so-called sunspots is beginning to make a little more sense. Since they are composed of almost nuclear density material, they would eject prodigous quantities of protons and electrons. The fact that they *appear* cooler is the result of evaporation type cooling from their surfaces. Some of the pictures of the sun (Fig. 8.7), look very much as if material was being ejected from the sunspots. Magnetic fields are associated with rotating charge distribution. Furthermore, the direction of the sunspots' motion along the surface of the sun is always in the same direction, indicating that their propulsion in part is a result of particle ejection by the dominant Mev protons.

Comparison with Galactic Phenomena

Compare and evaluate all physical and astronomical phenomena that were discussed in previous chapters and correlate them with this new galactic hypothesis.

What would these billions of DEBs look like at a distance

of a light year or ten light years? If every star went through similar developments, then the galaxy would be fairly crowded with these objects. They would block out a substantial amount of galactic light by virtue of the large size umbrella these DEBs would have created around them. These umbrellas resemble Saturn's rings in structure and also in chemical content. However, they would extend hundreds of thousands of miles beyond the core of each DEB. The "ring" around each DEB would consist of solid particles of various sizes, its gas molecules being trapped within a loose framework of snow-type condensations. A large quantity of small molecules would have escaped from these DEBs, since the velocity of escape would be larger than the gravitational ability for the core of the DEB to retain these gases. Consequently, the interstellar gases of hydrogen, sodium, CN, and CH, all would have originated from these DEBs. It is interesting to note that the presence of these constituents has been confirmed in comets and they are also seen in the interstellar medium. The nova phase of stars should not be too startling, since novas are seen often enough in our galaxy and in other galaxies. The nova brightness is accounted for in this model. It originates from the apparent large surface area that is generated when these DEBs are explosively ejected from the protostar. Since each DEB has a gas cloud around it, and is still radioactively hot, the excitation of the ejected atoms surrounding the DEB would emit sufficient light to make it appear as if the exploding star were far larger in diameter than it was originally. This would account for the increase in brightness. The amount of time involved in this explosive event is a few days. This would correspond to the time taken for the DEB to have travelled far enough away from the star and for their own radioactivity and heat to have decreased sufficiently so that their nuclear excitation would no longer be sufficient to excite their surrounding gas cloud. The DEB surface temperature, however, could easily be in the 300 to 500°K temperature range, which would account for the observed infrared radiation (IR). The IR radiation has been spectacularly discovered during the last decade in various parts of the galaxy. One must not forget that these DEBs are also spinning, and still have charged particles associated with them, generating magnetic fields. They also eject protons and electrons. Consequently, DEBs are the most likely source for charged particle emissions in such objects as the remnants of the Crab Nebula, or other emission nebula. When one examines the interstellar medium and observes the many areas in the galaxy which apparently seem dark, one is not seeing stars in the making, but rather stars in the past tense: stars and solar systems and DEBs and comets that are already formed.

It is preferable to differentiate DEBs from comets, even though they are, in fact, identical. One ordinarily thinks of very special objects when one discusses comets. The fact that the nucleus of the comets leads the way, is what one would anticipate if one of these DEBs decides to make a trip towards the sun. There must still be sufficient internal heat energy within each DEB to cause it to eject gas, or other material, to allow it to initiate their rocket-type action, which would change its orbit. This rocket action would account for the fact that the return of well-known comets are never precisely on time, largely a result of a comet still having the potential of ejecting gases. This ejection process would change its orbit sufficiently to cause a difference in predicted times of a return of the comet. It must be the potential of a comet to eject gases from its core that accounts for its decision to return to the sun in the first place, rather than so-called perturbations by Jupiter.

Polarization of starlight is now more readily accounted for by the reflection of light from the enormous number of particles associated with each DEB, constituting a quasi-mirror type surface in space, since any specular reflection from rough surfaces would cause light to be reflected in all directions. We would be receiving on the earth only the light that obeys the simple laws of reflection indicated in Chapter 13. When this law is satisfied, the light becomes automatically polarized. Studies of polarized light from comet tails have shown that the percentage of polarization could be between 7 and 11 percent. This cannot be accounted for by any other mechanism, only by plain reflection of light from particles of the tail. Similarly, the reflected light from the particles in Saturn's ring also show polarized light, which is again caused by reflection. Consequently, stellar light can be reflected too, and the reflection mechanism polarize the light.

This simple mechanism is more effective than the Davis-Greenstein model, which had been proposed in 1951 and which had never been verified experimentally. Figure 13.8 shows the overall polarization throughout the galaxy. Based on this reflection model, the distribution of DEBs in the plane of the galaxy is responsible for the preferential alignment along the galactic plane rather than a galactic magnetic field. Consequently, polarization is a result of the preferential distribution of matter in the plane of the galaxy. The deeper significance of this polarization picture is that it reflects the distribution of angular momentum and is suggestive of processes which account for the development of the galaxy.

The Development of the Galaxy

There are enough pictures of various types of galaxies exhibited in Figures 16.2, 16.3, and 16.4 to show the various structural galactic types: all the way from circular to varied shapes of elliptical. What stands out in these galaxies are their symmetries, particularly their bilateral symmetry.

We shall attempt to extend the Johnson Cosmological Principle to the development of the galaxy. If the stars develop by explosive means, why not the galaxy on a larger and more grandiose scale? Perhaps it develops from a very heavy rotating nucleus which becomes unstable and then splits up?

Figure 17.8 shows the evolution of radio galaxies which, in

turn, might be a clue to the galactic evolutionary development. The radio galaxies are symmetrically placed on either side of the galactic core. They emit large quantities of radio signals which, in turn, must have arisen from electrons travelling in magnetic fields. Where do these electrons come from? In all probability these electrons originated from the radioactive DEBs themselves, which in turn are spinning. If the DEBs contain an unbalanced charge, they would, of course, generate a magnetic field.

The Important Missing Link

The missing link in the cosmology of the 1970s is the fact that there are **underlying structures** in the galaxy, in the stars and in the universe. These structures are solid, and, as bones inside the body, are not obvious from afar, so that these structures in various parts in the galaxy, can easily be missed or overlooked. These solid structures consist of two types: (1) the dense cores and other solid structures within the stars, their development, and finally, (2) the DEBs. Consequently, what has previously been associated merely with dust and gas, in reality are DEBs, solids, and gas associated with DEBs. There is enormous structure, and this also implies that there is additional mass in the galaxy which had been searched for, but, until now, was unaccounted for. Thus, wherever previous theories talk about dust, one has to transpose the word "dust" for "DEBs," and where one talks about infrared radiation of dust, it is really the infrared radiation of the DEBs that is being exhibited. Obviously, there is little hope of observing the DEBs directly, but we have enough examples close by in the solar system to convince ourselves of their reality.

Is there any way these DEBs can be indirectly identified in other regions of the galaxy? The so-called interstellar clouds have velocities that can be measured by means of the Doppler shift. Whereas these clouds are thought of as just moving gas clouds, they are, in reality clouds of DEBs with gas associated with them. Since the gas is moving at the same speed as the DEBs, it is really the DEB velocity that one is measuring. One astronomer noticed a very simple relationship between velocities of various adjacent clouds in the same area in the galaxy. His explanation for some of these multiples of velocities was that it was due to radiation pressure. If we examine the data again, a little more carefully, we find that in addition to the relative factors of two by which these moving cloud velocities are supposed to be related, the relative velocities between adjacent clouds is really the square root of two. Now, this is a very significant number, since the velocity of escape, discussed in Chapter 5, is given by

$$V_{esc} = \sqrt{\frac{2GM}{R}}.$$

If our model is correct, and the stellar development proceeds as usual by core fission breakup and expulsion of mass, each time a DEB explosion occurs, the escape velocity of each successive nova group of DEBs will differ by $\sqrt{2}$, since the core mass has changed by a factor of two each time. Consequently, one can be almost certain that these DEBs will have originated from other stars whose developments are similar to our sun.

Look at what this implies. If these DEBs are universal throughout the galaxy and have all been ejected by similar processes, one can be fairly certain (almost) that there must also be planets that were ejected in processes similar to our solar system development. This evidence, inferred from the theoretical model, together with evidence of nearby stars whose motions are relatively erratic, as discussed in Chapter 12, indicate that they have nonradiating companions of masses comparable to that of our major planets. This is highly suggestive that virtually half the stars in our galaxy have solar systems like ours. There is one other bit of evidence that we ought to consider at this time. Table 12.3 was discussed in relationship to the rotational velocities of stars. It indicates that stars of spectral class G and lower show substantially very little rotation, whereas the earlier type stars O, B, and A show enormous rotation. Could this not be due to the fact that these later type stars have developed their solar systems and, consequently, have ejected DEBs and lost their angular momentum? I think so. From this, one can be a little more sure that it is the G, K, and M stars that are the most likely candidates for planetary systems in our galaxy. Previously, scientists had postulated that no more than ten percent of the stars in the galaxy might have solar systems. Based on *this* analysis, the number is more like fifty percent.

What are the chances that these solar systems are similar to our own? We can be sure that their planetary spacings would be given by Bode's law. Would there be one planet there which is similar to the earth? We don't know.

There are still a series of unanswered questions which have not yet been explored, and which, hopefully, some of our readers may take up. These include the following:

1. Detailed steps by which the fission process proceeds.
2. The ejection process; what causes the trigger, the instability?
3. The mechanism by which the protoplanets are ejected from the core and why they have different masses. Why are the initial protoplanets heavy, whereas the last four are much smaller in mass? (Why is this situation reversed with Jupiter's satellites?)

One might expect that the first set of ejected planets are more massive because the stellar core was far more massive. Then, as the core mass decreased, the size of the protoplanets might somehow decrease as well. The present masses of most of the planets do not give an accurate value of their initial masses, since the major planets were undergoing fission processes themselves.

The Moon (and Speculation)

There was a dramatic event subsequent to Jupiter's birth. The next scheduled planet ended up, instead, with its internal fragments (the asteroid belt) in orbit instead of itself. Maybe this catastrophic fate befell the planet Moon!!! At one particular stage in the protosun development, there was a dramatic change-over from large planetary mass to small mass ejection. It would be intriguing to explore whether the breakup at or near the protosun surface of the lost planet (moon??) (between the births of Jupiter and Mars) is exhibited by other mature star systems in the galaxy, i.e., whether indeed the third planet out from another stellar system contains an earthlike planet together with its "captured" moon. The chances are that this capture is a rather unusual and rare event.

The Moon Capture Hypothesis

The capture of a planet by another planet is presumably more readily accomplished inside a protostar than outside. Protoplanets can interact there with the stellar core magnetic field, increasing their velocity by having their ejected protons interact with the plasma environment. Consequently, it allows for some flexibility in their orbital paths, until they reach the protosun's surface.

Let us proceed with the assumption that the moon is that "lost asteroid planet" and speculate on its possible implications. Why did the moon fail to achieve orbital velocity and therefore miss being placed in orbit subsequent to one of the nova explosions? It returned back to the center (in a manner similar to what is exhibited by the present sunspots) of the protosun. Could it be that it received a few "fatal" impacts from high velocity DEBs either on their outward or return trip back to the sun? These impacts might have been sufficient to allow hot material from the inside, rotating "fluid" core to escape from the moon, resulting in the ejection of hot molten material (iron meteorites) which comprise the asteroids (see Figs. 6.4 and 6.5) and the large holes within the iron meteorites. The irony of this proposed scenario would be that we may have had lunar core samples long before the Apollo missions. There was some ejected material which did achieve orbital velocity, and thus constituted the asteroid debris.

Moon's Magnetism

Suprising evidence of ancient remnant magnetism, associated with some of the returned lunar samples is certainly consistent with this proposed lunar history. The moon once had a "live" liquid, fast-rotating core, just as the earth still has today. The lunar mass was at least one or perhaps two orders of magnitude greater initially. The substantial loss of its core (thus a greatly reduced internal energy source) would have stunted any geological development (such as the earth's tectonic history).

288

One should also take note that there was a recent discovery by Arrhenius of remnant magnetism in certain meteorites. This is strongly suggestive that this particular meteorite was once part of a planet or DEB.

Moon's Relevance to Life (and Some Philosophy)

The moon's role in the cause for tides was already discussed (Chapter 4). Did the moon possibly play a more important role in the first half billion year history of the earth? Would its possible meteorite shielding role have been significant? It seems unlikely, because of its smaller mass. (The far side of the moon looks more peppered with craters than does the near side, perhaps more of the near side craters were covered by lava flow.) Who knows?

The point I wish to explore is this: if the moon, indeed, is necessary for the evolution of life on earth (uncertain, but a subject worthy of study), then its capture by the earth involves a rather complex series of events. The probability of all this happening by chance is exceedingly low. Why did Mars not capture the moon, for instance? (Assuming of course that the original asteroid hypothesis is correct.) A low probability argues for a low probability of other solar systems having a similar Earth-Moon system, and maybe a reduced probability for life. Or the other conclusion: there must be far more preplanning and structure in the Universe than has been recognized (or admitted) by other scientists. It is far more likely that there exists cosmic intelligence on a grand scale than that there is utter chaos and no rhyme nor reason for all this vast complex array of organized matter, energy, molecules, and (limited) intelligent life.

Other Astronomical Phenomena Interpreted Via Johnson's Model: Neutron Stars and Supernovas

Supernovas are so drastic in their explosions that presumably the gases already built up around the star are removed by the nova process. Hence, the core of the star becomes visible. This is an unusual and very happy event for us, since it allows study of the inside of a star. Present theories are most likely incorrect in postulating that a neutron star is the end product, from the collapse of the rest of a star. The core of the star is the beginning, and all stars have such neutron cores. Once the outside gas is gone, the detailed phenomena associated with the core itself become visible. One such manifestation is the radiation that is emitted from some structural elements that still remain associated with the core and its immediate environment. This might be an inner-circle of DEBs that revolves close to the neutron core at enormous speeds. Each of the DEBs, as was discussed previously, is radioactively hot, and will emit electrons and protons. The core is also spinning and has its own very high intensity magnetic field. The electrons that are generated from the rotating DEBs are rotating in the core's magnetic field. Consequently, they will generate electromagnetic radiation known as a synchrotron radiation. The whole process is very similar to the operation of a giant magnetron.

Some of the enigmas which are not now understood regarding pulsars become simpler with this model. Even the interpulse of the pulsar NP 0532 begins to make sense, particularly since it is not symmetrically placed with respect to the main pulse. The subpulses "wandering across" would be DEBs that are loosened up from their bundle or swarm, as they are revolving around the neutron core. The DEBs are also spinning around their own axis, so that the ejected DEB electrons will make different orbital paths consistent with the DEB's spin and magnetic fields. The DEBs revolve about the central core and rotate simultaneously. The plane of the emitted electromagnetic radiation would, consequently, rotate, which would account for the observed polarization changes seen in the electromagnetic pulse emission structure, Figure 14.7. In fact, one can now work backwards and deduce the spinning rate of the DEBs from the rotating polarization vector. Electromagnetic radiation is being generated all the time, while the DEBs are circulating and emitting electrons. However, the beam that we intercept (or is projected towards us) gets generated only within a certain time slot or portion of the DEB's orbit. The rest of the radiation is beamed throughout the rest of the universe. There is a possible related mechanism at work in our solar system. Jupiter emits radio radiation which is controlled by its innermost satellite, Io. Perhaps this is giving us a clue as to how pulsars operate.

Interstellar Molecules

As we mentioned previously, all molecules, so necessary for life are generated from the DEBs. The larger and more stable molecules will be formed first, condense out the earliest, and also survive the longest. The lighter diatomic molecules, or radicals, such as CH, CN, CH, and Na atoms would leave the DEBs and enter the vast interstellar medium, whereas the heavier molecules would be bound gravitationally to the mother DEBs. Since the DEBs are radioactive for thousands of years subsequent to their birth, their ejected electrons and protons would continually cause the breakup of some of the bigger molecules and excite molecules and atoms to higher electronic states. This is the mechanism whereby the so-called interstellar molecules and minimolecules become excited. The DEBs would also still be hot enough (temperature-wise) to be in the 200° to 600°K range, which might be sufficient for excitation of molecules by the infrared pumping mechanism. The DEBs would be the biggest source of interstellar infrared radiation, a phenomena exhibited in various parts of the galaxy.

Extinction and Reddening

The DEBs would be responsible for the actual blocking of starlight (**extinction**). The loose, fluffy, snowlike structures associated with the tail of the DEB or, more picturesquely put, the Saturn-like ring configuration, would be very effective in scattering starlight. Scattered starlight removes the blue components preferentially, resulting in more reddish transmitted light (the so-called reddening effect). Polarization would be caused by reflection, as discussed previously.

Thus, regions which look very dusty and obscured in the galaxy are not (as was previously hoped) where stars are born, but where they already have formed and have developed planetary systems.

The Earth

In order to form a simple check on the DEB model, it was decided to see whether the continents could be fitted together on the size of a globe which would correspond to the original diameter of the earth, 3,440 kilometers. Indeed, within a few percent, the continents do overlap, as can be seen from the series of Figures 7.9, 7.10, and 7.11. The construction of this (original earth) globe and the matching of the continents was not accomplished with the precision with which Africa and South America had been matched previously by others using computer analysis. The model is a first order attempt, whose results, however, seem extremely gratifying.

We now have a chance to check this model in more detail, because some of the continental margins are touching on areas which previously were not considered. Parts of the original land masses had never before been combined: they obviously would not "touch" on the present size of the earth's diameter!! The DEB model can, in part, be substantiated by careful geologic matching of adjacent land masses since, if the original size of the earth was indeed the size of the present liquid core (3,440 km in radius, $\frac{1}{1.86}$ of present diameter), then it must have originated inside the sun in order to account for the large internal energy necessary for expanding the earth to its present size. Thus, instead of going back 200,000,000 years, we have attempted to go back about 4,000.000,000 years. Since the earth is close at hand, it still offers the easiest, readily available evidence concerning theories on the origin of the solar system. (There are many billion tons of rocks available for study; slightly more than the precious 800 pounds returned from the moon.)

The New Cosmological Picture—The Origin of Life in the Solar System

What emerges from this model is that the evolutionary paths in the universe are not from disorganization to organization, but the other way around. Highly organized, condensed structure at the core of the stars develops (see Figure 18.16). They explode and evolve, and they, in turn, project structures which evolve. Then some of those secondary structures, in turn, interact with the primary structures and so forth. This is the development pattern for stars, planets, and comets. It is very likely that the galaxies developed in a similar manner from even more complicated compact structures.

Now, if we want to extend this analogy one step further, perhaps the original "Big Bang" was not as is presently supposed, a hot gas and/or energy cloud, but a highly organized structure that also broke up into smaller organized substructures in an organized systematic manner. None of these discussions have any time frames associated with them (yet). So far, one can only attempt to measure and extrapolate time locally, using solar system radioactive nuclear clocks as references.

With the construction of organic molecules and water on the DEBs, and their subsequent bombardment of the planets at many stages during the first few billion years of the planet's existence, it was almost predetermined that the probability be high for "life" processes to start. A richness of molecules was already *prefabricated* on the DEBs. It was, therefore, not too difficult to get very primitive life started. Porphyrins must be important starting molecules. Present theories suppose that organic molecules are made from occasional lightning discharges in a reducing atmosphere. True, it is possible to make molecules by this means, but it is a relatively very inefficient process which would result in far *too few molecules* being generated. (Too little lightning.)

The mechanism being proposed here has the capability of generating billions of tons of organic molecules, and, what is more important, placing these molecules and the water on the planets at many times during their early existence, thus assuring that some aspects of life would get started, some of the time. When a variety of different competing processes are possible, the ones that have the highest efficiency will obviously dominate the evolutionary direction enumerated here. Using DEBs as the production site of organic molecules, seems to me to be far more efficient. Furthermore, there are many more places (billions) where this chemical development occurred, assuring adequate redundancy in the manufacturing and delivery system. Moreover, with the developments of DEBs from Jupiter and Saturn, *two* back-up systems were supplied for this production and delivery.

Summary

As we are looking at the Andromeda nebula, Figure 18.20, which is a galaxy very similar to our own galaxy, just a mere million light years away, we might ponder on the mystery of life in the universe. Our sun, one of a hundred billion stars, is not alone in its development, based on this model. Almost every star of similar spectral class would have a solar system like our own. It would have planets, obeying a Bode's type law. Since the laws of physics are universal, the laws of chemistry are universal. The chemicals will be virtually identical on all these planets. Whether or not life as we know it will develop, is not easily answered. However, since the laws of

292

biology are based on chemistry, we may have better answers in the future. The chances are that life will have developed everywhere. If there is one thing that we have learned in our history lesson, it is that we have continually underestimated the rest of the universe and grossly overestimated our own importance. We exist on a little planet associated with an ordinary star. Other life has developed in the galaxy and we (man) have only just emerged during the last few decades or so. We have discovered only a small fraction of what really is going on in the universe, and that during the last few years. What are the chances of other civilizations being more advanced than ours? The chances, I would say, are exceedingly high. I believe we are not alone and this is an opinion that is shared by other scientists as well. If we are not alone, do more advanced civilizations have superior knowledge of astronomy and physics, and are there laws that we still do not understand or comprehend? These questions would unnerve most scientists, because the answer to it must be in the affirmative. Based on our slowly emerging feeble understanding of the universe, it is incredible to suppose that others would not know much more than we do. However, this is a rather disconcerting admission.

I am, consequently, inclined to believe that we should pay a great deal more attention to UFO sightings, since there is a very good probability that they may be real, and that, indeed, we may be under study, but perhaps are considered far too backward to bother with establishing a two-way communication. Remember the following two analogies: in the nineteenth century it was considered impossible for meteorites to have come from outer space (see p. 106). Prior to fifteen years ago, organic molecules within these meteorites was considered an absurdity.

I anticipate that, within the next decade, the UFO phenomena will be acknowledged to be real, and more serious discussions will ensue regarding their nature and origin. I believe that the phenomena deserve far more serious scientific study than is presently afforded on all fronts.

Conclusion

There are many mysteries for which there are no answers. Where did all the initial material and/or energy come from? If, as it now seems, there had to be structure and organization to begin with, how did that get there? At this point astronomers usually refer to philosophy and religion; maybe this is what it would take.

It is hard to comprehend that all this should have happened for no apparent reason or by sheer chance; that life is just an accident, like ships passing in the night travelling aimlessly on the oceans of space-time. That is very hard to believe. There must be a deeper significance, a more profound mystery and significance that lies beyond what is expounded in this book. It remains for the next generation, however, to explore and carry the solution further.

Again, let us ask: Could all this have happened by chance? One can calculate the probability of each of the necessary steps leading to life to have happened purely by random chance. (Example: what is the probability that a monkey would type out an exact replica of the Bible by randomly pressing the keys of a typewriter? How long would it take, assuming he kept going indefinitely? The answer: It exceeds the lifetime of the solar system!!) If everything in the universe were to have happened by pure chance, there would not be enough time available to arrive at the present state of development. A very sobering thought.

Einstein did not believe that the Almighty plays dice with the Universe. Most scientists today believe in dice (chance). There is room for dice at the local level (Nevada) within narrow confines, but certainly not for the grand picture. I think, that Einstein, as usual, has a high probability of being correct.

Figure 18.20. The Andromeda Galaxy (M 31). (The satellite galaxies NGC 205 and 221 can also be seen in this photograph, Lick Observatories).

This is one of our neighbor galaxies about a million light years distant. Light from its brightest stars are recorded in this photo.

Examine this picture carefully. We assume that our galaxy will look very similar when studied from a comparable distance.

Our sun, one of the 10^{11} stars in our galaxy, together with its complement of planets, constitutes but a miniscule point on such a scale. There are many billions of such galaxies. All moving away from each other in a mad rush.

Should we assume that all this came about just for *our* benefit only? Do we dare to be so egocentric?

There, most likely, is an enormous amount of intelligence all over the universe. Contrary to everyone's impression, there may even be some, somewhere on this small earth. We are not alone.

Thank you for joining me on the last trip of our universal tour.

TECHNICAL NOTES—
THE NITTY GRITTY SECTION

Introduction to Technical Notes

The purpose of placing some of the more complicated material in the appendix is to allow the more dedicated, and perhaps more adventuresome, student to tackle material presented in earlier chapters in greater depth, using the familiar tools of algebra, some easy equations, and a little physics.

Regard the equations and the algebraic symbols contained within them as merely shorthand devices for expressing relationships between various physical quantities. One can, if needed, always express these relationships in words.

Some students in college today are unfortunately panicked by mathematics or algebra, which is probably a reaction to their earlier unhappy encounter with the subject in elementary and high schools.

Mathematics is a language and a tool whose concise principles and rules can be readily mastered, once they have been adequately explained.

One does not require complicated mathematics to understand nor to express ideas of cosmology and the physical principles discussed in this course. The tendency of some authors in astronomy has been to eliminate equations completely.

These technical notes are to encourage gifted and inquiring students to try their hand at some of the important principles involved.

Like music, food, and many of the other good things in life, it takes an acquired taste to appreciate them. There is a great sense of aesthetic beauty and elegance associated with the simple equations that are given here. Think of them as masterpieces of human thought, as a Rembrandt, as a Leonardo da Vinci. They epitomize and encapsulate concepts that have taken thousands of years to develop and mature and to finally reach this stage.

Tech. Note No. 1

Simple Mathematics Review

Abbreviations for Big and Small Numbers

$\log_{10} N$	N	N	N
-6	10^{-6}	$\dfrac{1}{10^6}$	$\dfrac{1}{1,000,000}$
-4	10^{-4}	$\dfrac{1}{10^4}$	$\dfrac{1}{10,000}$
-2	10^{-2}	$\dfrac{1}{10^2}$	$\dfrac{1}{100}$
0	10^0	1	
1	10^1	10	
3	10^3	$1,000$	one thousand
6	10^6	$1,000,000$	one million
9	10^9	$1,000,000,000$	one billion
11	10^{11}	eleven zeros (hundred billion)	

Review *Some Algebra:*

If $\dfrac{A}{B} = \dfrac{C}{D}$ then, $A \times D = C \times B$

$$\text{or } D = \frac{C \times B}{A}$$

and $\dfrac{A + B}{B} = \dfrac{C + D}{D}$

Check this with simple numbers.

Example:

$$\frac{1}{2} \equiv \frac{2}{4}$$

then

$$\frac{1 + 2}{2} \equiv \frac{2 + 4}{4}$$

Tech. Note No. 2

Fundamental Constants and Astronomical Data

Mass of Proton = 1.672661×10^{-24} g = 1.00727 amu

Mass energy of unit atomic mass (Mc^2) = 1.49241×10^{-3} erg

$$= 931.481 \text{ MeV} = 9.3148 \times 10^8 \text{ eV}$$

Photon wavelength associated with 1 eV	λ_o	= 1.2398×10^{-8} cm
Energy of 1 eV	E_o	= 1.602192×10^{-12} erg
Speed of light	c	= 2.997925×10^{10} cm/s
Gravitational constant	G	= 6.670×10^{-8} dyne cm^2 g^{-2}
Planck constant	h	= 6.62620×10^{-27} erg/sec
(Radiation) Stefan-Boltzmann constant	σ	= 5.66956×10^{-5} erg cm^{-2} deg^{-4} sec^{-1}
Boltzmann constant	k	= 1.38062×10^{-16} erg deg^{-1}
Joule equivalent	J	= 4.1854 joule cal^{-1}
Avagadro number	N	= 6.02217×10^{23} mole^{-1}
Mass of Sun	$M_\odot$	= 1.989×10^{33} gram
Radius of Sun	$R_\odot$	= 6.9599×10^{10} cm
Surface Area of Sun	A	= 6.087×10^{22} cm^2
Luminosity of Sun	$L_\odot$	= 3.826×10^{33} ergs sec^{-1}
		= 3.826×10^{26} watts

10^7 erg sec^{-1} = 1 watt = 1 Joule per sec

10^7 erg = 1 Joule

Mass of Earth	$M_\oplus$	= 5.976×10^{27} gram
Mean radius of Earth	$R_\oplus$	= 6,371 km
Surface area of earth	$S_\oplus$	= 5.1×10^{18} cm^2

Heat flow from inside earth (at surface) = 5.9×10^{-6} watt cm^{-2}

Surface temperature gradient $= 2 \times 10^{-4}$ °K/cm

Earth central temperature (extrapolated from the temperature gradient) = 1.2×10^5 °K. Equivalent temperature, see text for interpretation.

Mass of Moon	$= \frac{1}{81} M_\oplus = 7.35 \times 10^{25}$ gram
Heat flow from inside moon (at surface)	1×10^{-6} watts cm^{-2}
Radius of moon	1,738 km
Wavelength unit	1 Å (Angstrom) = 10^{-8} cm

Tropical year = 365 d 5hrs 48 min 46 sec = 3.15569×10^7 sec

Sidereal year = 365 d 6 hrs 9 min 10 sec

Tech. Note No. 3

Foucault Pendulum

Latitude	sin (latitude)	Period of Rotation	
		$= \dfrac{23 \text{ hrs. } 56 \text{ min.}}{\sin \text{ (lat.)}}$	
Degrees		Hours	Minutes
5	.087	275	5
10	.174	137	32
15	.259	92	54
20	.342	70	0
25	.423	56	35
30	.500	47	52
34 L.A.	.559	42	49
35	.574	41	42
40	.643	37	13
45	.707	33	51
50	.766	31	14
90	1.000	23 hrs.	56 min.

Tech. Note No. 4

The Inverse Square Law

The Principle: All effects or manifestations resulting from symmetrical ejection (or radiation or fields) from a point source, obey the inverse square law relationship; i.e., all such effects diminish in intensity in inverse proportion to the distance squared.

Algebraically, if the strength of the effect is I, then

$$I \propto \frac{1}{d^2}$$

Where the symbol of proportionality is expressed thus: $\propto$
Examples:

1. The **light intensity** I, at distance d from a light point source is: $I \propto \dfrac{1}{d^2}$

   This applies to light bulbs, as well as to the stars.

2. **Newton Law of Gravity:**
   The force of attraction between masses M_1 and M_2 is inversely proportional to the distance squared between them

   $$F \propto \frac{1}{d^2}$$

3. **Electric fields:** same relationship.

4. **Nuclear radiation:** same relationship.

A simple example: If this seems difficult, consider the

example of a *self-ejecting money tree.* Suppose this tree ejects pennies at a uniform rate, equally in **all** directions. Imagine you are 10 feet from such a tree and collect in your hat 36 pennies per minute. You see pennies flying out in all directions and naturally become a little greedy. You wish to collect more. You decide to proceed to a distance of 20 feet. Doubling your distance; you will collect:

$$\frac{36}{2^2} = \frac{9 \text{ pennies}}{\text{per minute}}$$

(Check your hat and verify the number.)

Next, you proceed to 30 feet, tripling your distance. The expected number of pennies reduces to:

$$\frac{36}{3^2} = 4 \text{ pennies per minute.}$$

Catch on? That's how the inverse square law works. The moral of the story is:

> If you want more, of money free,
> Get closer to the money tree!!

Tech. Note No. 5

Properties of Ellipse and Planetary Motion

The Figures 5.1 and 5.2 show various conic sections derived by slicing pieces of a solid cone. It is shown here to exhibit possible geometrical shapes. It so happens that the ellipse, parabola, hyperbola, and the circle are all possible orbits or trajectories involved with motion under the influence of gravity. (The actual slicing shown is irrelevant to orbital motion. It may tend to give the erroneous impression of astronomical cut-up!)

For the more sophisticated reader, we shall list all the gory algebraic relationships applicable for orbital motions.

First, why all the geometric shapes? Under the influence of a central massive object, such as the sun, an object may travel in an ellipse (as all planets do) or circle in almost parabolic orbits (as some of the more distant comets do). If we get visited by an object from far out, say from another star, a possible trajectory would be hyperbolic. Astronomers have long sought after such (diabolic) hyperbolic orbits in comets, alas, without success.

Now, let's get down to the elliptical orbits only, as applied to the planets.

The largest distance across the ellipse is called the major axis. It is 2a in length. The minor axis (the shortest distance across) is 2b in length. The eccentricity of an ellipse, e, is a measure of its shape. It is defined as follows:

$$b = a\sqrt{1 - e^2}$$

When an ellipse is close to being circular, e is close to

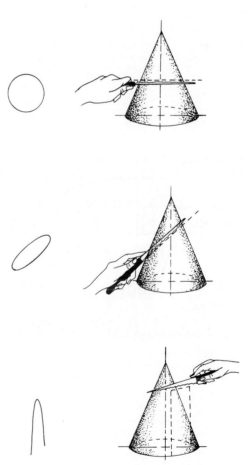

Figure TN. 5.1. Conic sections. The various shapes are generated by slicing sections in various directions in the cone. See also Figure TN. 5.2.

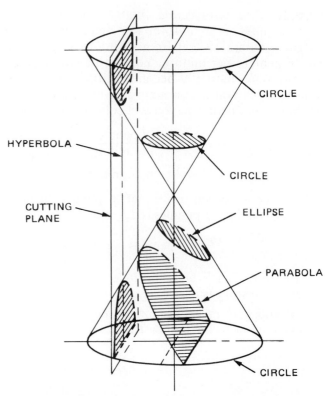

Figure TN. 5.2. The various conic sections generated by slicing a cone along different directions. Each conic section happens to have an application in the dynamic motion of masses in a gravitational field. The ellipse shown in Figure TN. 5.3 is the most useful in planetary motions.

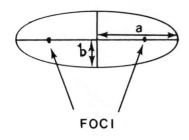

Figure TN. 5.3. The ellipse. Semimajor axis—a. Semiminor axis b.

zero. In fact, if e = o, b = a and we have a circle. As e approaches unity, the ellipse becomes progressively elongated at its waist. At e = 1, we have a parabola. For e > 1, we have hyperbolas.

Now, we shall list the properties associated with orbital motion of a body of mass, m, about the governing central mass, M (the sun, for example).

Let a be the semi-major axis of the ellipse (for the earth this is I.A.U.).

r = distance from sun to planet, at any point in orbit.

v = velocity of planet, relative to sun.

Then, the angular momentum of a planet is

$$J = m \sqrt{a(1 - e^2) \, G \, (M + m)}$$

Total energy, E, of planet is

$$E = -\frac{GMm}{2a} = 1/2 \, mv^2 - \frac{GMm}{r}$$

Note that both the total energy and its angular momentum stay the same for all time, provided m, M, and a remain unchanged.

Other useful quantities are the closest distance to the sun perihelion = a(1 − e), and the furthest distance, aphelion is a(1 + e).

300

Tech. Note No. 6

Energy, Work, Conversion Units

The energy field incorporates many disciplines, each with its own set of units (our heritage from the nineteenth century). Consequently, keeping Figure 9.1 in mind, it is important to convert from one form to another effortlessly.

This technical note is designed to help you move from one form of energy to another as smoothly as a money-changer changes currency in a European airport.

1 British Thermal Unit (B.T.U.)

Unit of Energy

$= 2.930 \times 10^{-4}$ kilowatt hours
$= 0.2930$ watt hour
$= 3.9292 \times 10^{-4}$ horsepower hour
$= 1054.8$ Joules
$= 778$ foot-pounds
$= 252$ calories
$= 1.055 \times 10^{10}$ ergs

The original definition of the B.T.U. is the amount of heat required to heat 1 lb. of water 1°F.

---

1 *Foot-pound*

Unit of Work

$= 3.766 \times 10^{-7}$ kilowatt hour
$= 5.05 \times 10^{-7}$ horsepower hour
$= 3.7662 \times 10^{-4}$ watt hour

---

1 gram calorie $= 4.185$ Joules

Heat required to raise 1 cc
of water by 1°C(at 15°C)

$$\begin{matrix} \text{Force} \\ \text{(in dynes)} \end{matrix} \times \begin{matrix} \text{distance} \\ \text{(cm)} \end{matrix} = \begin{matrix} \text{Work} \\ \text{(ergs)} \end{matrix}$$

$$10^7 \text{ ergs} = 1 \text{ Joule}$$

Rate of doing work: 1 Joule per second = 1 watt

$$\text{i.e.,} \left(\frac{\text{Joules}}{\text{Time in seconds}} \right) = \text{watt}$$

Newton's law of gravity in c.g.s. (cm-gram-second) units, measures the force between mass objects in units of *dynes*, if the masses are in grams and G is also in c.g.s. units.

Power is the rate of doing work or the rate at which energy is expended.

$$\text{Power} = \frac{\text{Energy}}{\text{Time}}$$

1 Horse Power $= 550$ foot-pounds per second
$= 42.418$ B.T.U. per minute
$= 745.7$ watts

Voltage (Volts) $\times$ Current (Amperes) = Electrical Power (watts)

301

Suggestion: Since engineers and scientists use a large variety of units, standardization in units is recommended: The use of Joules and watts may be the most useful.

Example: A 1 H.P. electric motor (if 100% efficient) should deliver this much mechanical power.

Its electric power = 745.7 watts

At 110 Volts, it uses $\dfrac{745.7}{110}$ = 6.78 Amperes

Tech. Note No. 7

Useful Numbers, Energy, Land Areas, etc.

1 gallon = 3.785×10^3 cc
1 acre = 43,560 sq. ft.
1 acre = 4×10^7 sq. in.
Mass of ocean water = 1.42×10^{24} gram

Water requirements:

1 person requires 2,000 gallons/day or 7×10^6 cc per day. (Not all is for drinking! Water is mainly needed for growing food.)

Population of 4 billions requires:

$4 \times 10^9 \times 7 \times 10^6 = 2.8 \times 10^{16}$ cubic cm of water per day.

Total* amount of water from rain and run-off = 3.6×10^{17} cc

Thus, world population water requirements seem to approach 10% of total circulating supply!!

Tech. Note No. 8

Supplement to Energy

The Second Law of Thermodynamics can be written in terms of the **input temperature** (T_1) and the **output temperatures** (T_2) of a heat engine, where the temperatures are expressed in absolute units (°Kelvin).

The best possible theoretical efficiency, η, known as the **Carnot efficiency** is given by

$$\eta = \frac{T_1 - T_2}{T_1}$$

This implies that when the input and output temperatures are equal, the engine ceases to work! Everyone knows that. However, the best efficiencies are obtained by increasing the input temperatures as high as possible, or by lowering T_2 as low as possible. ($T_1 - T_2$) has to be maximized.

Example: $T_1 = 327°C = 327° + 273° = 600°K$
$T_2 = 27°C = 27°C + 273° = 300°K$

*Of this total only a fraction is used (or available) for agriculture.

302

The best possible theoretical efficiency

$$\eta = \frac{600 - 300}{600} \times 100\% = 50\%$$

Steam engines are, therefore, operated with superheated steam and approach practical efficiencies of about 40%.

Now, here comes the surprise in the Second Law of Thermodynamics: If the engine has only 40% efficiency, what happens to the remaining 60%?

It exhausts as heat. That's why power generators are always close to water reservoirs, oceans, or rivers in order to "dump" this excess heat. Is it necessary to dump the heat? Of course not. But who cares to design an integrated system that utilizes this excess heat, for example, for hot water home use? It would require planning and plumbing and would result in a better utilization of precious energy (which is presently being wasted). There are an infinite variety of manufacturing or chemical processing operations, such as distillation, which require heat. Does anyone consider combining power plants with chemical or manufacturing plants? Of course not. Each is in business for himself and the cost can always be passed on—so far.

"Waste" heat could be used in the manufacture of methyl alcohol—which would constitute a breeder-type reaction. The otherwise lost heat would produce potential new fossil fuel. One could also use the heat for water (purification) distillation, i.e., production of drinking water from salt water (desalinization).

There is no law on the books or in physics that mandates waste of precious fuel.

The energy waste has a corresponding counterpart in food waste (which is also a form of energy). In the food distribution chain, from producer to consumer, there is a 20-50% loss of (life-giving) food. Food losses result from spoilage, damage by rats, locusts, etc. This figure does not include the food wasted by a large fraction of the well-fed consumers.

With proper planning, the food chain (even the wasted kind) can, in principle, be recycled. Not so with the hydrocarbon fuel, which, on burning, is converted to carbon dioxide. The plants cannot absorb all the excess CO_2 in their processing.

Tech. Note No. 9

TABLE A
Heats of Combustion

Coal gas	600 BTU/ft.^{3}
Natural gas	1,000-2,500 BTU/ft.^{3}
Coal	1,100-1,400 BTU/lb.
Ethyl alcohol	14,000 BTU/lb.
Fuel oil	20,000 BTU/lb.
Hydrogen	100,000 BTU/lb.

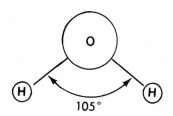

Figure TN. 10.1. The water molecule.

Figure TN. 10.2. Hubbard Glacier, Alaska (photo U.S. Dept. of the Interior, Geologic Survey).

Water—The Magic Fluid of Life

Man takes a great deal for granted. The more common the substance, the less it is appreciated. Wait until you don't have any water, though; your body will quickly let you know of its absence! Ancient prayers (still used today) always include a request for dew and rain—if your life depends on it, you tend to pay slightly more attention to the subject, that is *relevant* astronomy.

In a previous discussion, the role of the sun in driving the hydrological cycle was discussed. Here we wish to concentrate on the intrinsic physical properties of the water, and why each one of them is essential for the processes of life.

H_2O. The molecule of water, as everyone knows, is composed of two atoms of hydrogen and one of oxygen. From an astronomical point of view, we can appreciate the universal abundance of water, since hydrogen is *the* most abundant element in the universe, and oxygen is not far behind (Table 6.12). The *bent* structure of the water molecule gives it a **polar** nature (in analogy with a magnet having a north and south pole). This gives water some unusual properties. However, one of the most unique properties of liquid water, not shared by any common substance, is its ability to expand on freezing. This property alone is what allows life to function, since, otherwise, ice would sink to the bottom of a lake or ocean and, eventually, no life could have survived in the water. It would have frozen from the bottom up. Ice has a density of about 0.9. Being less than 1, it floats on water, allowing aquatic life to continue below the ice.

Water exists in three possible forms: solid (ice), liquid, and vapor (gas). The earth has all three forms present at the same time and water changes its state from one form to another continually. The hydrological cycle involves all three possible states and, in fact, our life very much depends on water performing these changes. Let's examine this a little deeper.

If we take some water in the laboratory and place it in a cylinder, where we could monitor its temperature and the pressure in the water as well as the pressure around it, and then change conditions of pressure and temperature, we would get a set of curves as shown in Figure 10.4, where the lines indicate a set of stable conditions between any two states. Examine the figure carefully. For water to be in *liquid* form, not only must its *temperature* be within a certain range, but also its *pressure*. This has a lot of practical significance. If you boil water at a location where the atmospheric pressure is lower, for instance, Mexico City or Machupicho, Peru, water will not boil at 100°C but considerably lower. On top of Mt. Everest, where the atmospheric pressure is about 300 millibars, the boiling point of water would be about 70°C, not hot enough to boil your eggs adequately. It also means that at such low pressures, the sun's heat can more easily vaporize liquid water, which then becomes our familiar clouds. Note from Figure 10.4 that if at low pressure the temperature were to be dropped, the water vapor would become solid, i.e., snow or ice, depending on its dispersion and density. The transition at low pressures is *directly* from gas to solid without going through the liquid phase. In another pressure range, water can cross the boundary between gas and liquid curve T-C. To cross from solid to liquid it has to cross the D-T line in the figure. At one and only one unique pressure and temperature can water exist in all three phases simultaneously. This point is known as the triple point, T. It is at a temperature of 273.16°K and pressure of 4.58 Torr. (1 Torr is the pressure equivalent of 1 mm of Hg.) Examine the line T-D, which is the solid-liquid equilibrium line. The slope of this line is negative—it leans backwards slightly. So what? Well, this is one of the unique properties of water, not shared by other substances. What does it mean? It means that if one applies pressure to ice which is at the temperature of the triple point or slightly below, the ice will melt. Figure 10.2 shows some examples of galciers which can be observed to slide over some very rough terrain at the bottom of its ice surface. How can these glaciers move? The answer is the *negative* slope of the T-D line. Ice melts under pressure, and this offers the necessary lubrication for the glaciers. The same property allows ice skating. The pressure exerted via your body weight on the ice skates and against the ice makes the ice melt and creates a small amount of water at the interface, allowing you to glide gracefully across the ice surface. If this property of water were otherwise, your skates would freeze fast to the ice.

Where else does this property of water perhaps play an important role? Maybe on Mars. The vapor pressure in the Martian atmosphere is low at the present time. There seems to be evidence of solid ice, as well as solid carbon dioxide near the polar caps. One method by which liquid water could exist, therefore, would be below the surface of the glaciers at the ground-glacier interface. Another thing to keep in mind about the liquid water problem on earth, as well as on Mars, is this: Water is in liquid form on earth whenever the atmospheric pressure is in the right range *and* the right pressure range is provided by gases of nitrogen and oxygen, *not* water vapor. Hence, for water to exist in liquid form on Mars, all one would need is occassional emission or outgassing of sufficient quantity of gas, of any kind, to bring the atmospheric pressure above the triple point of 4.58 Torr. The measurements taken by Mariner 9, indicate a pressure on Mars not too far below the triple point; hence, it should be fairly easy to achieve the liquid condition on Mars, since the mean temperature near Mars' equator is certainly adequate, about 50°F. Why all the fuss about water on Mars? First of all, there is a great deal of geologic erosion, like Mars' Grand Canyons, for instance, which obviously requires the presence

Figure TN. 10.3. The Magic Fluid—*Water.* Auburn—Folsom South Unit, near Sacramento, California (photo U.S. Bureau of Reclamation).

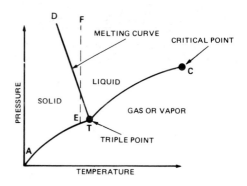

Figure TN. 10.4. A schematic diagram of the important properties of water as a function of temperature and pressure, indicating the various equilibrium states. Note that the melting curve DT is sloping towards the left, which is rather unusual, compared to other compounds. See text.

of water. Then there is the speculation and hope that perhaps life could have started on Mars as well. We know that one of the conditions for life as we know it is the presence of water.

Keep in mind, however, that a great deal of life at the lower evolutionary scale can exist with very little water, e.g., type Kaoline termites, to the consternation of southern California homeowners. These termites survive from water extracted from the moisture in the air. Nature has shown us on earth many unusual, but successful, adaptations of life to very dry and harsh conditions: deserts support a great diversity of living systems, including a species of rats (mammals) which survive without drinking a single drop of water. These rats obtain water from plants or internally, through body carbohydrate processing. This knowledge leads one to have an open mind about life on Mars. We may have an answer soon, but if the answer is negative, remember this: what are the chances of finding another human being if you were suddenly placed anywhere among the vast unpopulated regions of the world? (We are now 4 billion people, with at least 20% of the solid earth's surface uninhabited and inhospitable.)

Let's now examine some of the other properties of water. How much of it is there on earth? The table in Tech. Note No. 7 gives a rough indication of the distribution of water over the earth's surface (see also Fig. 9.9, p. 149). About 97% of all water is tied up in the oceans. The bulk of the remainder is in the form of ice. Only 1 part of water out of ~2,000 parts of ocean water is in the form of available fresh water, and only about 1/30 of all the fresh water is in the vapor state (including clouds). These numbers show how little fresh water is actually in *circulation* to sustain life. The ocean is an enormous, nondrinkable reservoir. The sun performs the vaporization, or distillation, process, thereby producing the pure water. (See discussion on hydrological cycle and Fig. 9.9.)

Solubility of water

The solubility of water is another property indispensible for life. Table A gives the major dissolved constituents in sea water. The ability of water to dissolve a large number of chemicals allows for erosion of the earth's surface, bringing essential chemicals and minerals with the flow of rivers into lakes and oceans, thus supporting life. Man's interference in these natural processes has immediate deleterious consequences, as for instance the construction of the Aswan Dam. This dam now prevents the previous flooding and nutrient-bearing lower Nile from fertilizing and "feeding" the ground and life in the previously fertile Nile delta.

The oceans can also dissolve solids or suspend colloidal particles. However, the most important property of water, which presently prevents our immediate demise from pollution, is the ocean's ability to absorb gases and wastes. Table B gives the dissolved gases in the ocean water. It is important to

TABLE A
The Major Dissolved Constituents of Sea Water

Ion	Percent
Cl	55.05
Na	30.61
SO_4	7.68
Mg	3.69
Ca	1.16
K	1.10
HCO_3	0.41
Br	0.19
H_3BO_3	0.07
Sr	0.03
P	0.00
Total	99.99

TABLE B
Dissolved Gases in Sea Water

	Concentration (cc/liter)
Oxygen	0—9
Nitrogen	8—15
Total carbon dioxide	34—56
Argon (residue after removal of N)	0.2—0.4
Helium and neon	1.7×10^{-4}
Hydrogen sulfide	variable

keep in mind that the oceans can only absorb a certain *finite quantity* of carbon dioxide (CO_2) before it begins to saturate them. The limit of the ocean will effect us if the continued burning of hydrocarbons, whose end products include CO_2, reach the ocean saturation stage. Once this saturation stage is reached, which can easily be calculated from known hydrocarbon burning rates, then the "fat is really in the fire" or, to put it more explicitly, "our goose is cooked."

With an increasing amount of vapors in the atmosphere, the amount of sunlight absorbed by the "greenhouse" effect would increase. Once the global temperature rises, the solubility of CO_2 in the oceans decreases (slowly at first), then the amount of water evaporated from the ocean would increase, which, in turn, would increase the solar greenhouse effect and increase the temperature even more. Once this "run-away" condition sets in, it would probably continue until all the glaciers and polar ice is melted (which would inundate all low-lying land masses, about 70% of the world's population). Then, with an increased water surface area, the evaporation of water would increase even more rapidly. Figure TN 10.5 is again pertinent for this discussion. With more vapor in the atmosphere, the pressure would also increase. This pessimistic scenario could more than likely come about within the next two centuries.

Let us discuss the global *Carbon Dioxide (CO$_2$) Problem* in more detail.*

First the facts. The measured CO_2 content in the atmosphere has been steadily increasing this century (Fig. TN 10.6). It seems to go up linearly as a result of fossil fuel burning. The steady increase indicates that our plant life cannot take up the increased CO_2 fast enough, nor do the oceans apparently take care of all the excess—otherwise, we should see a straight horizontal line in Figure TN 10.6; instead it goes up!! According to Fowler, CO_2 concentration was 290 ppm in the nineteenth century; it is projected to be 345 ppm by the year 2000—about an 18% increase. By that time, we will also have burned (ravaged) between 2 and 12% of our total fossil fuel reserves (there is uncertainty regarding the amount of reserves). Fowler projects that burning the rest would increase the CO_2 content in the atmosphere by as much as a factor of 4.

Examine the distribution of CO_2 in the biosphere. (Once all the oceans are evaporated, the atmospheric carbon [Table C] content would increase by a factor of 60, the earth's atmosphere would initially be mainly water vapor, however.)

Note that roughly comparable amounts of carbon are distributed between the atmosphere, living matter, and the top mixing layer of the ocean.

The sun, of course, interacts strongly with all three. Both the carbon and the hydrological cycle are most delicately coupled to the atmosphere. It is the functioning of the atmosphere which can be altered by very minute changes in its content and bring about major changes in our weather. This is called amplification. It appears that man's activities are now on such a sufficiently large scale that he can covertly or inadvertantly bring about major changes. Unfortunately, meteorology is not well enough understood to provide the firm analysis needed. By the time we understand what's going on, it will probably be too late.

There are already noticeable changes in the atmosphere's temperature. However, these changes may be only indicative of subtler changes in the chemistry and photochemical interactions in the upper atmosphere. There was an increase of 0.6°C in the atmosphere temperature from the nineteenth century to 1940. Since then it decreased by 0.2°C in the northern hemisphere. These temperature changes may not seem spectacular, but remember, the energy balance and reactions in the atmosphere are so delicate that a mere 1 or

*Reference: John M. Fowler, "Energy and the Environment," Mc-Graw Hill, 1975.

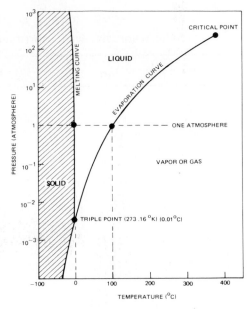

Figure TN. 10.5. An exact pressure-temperature diagram for water, showing the solid, liquid, and gas phases. Note the temperature and pressure ranges which permit water to exist in the three possible phases. Only at the triple point can it exist in all three, simultaneously. Since water is so important to life, its properties should be studied carefully.

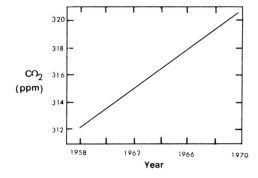

Figure TN. 10.6. The mean carbon dioxide (CO$_2$) yearly increase. The curve is based on 4 different earth locations. (Source: Report of the Study of Critical Environmental Problems, MIT Press, Mass.)

2% change in the energy available at the earth's surface can bring on a new ice age or melt the polar caps.

The atmosphere of the earth is clearly the "jugular" of the biosphere. We should obviously treat it with far greater respect and not tamper with it, unless its consequences are better understood.

TABLE C
The Carbon Reservoir*

Atmosphere	750 B tons
Oceans mixing layer	800 B tons
Living matter	1,740 B tons
Deep layers of ocean	43,500 B tons
Fossil fuel burning	4.4 B tons/year

*Data from J.W. Fowler.

Water, water, everywhere
And all the boards did shrink
Water, water, everywhere
Nor any drop to drink

The ice was here, the ice was there,
The ice was all around.
It cracked and growled and roared and howled,
Like noises in a swound!

The Rime of the Ancient Mariner
    Samuel T. Coleridge

TABLE D
A Few of Life's Key Constituents

Mass of atmosphere	5×10^{21} gram
Mass of CO_2 in atmosphere	2×10^{18} gram
Mass of H_2O in atmosphere	between $1 - 3 \times 10^{18}$ gram
Total fossil carbon (estimated)	7×10^{21} gram
Mass of O_2 in atmosphere	1×10^{21} gram
Recoverable carbon	$\sim 8 \times 10^{18}$ gram
Solubility of CO_2 in water	
at 20°C	1 gram per 500 liter of H_2O
at 60°C	$\sim 1/4$ gram per 500 liter of H_2O
Mass of ocean water	
(our reservoir)	1.5×10^{24} gram
Ocean area	3.6×10^{18} cm^2

About 14 meter depth of ocean water has the mass of the whole atmosphere. Roughly 3 meter depth is required to retain the circulating CO_2 supply in the ocean.

Incidently, weight of 4 billion people $\sim 2 \times 10^{14}$ gram (mostly H_2O). Thus people weight constitutes already 10^{-2}% of total atmospheric water content.

Your perspiration does not go unnoticed!

Tech. Note No. 11

Sun's Luminosity and the Solar Constant

If the sun's luminosity is 4×10^{26} watts, calculate the solar constant.

Solution: Compute the total surface area at 1 A.U., i.e., at the earth's location, all the sun's energy passes through an imaginary spherical surface of radius 93,000,000 miles.

The area of this surface is 3×10^{24} sq. ft. Hence:

$$\text{One square foot intercepts } \frac{4 \times 10^{26} \text{ watts}}{3 \times 10^{24} \text{ sq. ft.}}$$

Thus, the solar constant is about *130 watts/sq. ft.* We round it off to 100 watts, since at least 30 watts is reflected by the earth's atmosphere. (In actual practice, the solar luminosity is deduced from the measured value of the solar constant.)

Some useful energy conversion factors:

1 Mev = 1.6022×10^{-6} erg
1 Kiloton of TNT = 4.2×10^{19} erg
pp reaction yield = 26 Mev
CNO reaction yield = 26.7 Mev
typical fission yield = 150–200 Mev

Tech. Note No. 12

*Simple Log Tables to Calculate Absolute Magnitude
(For Chapter 10)*

TABLE A

To compute absolute magnitude (M) from apparant magnitude (m) and parallax (p), logarithms are needed.

Number	Logarithm
1.0	0.0
2.0	0.301
3.0	0.477
4.0	0.602
5.0	0.699
6.0	0.778
7.0	0.845
8.0	0.903
9.0	0.954

Examples:

log 1,000 = 3.000
log 5,000 = 3.699
log 7,000 = 3.845
log 70,000 = 4.845
log 70 = 1.845

Tech. Note No. 13

Definitions of Some Angles. (See parallax application, Chapters 17 and 10.)

A circle is divided into 360° (degrees).
A circle of radius d may also be divided into 2π radians.

Hence, $360° = 2\pi$ radians
$60' = 1°$
$60'' = 1'$

206, 265 seconds of arc = 1 radian

$\dfrac{\text{Arc}}{d} = \theta$ (measured in radians)

or $d = \dfrac{\text{Arc}}{\theta} = \dfrac{(\text{Arc}) \times 206{,}265}{p'' \,(\text{seconds})}$

For small angles, the arc can be approximated as a straight line. If d is the distance from our sun to a nearby star and the arc is 1 A.U.,

then $d = \dfrac{206{,}265 \text{ A.U.}}{p''}$

We now let 206,265 A.U. = 1 parsec, defining a new unit of length, then $d = \dfrac{1}{p''}$ parsec.

Tech. Note No. 14

Summary of equations, assumptions and definitions of our

INSIDE STAR TRIP (Strictly X-rated)

Assume:

1. x = % hydrogen
   y = % helium
   z = % heavy elements
   x + y + z = 100%
2. Ionized Gas
3. Symmetry
4. Dynamic Equilibrium
5. Set up *4 equations* and solve for *internal self-consistency*

Buoyant Force

$\Delta M(r) = 4\pi r^2 \rho(r)\Delta r$ $\Delta M(r)$ = mass of shell
 $M(r)$ = mass of matter within radius r

$\Delta P = -\dfrac{GM(r)}{r^2}\rho(r)\Delta r$ pressure equilibrium

$\Delta L = 4\pi r^2 \cdot \rho(r) \cdot \Delta r \cdot \epsilon$ energy generation

$\Delta T = -\dfrac{3\kappa}{16\pi ac}\dfrac{L(r)}{r^2}\dfrac{\rho}{T^3}\Delta r$ radiation transport, ΔT = temperature gradient

Where $\quad\quad\quad\quad\quad \Delta r$ = shell thickness

ϵ = rate of energy generation per gram

κ = opacity

$a = 4\pi\sigma/c \quad\quad$ where σ = Stefan Boltzmann Constant

$\rho(r)$ = density at position r from center of star

G = gravitational constant

ΔP = change in pressure

$$\mu = \frac{1}{2x + (3/4)y + (1/2)z} = \text{mean molecular weight}$$

(Opacity) $\quad\quad \kappa = 5 \times 10^{25}\,\dfrac{g}{t}\,\dfrac{\rho}{T^{3.5}}\,(1+x)\,(1-x-y) \quad\quad\quad g$ = Gaunt factor

t = guillotine factor

$L(r)$ = luminosity at position r from center of star

Eliminate $\rho = \dfrac{H}{k}\mu\,\dfrac{P}{T}$ $\quad\quad\quad\quad\quad\quad$ where H = mass of proton in grams

k = Boltzmann constant

Then solve all 4 equations simultaneously:

Energy generation : Each gram yields 7×10^{18} ergs

$\quad\quad\quad\quad\quad\quad\quad 10^7$ ergs/sec = 1 watt

p-p cycle or CNO cycle — carbon cycle

Energy transport: conduction, convection, radiation ˎ

$$\boxed{\begin{aligned} \epsilon_{pp} &= 1.05 \times 10^{-29}\,\rho\,x^2\,T^4 \\ \epsilon_{cc} &= 1.6 \times 10^{-142}\,\rho.x.\frac{z}{3}\,T^{20} \end{aligned}}$$

Energy generation

temperature dependence

Models: 2 or 3 zones

For more details see e.g., L. Motz and A. Duveen, *Essentials of Astronomy*, Columbia U. Press, Chapt. 22.

Tech. Note No. 15

The Sun's Own Energy (for Chapter 12)

What percentage of the sun's mass and percent of hydrogen is used up, in 4 1/2 billion years for its energy production?

Assume proton-proton reaction

Luminosity of sun = 4×10^{33} ergs per sec.

E_T = total energy used = $4 \times 10^{33} \times \underbrace{1.45 \times 10^{17}}_{\text{(no. of seconds in 4 1/2} \times 10^9 \text{ years)}} = 5.8 \times 10^{50}$ ergs

Energy generated by mass loss Δm

$\quad E_T = \Delta m c^2 \quad\quad\quad\quad\quad\quad c = 3 \times 10^{10}$ cm/sec.

$\quad \Delta m = \dfrac{5.8 \times 10^{50}}{9 \times 10^{20}} = 6.4 \times 10^{29}$ gram $\quad$ (This is the minimum idealized mass loss due to energy production by mass annihilation)

Each pp cycle requiring 4 protons yields 26 Mev = 4.2×10^{-5} ergs

Assume 100% efficiency, no. of reactions in 4 1/2 billion years

$$\text{is} \quad \frac{5.8 \times 10^{50} \text{ ergs}}{4.2 \times 10^{-5} \text{ ergs/reaction}} \qquad = 1.38 \times 10^{55} \text{ reactions}$$

Minimum no. of reactions: 1.38×10^{55}

Hence minimum no. of protons required = $4 \times 1.38 \times 10^{55} = 5.5 \times 10^{55}$

Minimum mass of sun required to produce E_T is

$$5.5 \times 10^{55} \times \underbrace{1.67 \times 10^{-24}}_{\text{mass of proton}} = 9.21 \times 10^{31} \text{ grams of protons}$$

Present mass of sun = 2×10^{33} grams

Fraction of sun's hydrogen used up is $\dfrac{9.21 \times 10^{31}}{2 \times 10^{33}} = 4.6\%$

This calculation shows that the p-p ratio is efficient enough to produce sun's energy. It is a necessary (but not sufficient) condition.

Tech. Note No. 16

Einstein's Special Relativity

Lengths Shrink

Consequences: consider a rod of length (1) travelling with speed (v) in the direction of the rod.

Special relativity says: The length of a measuring rod shrinks by an amount proportional to $\sqrt{1 - (v^2/c^2)}$ with respect to an observer at rest. If the observer were to be moving *with* the rod, he would also infer that the fixed rod has shrunk by the same factor, provided he uses as a frame of reference that of the fixed observer.

Clocks Run Slow

If a stationary observer compares his clock with that of a moving observer, the fixed observer would infer that the moving clock runs slower by a factor of $\sqrt{1 - v^2/c^2}$.

If the moving observer were to check his own clock with that of the fixed observer, he would infer that the stationary clock is running slower by the factor $\sqrt{1 - v^2/c^2}$ over his clock.

Note that there is a symmetry in space-time. There is no absolute reference frame. Each observer thinks the other one's clock is running slower, and the other one's meterstick has shrunk.

Einstein Mass-Energy Relation

One other consequence of special relativity is the following relationship:

$$E = mc^2$$

This is the rest energy of all matter of mass (m), where c is the speed of light.

Tech. Note No. 17

Red Shift

There are two and only two ways by which present-day (1976) physics can explain a red shift of spectral lines. One, is the Doppler effect and two is the gravitational red shift. A spectral line which originates in a laboratory at rest has a wavelength λ_0. Let this line be shifted by an amount $\Delta\lambda$ to $\lambda \pm \Delta\lambda$. From Einstein's special relativity, if the relative speed is v between emitter and observer,* then

$$\Delta\lambda/\lambda = \frac{1 \pm v/c}{(1 - v^2/c^2)^{1/2}} - 1 \text{ where } c = \text{speed of light.}$$

The expression $\Delta\lambda/\lambda$ is referred to as z in the literature.

$$z = \Delta\lambda/\lambda$$

If the speed v is close to the speed of light c, then the relativity expression has to be used as is. If, on the other hand, v is much less than c, the expression reduces to

$$z = \Delta\lambda/\lambda = v/c$$

Hubble's law is

$$H \cdot d = c\Delta\lambda/\lambda$$

or $\boxed{d = cz/H}$

where H = Hubble's constant
d = distance of receding galaxy.

H is supposedly a constant, but its value has changed many times during the last 40 years, not because the constant H is variable, but because astronomers are constantly improving and refining their distance measuring "yardsticks." The most recent value for H is 50 km/sec. per million parsecs, i.e., for every million parsecs, the velocity of recession increases by 50 km/sec. Galactic distances inferred by this technique are referenced as arising from the *cosmological Doppler effect*.

Example 1. What is the distance to a galaxy whose recession speed is 300 km/sec?
(Answer: 6×10^6 parsecs)

Example 2. What is the distance to the quasar is z = 2?

From equation $d = \frac{cz}{H} = \frac{3 \times 10^5 \times 2}{50}$ Mega parsecs

Note: $c = 3 \times 10^5$ km/sec.

($d = 1.2 \times 10^{10}$ parsecs)

*Use + for a receding source;
use − for an approaching source.

314

This is an incorrect answer, because z is large enough to require the use of the relativistic Doppler equation.

Now, do it right:

1. Get (v/c) from Doppler equation. Hint: Solve as quadratic equation
2. Then get v
3. Then calculate distance from d = v/H

Correct answer: $\dfrac{v}{c} = 0.8$

d = 4.8 billion parsecs

Tech. Note No. 18

The Gravitational Red Shift

If a photon is emitted from a massive body having a strong gravitational field, it will lose a small part of its energy on making its departure from the body.

If ν_0, λ_0 are its original rest frequency and wavelength, and ν and λ the observed frequency and wavelength after the photon has left the object

$$\nu = \nu_0 \left[1 - \frac{2GM}{c^2 R} \right]^{1/2}$$

Where M = mass of object
R = Its radius
c = speed of light

These red shifts were confirmed by a study of spectra from white dwarfs.

The gravitational red shift is:

$$\frac{\Delta\lambda}{\lambda} = z = \left[1 - \frac{2GM}{Rc^2} \right]^{-1/2} - 1$$

Tech. Note No. 19

Calculate the Radius of a Neutron Star

Calculate the radius of a neutron star of

a. Solar mass
b. 100 times solar mass
c. Also calculate its density

Mass of hydrogen nucleus = 1.67×10^{-24} gm
Mass of Sun = 2×10^{33} grams
No. of nuclei in star
of solar mass $= \dfrac{2 \times 10^{33}}{1.67 \times 10^{-24}} = 1.2 \times 10^{57}$ nuclei

Imagine all nuclei compressed into one giant nucleus, whose radius is R or size of neutron star.

The equation for the radius R is given by:

$R = 1.5 \times 10^{-13} \quad A^{1/3}$ cm   where A = no. of nuclei
$R = 1.5 \times 10^{-13} \quad (1.2)^{1/3} (10^{57})^{1/3}$
$R = 1.6 \times 10^6$ cm = 16 km (Answer)

If mass were $100M_\odot$, then neutron star radius would be 74 km.

The volume of a 16 km radius neutron core is $= 1.71 \times 10^{19}$ cc

its density is $\dfrac{\text{mass}}{\text{volume}} = \dfrac{2 \times 10^{33}}{1.71 \times 10^{19}} = 1.1 \times 10^{14}$ grams/cc.

Thus 1 cc of neutron core has a mass of about 10^8 metric tons.

Note: The core of an atomic nucleus has the same density.

Tech. Note No. 20

Q. What would be the orbital radius for DEBs if they were emitting electrons and revolving around the neutron core; if P = 0.033 seconds?

Hint—Use $\dfrac{P^2}{a^3} = \dfrac{4\pi^2}{G(M+m)}$ assume $(M+m) \sim M_O$

$$a^3 = \dfrac{P^2}{4\pi^2} G(M+m)$$

Substitues numerical values for P, G, and (M+m)

$a^3 = \dfrac{(0.033)^2 \; 6.67 \times 10^{-8} \times 2 \times 10^{33}}{4\pi^2} = 3.67 \times 10^{21}$

$a = (3.67)^{1/3} \cdot 10^7 = 1.54 \times 10^7$ cm $= 154$ km

Thus the radius of orbiting Debs would be about 10 neutron core radii away.

Tech. Note No. 21

Q. What would be the speed of these orbiting DEBs?

A. They would be traveling in an orbit of 154 km radius in a time of 0.033 seconds.

Assume circular orbit for simplicity.

$\dfrac{\text{Circumference}}{\text{Period}} = $ speed in orbit $= v$

$v = \dfrac{2\pi r}{P} = \dfrac{2\pi 154}{0.033} = 29,300$ km/sec.

or $v = 2.93 \times 10^9$ cm/sec.

Now light travels at speed of $c = 3 \times 10^{10}$ /sec.

Hence, DEBs would travel at approximately $\dfrac{1}{10}$ speed of light.

Note: that for the case of the Crab Pulsar, whisps of lumi-
    nous clouds have been observed occassionally to move
    away from the neutron core at speeds of $\frac{1}{10}$ c.

The overall expansion of the Crab Nebula is about $\frac{1}{300}$ c.

Tech. Note No. 22

Exercise: Crab Nebula (continued)
    Assume its distance is 2,000 parsecs from us. Its apparent
magnitude is 16.

   a. What is its absolute magnitude?
   b. What is its luminosity?
   c. What is its apparent effective temperature assuming it
      radiates like a black body?

$$\text{Hint:} \quad d = 1/p''$$
$$M = m + 5 + 5 \log p''$$
$$M = 16 + 5 - 16.5$$
$$\underline{M = 4.5}$$

Since, $\log \left(\dfrac{1}{2,000} \right) = -\log(2,000) = -3.30$

Now the absolute magnitude of the sun is 4.8. Hence, sun
and pulsar supposedly radiate comparable energies, even
though the mechanisms of their energy sources may be completely different, as well as spread out over different regions
of the electromagnetic spectrum.
From exercise No. 19 we discovered that the radius of pulsar
is 16 km. (Now, surface area $= 4\pi R^2$.)

$$\text{Let } q = \frac{\text{Surface area of sun}}{\text{Surface area of pulsar}}$$

$$q = \frac{(6.95 \times 10^5)^2}{16^2} \cdot \frac{4\pi}{4\pi} = 1.88 \times 10^9$$

From Black body radiation law, calculate the ratio of their
luminosities:

$$\frac{L_{sun}}{L_{pulsar}} = \frac{4\pi R_\odot^2 \; \sigma \; T_s^4}{4\pi R_p^2 \; \sigma \; T_p^4} = \frac{T_s^4}{T_p^4} \frac{R_\odot^2}{R_p^2} = q \cdot \frac{T_s^4}{T_p^4}$$

$$\left(\frac{T_p}{T_s} \right)^4 = 1.88 \times 10^9 \qquad \text{Since } \frac{L_{sun}}{L_{pulsar}} \simeq 1$$

$$\frac{T_p}{T_s} = 208 \qquad\qquad \begin{aligned} T_p &= (208) \times 6,000 \\ T_p &= 1.2 \times 10^6 \; {}^\circ K \end{aligned}$$

Imagine now putting a gas cloud of low density (say 1.41) surrounding this pulsar, of radius 430,000 miles. Would this object's radiation pattern possibly resemble any known source?

Tech. Note No. 23

Physical Properties of the DEBs*

It is possible to obtain a rough measure of the mass and radius of the DEB by the following considerations: If molecules are formed on the DEBs and if we assume that heavy molecules such as the porphyrins are retained and the lighter molecules such as CH and CN escape from the DEBs then one can write down the following inequality (based on velocity of escape considerations): See Chapter 5.

$$6\sqrt{\frac{3kT}{m_{heavy}}} < \sqrt{\frac{2GM}{R}} < 6\sqrt{\frac{3kT}{m_{light}}}$$

where m = the mass of the molecule. That is, one could put lower and upper bounds on the M/R ratio of the DEB. If one assumes a temperature of, say 700°K. and takes a range of values for the radius commensurate with known radii for the comets, namely 10-1,000 km as an outside limit, that is, from a comet to a planet, then Table A shows the expected range of mass and density of the original DEBs. It is quite apparent that the original densities are extremely high and that only after sufficient ejection processes have occurred will equilibrium set in to stabilize the internal structure of the DEB. However, such stabilization may take millions of years, and in fact, has not yet set in for the earth, since the earth is still extremely active.

By invoking principles of conservation of angular momentum and conservation of mass, it is possible to write a series of equations from which one can calculate the initial density of the earth, since we have a very good expectation that the initial radius is ≈ 3,400 km; the initial density comes out to be 35.6. The mean density after 4 1/2 billion years, of the central core, is now ~14. Hence, sufficient internal pressure

TABLE A
Mass/Radius of Debs

R (km)	M (grams)	Initial Density (gr./cc)
10	7×10^{23}	1.7×10^5
100	7×10^{24}	1.7×10^3
1,000	7×10^{25}	17

*Reference F.M. Johnson, Mem. Societe Royale des Sciences de Liége, 6th series, Volume III, pp. 609-627 (1972).

is still available to cause eruption of new volcanoes and perform mountain building, phenomena that were perhaps more prevalent in the past.

This table is constructed on the assumption that light molecules, like CH and CN, escape and heavy molecules, such as porphyrins, are retained in the atmosphere. Hence:

$$1.0 \times 10^{14} < \frac{M}{RT} < 25 \times 10^{14}$$

$$\text{Take } \frac{M}{RT} \simeq 10^{15} \text{ and } T = 700°K$$

Tech. Note No. 24

The Earth* (See Chapter 7)

The earth provides a good test for the DEB model. Each planet was once a DEB! As the protosun developed, the planets were successively launched into orbit. There is abundant evidence to support the hypothesis that the earth's radius is expanding at the mean rate of 0.65 mm/yr. Proponents of the hypothesis include Egyed, Carey, Dicke, and Heezen. Although there seems to be no agreement as to the causes of the actual amount of expansion, the evidence for the expanding earth includes:

1. Precambrian crustal geotechtonic data which, according to Dearnley, corresponds to an expansion of 0.65 mm/yr. This would extrapolate to an original radius of 3,440 km (at 4 1/2 billion years ago).

2. Nontidal slowing of the earth's rotation corresponds to 8.8×10^{-6} sec/yr., which in 4.5×10^9 years amounts to 11 hours, i.e., original period is approximately 13 hours.

By invoking conservation of angular momentum, values for the initial rotational speed and densities are derived. However, they do imply that some angular momentum was somehow shared with the moon.

3. If all the present land areas coalesced to form a sphere of radius R_O (reverse continental drift and shrink earth), then the value of R_O can be calculated.

$$\left(\frac{\text{Land Area}}{\text{Total Surface Area}} \right)^{1/2} = \left(\frac{1.48}{5.11} \right)^{1/2} = \frac{1}{1.86}$$

Hence, R_O = 3,430 km, since (present radius) = 6,370 km divided into 1.86 gives R_O. See Figures 7.10, 7.11, and 7.12 for such a reconstruction.

4. Finally, the radius of the liquid core is 3,470 km.

The difficulties encountered with the continental drift and expanding earth models, previously, had been that they floundered because they required high initial densities: 25-40 according to Beck (our calculation 35.6) and enormous internal energy sources. Since no one had previously considered the original energy sources associated with

*Reference F.M. Johnson, Mem. Societe Royale des Sciences de Liége, 6th series, Volume III, pp. 609-627 (1972).

remnants of protosun nuclear energy generation, these theories were discarded.

A rough calculation of the energy requirements can be obtained by evaluating the gravitational potential energy before and after earth expansion, and equating this to (3/2) nkT, assuming equipartition of nuclei energies in the interior (where n = number .of atoms, k = Boltzmann constant).

Such an order of magnitude calculation yields a heat energy source corresponding to a temperature of about 2×10^6 °K (a more precise knowledge of the relevant parameters might yield numbers anywhere in the range from 100,000 to 50,000,000°K). Such an enormous potential heat energy reservoir could only have been supplied inside the earth from the protosun and not by the small amounts of radioactive decay heating as is presently postulated (to account for the much lower assumed central temperatures). *Large scale* radioactive processes are a distinct possibility for providing the earth's internal energy. (See pg. 280.)

Note that the four above independent methods yield almost identical values for R_O (± 20 km), hence, providing good arguments for the DEB model.

The earth's radius expands due to the high internal core pressure and temperature, resulting in the ejection from the central core of hot material into the mantle (Fig. 7.15).

Tech. Note No. 25

Periodic Comets

Name	P (yrs)	e	q	i(°)
Encke	3.30	0.847	0.339	12.0
Grigg-Skjellerup	4.91	0.703	0.858	17.6
Honda-Mrkos-Pajdusakova	5.21	0.815	0.556	13.2
Tempel (2)	5.26	0.549	1.364	12.5
Neujmin (2)	5.43	0.567	1.338	10.6
Brorsen	5.46	0.810	0.590	29.4
Tuttle-Giacobini-Kresak	5.48	0.639	1.123	13.8
Tempel-Swift	5.68	0.638	1.153	5.4
Tempel (1)	5.98	0.463	1.771	9.8
Pons-Winnecke	6.30	0.639	1.230	22.3
de Vico-Swift	6.31	0.524	1.624	3.6
Kopff	6.31	0.555	1.520	4.7
Giacobini-Zinner	6.41	0.729	0.934	30.9
Forbes	6.42	0.553	1.545	4.6
Schwassmann-Wachmann (2)	6.53	0.383	2.157	3.7
Wolf-Harrington	6.54	0.538	1.614	18.5
Biela	6.62	0.756	0.861	12.6
Wirtanen	6.67	0.543	1.618	13.4
d'Arrest	6.67	0.614	1.369	18.1
Perrine-Mrkos	6.71	0.643	1.271	17.8

Name	P (yrs)	e	q	i(°)
Reinmuth (2)	6.71	0.457	1.932	7.0
Brooks (2)	6.72	0.505	1.763	5.6
Harrington	6.80	0.559	1.582	8.7
Arend-Rigaux	6.82	0.600	1.437	17.8
Johnson	6.86	0.377	2.247	13.9
Finlay	6.90	0.703	1.077	3.6
Borrelly	7.02	0.604	1.452	31.1
Daniel	7.09	0.550	1.661	20.1
Harrington-Abell	7.22	0.522	1.785	16.8
Holmes	7.35	0.379	2.347	19.5
Faye	7.38	0.576	1.608	9.1
Whipple	7.46	0.353	2.471	10.2
Ashbrook-Jackson	7.49	0.396	2.314	12.5
Reinmuth (1)	7.60	0.487	1.983	8.3
Arend	7.79	0.534	1.832	21.7
Oterma	7.88	0.144	3.388	21.7
Schaumasse	8.18	0.705	1.196	12.0
Wolf	8.43	0.395	2.507	27.3
Comas Sola	8.59	0.576	1.777	13.4
Vaisala (1)	10.46	0.636	1.741	11.3
Neujmin (3)	10.95	0.588	2.032	3.8
Gale	10.99	0.761	1.183	11.7
van Biesbroeck	12.41	0.550	2.409	6.6
Tuttle	13.61	0.821	1.023	54.7
Schwassmann-Wachmann (1)	16.10	0.132	5.538	9.5
Neujmin (1)	17.97	0.774	1.547	15.0
Crommelin	27.87	0.919	0.743	28.9
Tempel-Tuttle	32.91	0.904	0.981	162.7
Stephen-Oterma	38.96	0.861	1.596	17.9
Westphal	61.73	0.920	1.254	40.9
Brorsen-Metcalf	69.06	0.971	0.485	19.2
Olbers	69.57	0.930	1.179	44.6
Pons-Brooks	70.86	0.955	0.774	74.2
Halley	76.04	0.967	0.587	162.2
Herschel-Rigollet	156.0	0.974	0.748	64.2
Grigg-Mellish	164.3	0.969	0.923	109.8

Tech. Note No. 26

Comets from Way Out There in the Solar System

Name and Year	P(yrs)	e	q	i(°)
Kilston 1966 V	162,000	0.9	2.385	40.3
Rudnicki 1967 II	—	1.0	0.420	9.1
Wild 1967 III	—	1.0	1.327	99.1
Seki 1967 IV	4,420	0.9	0.457	106.5
Mitchell-Jones-Gerber 1967 VII	—	1.0	0.178	56.7
Ikeya-Seki 1968 I	89,400	0.9	1.697	129.3
Wild 1968 III	—	1.0	2.660	135.3
Tago-Honda-Yamamoto 1968 IV	—	1.0	0.680	102.2
Whitaker-Thomas 1968 V	—	1.0	1.234	61.8
Honda 1968 VI	—	1.0	1.100	128.0
Bally-Clayton 1968 VII	—	1.0	1.772	93.2
Thomas 1969 I	18,400	0.9	3.316	45.2
Fujikawa 1969 VII	—	1.0	0.774	9.0
Tago-Sato-Kosaka 1969 IX	419,000	0.9	0.473	75.8
Daido-Fujikawa 1970 I	—	1.0	0.066	100.2
Bennet 1970 II	1,730	0.9	0.538	90.0
Kohoutek 1970 III	83,100	0.9	1.719	86.3
Suzuki-Sato-Seki 1970 X	—	1.0	0.406	60.8
Abe 1970 XV	—	1.0	1.113	126.7

Tech. Note No. 27

(Johann)² Bode-Titius Law

We shall now derive a law which was on the books for 200 years without anyone appreciating its physical significance. In fact, it was recently denied its official "law" status (shades of astronomical *star* chamber disbarment procedure!). The argument for denigrating it to the lower status was: "random-access-number-coincidence phenomenon." Which, translated into English, means: "We have not the foggiest idea of its significance, hence, it must be unimportant." Feeble rebuttal voices by some who argued that this so-called law at least does predict the mean distances of planets quite well, were drowned out by shouts of:

1. "It's all just accidental coincidences" (8 of them!!).
2. "Any half-baked theory will come up with a logarithm type sequence." (But not this exact one!)
3. "It does not explain Neptune and Pluto." (That's because the law was not adequately used—see Table A. It works well for Pluto, if you skip Neptune.)

The basic physics behind this law is the conservation of angular momentum. Each protoplanet in orbit at the protosun surface is assumed to have orbital velocity appropriate to the stellar mass. We shall assume that Pluto and Neptune are launched simultaneously as the first planets.

We shall now develop a set of simple equations which contain only two unknowns. (1) The initial mass of the protosun's core, $\overline{M}_0$, and (2) the size of the orbit from which all the planets were launched, a_0. For simplicity, we shall assume that the size of the protosun did not change subsequent to each nova explosion. Using this analysis, we can write down eight simultaneous equations with two unknowns which are as follows (using the fact that the expression for the angular momentum is given thus):

$$J = m \sqrt{a(1 - e^2)\, G\, (M + m)}$$

Where m = mass of plant
a = mean orbital distance
e = eccentricity
M = total mass of protosun

Instead of writing all 8 equations, we shall write 3 of them only, which will illustrate the pattern of the equations. Note that after each nova, the increase in distance corresponds to the ratio of $\dfrac{\text{solar mass before nova}}{\text{solar mass after nova}}$. For a succession of such novas, cancellation of factors in numerator and denominator result, which finally results in a set of very simple equations.

Let M_0 (M_{Sun}) = mass original core = $\overline{M}_0$

a_0 = orbit at launch

We assume that every protoplanet, in turn, has achieved orbital velocity at the protosun surface (radius a_o) prior to its launch via nova explosion.

e.g., MARS

$$\frac{\left(1 + \frac{M_o}{32}\right)}{\left(1 + \frac{M_o}{64}\right)} \cdot \frac{\left(1 + \frac{M_o}{64}\right)}{\left(1 + \frac{M_o}{128}\right)} \cdot \frac{\left(1 + \frac{M_o}{128}\right)}{(1 + 0)} \cdot a_o = 1.523$$

Earth

$$\left(1 + \frac{M_o}{64}\right) a_o = 1$$

Venus

$$\left(1 + \frac{M_o}{128}\right) a_o = 0.723$$

(Note the cancelation of factors in numerator and denominator.)

The right hand side is the present distance of the planet. All eight equations, with only 2 unknowns are consistent with $\overline{M}_O = 96\,M_O$ and $a_O = 0.393$ A.U.

The logic behind the equation is as follows: We shall assume that a basic quantity of matter is always associated with the sun, comparable to the present mass of the sun, and, by the principle of conservation of angular momentum, whenever the total protosolar mass is diminished, a corresponding increase in the orbital radius results. Subsequent to each nova explosion, we multiply the distance of each planetary orbit by the appropriate ratio of protosun masses (involving its initial mass) divided by its final mass. This ratio is directly proportional to the distance which the planet moves, subsequent to each nova explosion.

Note, e.g., when the earth was launched from the protosun surface (following solar nova No. 7) its distance increased from a_O to

$$\frac{\left(1 + \frac{M_o}{64}\right) a_o}{\left(1 + \frac{M_o}{128}\right)} = \frac{\left(1 + \frac{6}{4}\right) a_o}{\left(1 + \frac{3}{4}\right)} = \frac{10}{7} a_o$$

See Figure 18.17, page 271. At Pluto's launch the initial change in core mass is large so that the additional mass of the outside gas (which is close to unity) is insignificant, compared to M_O. However, when one gets closer to the final nova states, the final mass of the sun shows up very dramatically, and, in fact, provides the *exact* coefficients in Bode's law.

Thus, proceeding with each planet, the previously discussed equations are written down, where a_O is the orbital

323

The Bode-Titus Law of 1772
(Interpreted by F.M. Johnson 1972)

n	∞ Mercury	8 Venus	7 Earth	6 Mars	5 Asteroids	4 Jupiter	3 Saturn	2 Uranus	1b Neptune	1a Pluto
	0	3	6	12	24	48	96	192	—	384
Add 4	4	4	4	4	4	4	4	4	—	4
Divide by 10	0.4	0.7	1.0	1.6	2.8	5.2	10.0	19.6	—	38.8
Actual distance	0.387	0.723	1.0	1.523	(2.8)	5.202	9.540	19.18	30.0	39.44

$$d = 0.4 + (0.3)\, 2^{8-n}$$

Where n = order of birth. Pluto and Neptune were launched simultaneously from slightly different original orbits. Mercury (n = ∞) signifies that it was left in original orbit from whence all its sister planets originated. No core fission or explosion were necessary to launch Mercury. Subsequently, the protosun gas cloud shrank to its present size.

protosun radius and M_O the initial mass of the core in units of solar masses. Note that when the earth is launched, it increases its distance by factor (10/7). It does not actually double its distance from the protosun radius, because the factor of one is already significantly large in comparison to remnant solar core. Its fractional increase in distance is an additional 7/4 when Venus is finally launched. At the time of Venus' nova, it is assumed that **almost** the whole stellar core disappears.

Solving these equations, one obtains the initial radius for launching the planets as 0.393 A.U., and the initial solar mass $\overline{M}_O$ as 96 solar masses.

Table B is a summary of the calculated distances and the actual planetary mean distances. This first calculation had assumed that a_O did not change, and, more seriously, the mass of proto-Jupiter was neglected in the angular momentum equation. The improvement becomes apparent if one takes into account the mass of Jupiter (about $0.2M_O$) upon launching. The results, when this is done, are also indicated in Table B. Essentially, one obtains good agreement with the actual planetary distances, with a very small error in Venus' orbit. Since Venus, in any event, was the last planet to be launched, one might check this out a little more carefully to see whether one can improve the calculation still further. It seems a unique opportunity since with eight equations and only two unknowns, more information can be extracted.

TABLE B

Assumed Protoplanet Mass m	Actual Distance	Caicul. Distance	% Error
Pluto	39.44	38.1	+3.3
Uranus	19.18	19.2	0
Saturn	9.54	9.8	−2.7
Jupiter (0.2)	5.20	5.2	0
Ceres	2.77	2.75	0.6
Mars (0.1 return)	1.523	1.52	0.2
Earth	1.00	1.00	0
Venus	0.723	0.73	−1
Mercury	0.387	0.393	−1.5

Tech. Note No. 28

Pulsars

We wish to very briefly examine the remnant of a supernova, i.e., the central core of a star, assuming that almost all the DEBs have been ejected and an innermost collection of remaining DEBs rotate around this central core. Assume that this would be the case subsequent to a typical supernova explosion and that the remnant constitutes a pulsar as shown in Figure 28.1. The pulsar emits, first of all, non-symmetrically spaced signals. For instance, the prototype NP 0532, the Crab Nebula pulsar, emits signals which are spaced 13 milliseconds and 20 milliseconds between the pulses. The model shown in Figure 28.1 will satisfy such a condition. That is, maximum radiation is received when a collection of DEBs are 90° with respect to the central core. This would correspond to the case of radiation from Jupiter, where maximum radiation occurs when Io is 90° with respect to Jupiter. From the asymmetry of the pulses and other information, one might be able to approximate the orbit of these DEBs. In position 1 the DEBs are closer to the central core and hence, have a larger magnetic field, causing the output emission due to the synchrotron radiation of electrons moving around the collection of DEBs to be larger. The model adopted here is that high energetic electrons or other high energetic particles revolve in orbits around these DEBs and when the DEBs are in a position of alignment as shown in Figure 28.1, maximum radiation occurs. Each maximum intensity is related to the strength of the magnetic field at the position of the DEB swarm due to the field emanating from the rotating core (as well as due to the DEBs own magnetic field).

If we adopt this model then for NP0532 from the equation

$$P^2/a^3 = 4\pi^2/(G(m + M))$$

$a \approx 1.5 \times 10^7$ cm, since P = 0.033 seconds, and (m + M) was taken roughly equal to the sun's mass. The orbital speed of the DEB collection is about c/10, where a is the size of the semimajor axis. (Tech. Note No. 21, page 316.)

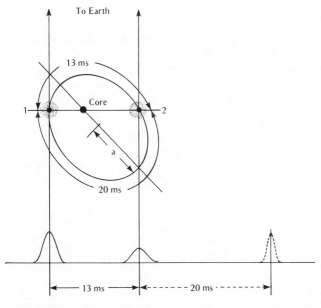

Figure 28.1. Schematic projection of the pulsar NP 0532. Pulses are presumably emitted when the group of DEBs is in either sites 1 or 2.

The slowing of the pulses, at the rate of dP/dt = 36.5 nsec per day would be due to the fact that the orbit increases as energy is being radiated and also mass lost. Every two years or so, one observes motions of plasma regions adjacent to the pulsar with speeds of about 1/10 the speed of light. This would correspond to the fact that as this DEB collection moves successively further away from the central core, one of the more remote DEBs escapes* at c/10 and this event would manifest itself by the ionizing radiation which it would impart to the surrounding gases with which it would interact. These effects have been studied by a number of observers. The spin-up would be due to the rearrangement of DEBs subsequent to the loss of one of its kind and the resulting tightening up of the orbit by a very small amount. (The observed value of the spin-up is $\frac{\Delta w}{w} \approx 2.5 \times 10^{-9}$). If no rearrangement occurs, a sudden spin-down would occur: *antiglitch*.

Based on the above model, the slowing down of the pulsar is due to mass loss of high energetic particles orbiting the DEB collection. From the modified Kepler's equations, on differentiating with respect to mass:

$$\Delta P/P = -\Delta m/(2[m + M]).$$

Substituting the values for the observed fractional changes, $\Delta P/P = 3.65 \times 10^{-9}/3.3 \times 10^{-2}$, then, since 1054 A.D., the mass loss amounted to about 7.4% of $(m + M)$, where M is the mass of the central core and m is the combined mass of all the orbiting DEBs.

Such an enormous particle mass loss in 923 years implies that the total mass of the orbiting DEBs be either comparable to the mass of the core or that the high energy particles be emitted from the core itself. The fact that the loss of a single DEB during the "Glitch" spin-up, however, only changes the orbit radius by a very small amount (10^{-2} cm) implies that the number of DEBs in the orbiting cluster must indeed be large. The high-energy particles which escape the pulsar (core and DEBs) interact with the remainder of the Crab Nebula, providing it with the necessary energy to maintain the well-known "amorphous mass" excited by means of synchrotron radiation. The magnetic fields in the Nebula presumably are supplied by the DEB remnants of the original supernova explosion. The intrinsic X-rays emitted from the DEBs in the Crab Nebula are expected to be noncoherent and unpolarized.

*Another likely escape mechanism is DEB core fission, resulting in an increased velocity of one of the fragments.

LABORATORY
AND
HOME EXERCISES

EXERCISE NO. 1
BASIC COORDINATE SYSTEMS
Getting Oriented

Our first experiment deals with the basic principles of locating objects on the celestial sphere. For this purpose, each one of you will have a celestial globe in front of you. Your mission, if you will accept it, will be to study the following: the **Horizon System**; altitude and azimuth; and locating the important points on the horizon and on the observer's celestial meridian. Locate the zenith, the North Celestial pole, the sigma (Σ) point (Fig. Ex. 1.1) and then locate an object using the azimuth and altitude as coordinates.

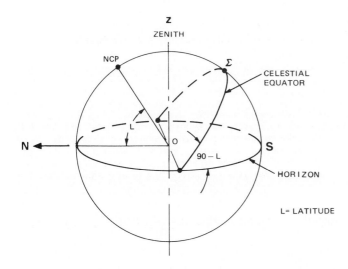

Figure Ex. 1.1. Shows the celestial equator, NCP, and the horizon. The altitude of the NCP is equal to the observer's latitude. The sigma (Σ) point is shown. Note that the plane of the celestial equator makes an angle of 90 minus the latitude with respect to the horizon. Or another way of looking at it, the angle ($ZO\Sigma$) is equal to the latitude.

The next exercise involves the **Equator System.** The same celestial object will now be located with respect to coordinates illustrated in Figures 1.18 and 1.19. Show with your finger how you would measure on the celestial globe, right ascension (R.A.) from the Vernal Equinox and declination from the celestial equator along the star's hour circle.

Trace out the path that the sun describes on the celestial sphere along the ecliptic. Note where the ecliptic intercepts the celestial equator: at the vernal equinox (about March 21) when the sun moves from the south to the north. Then locate the autumnal equinox where the sun crosses the equator going from north to south (about Sept. 21). Place little objects, not chewing gum, but little rubber grommets on the celestial sphere, rotate this sphere, and see what the sky looks like. Exercise Number 3 involves the study of sunrise and sunset (Fig. Ex. 1.2).

Move the sun, by means of the small auxiliary knob, to the various positions indicated. First, have the sun at the **Vernal Equinox,** then at the **Autumnal Equinox,** then the **Summer Solstice,** and then at the **Winter Solstice,** and at each time demonstrate sunrise and sunset. Particularly, pay attention to the crossings of the sun at the observer's meridian, at high noon. Whenever the sun crosses the observer's celestial meridian, we have the highest altitude of the sun for that day. See how you obtain the maximum altitude of the sun for various times of the season. For Los Angeles, you will note that the altitude of the (Σ) Sigma point is 56°. On March 21 and September 21, the sun will have a maximum altitude of 56°, since the sun is exactly on the celestial equator. For June 21 and December 21, that will be 56° plus 23 1/2° and 56° minus 23 1/2°, respectively. Demonstrate these on the globe. Finally, as an exercise, the instructor will ask you to locate an object on the celestial sphere, given right ascension, declination, and sidereal time.

Exercise Number 4 involves the measurement of sidereal time. Note that the hour angle of the Vernal Equinox is a measure of sidereal time. Rotate the celestial sphere in the proper direction and note how the sidereal time changes. When the Vernal Equinox crosses the observer's meridian,

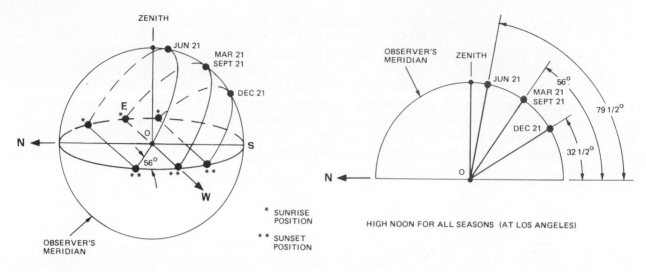

SUNRISE— SUNSET AT DIFFERENT SEASONS

Figure Ex. 1.2. This shows positions of sunrises and sunsets at different seasons for the latitude of Los Angeles. Note that the altitude of the sigma point (Σ) on the plane of the earth's equator, makes an angle of $56°$ (at Los Angeles), with respect to the horizon. The maximum and minimum altitudes of the sun's orbit are shown on this figure at high noon. For other latitudes, replace 56 degrees with your own latitude (L). In each case, add and subtract 23 1/2 degrees from $(90 - L)$ to obtain the highest altitude of the sun at the summer solstice and winter solstice, respectively. Note the large range in altitudes that one obtains during the course of a year. It is also interesting to note that the sun does not go directly overhead at Los Angeles at any time.

the sidereal time is zero (0). Note how the diurnal rotation of the sky is, in effect, a clock, a **sidereal clock***.

What is the effect of changing the latitude? This can also be demonstrated with the globe by changing the latitude to the North Pole. Rotate the sky; see what the sun looks like for an observer at the North Pole (Fig. Ex. 1.3). Next, position the globe such that you are on the equator. Remember the altitude of the North Celestial Pole is equal to observer's latitude.

You are now on the equator; note how the north celestial pole lines up exactly with the north point on the horizon and the south celestial pole with the south point on the horizon (see Fig. Ex. 1.3). Note how the sun rises, perpendicular to the horizon on the equator. Compare that again with the motion of the sun as seen on the north pole. There the sun describes circles parallel to the horizon, and, on March 21 and September 21, the sun is exactly on the horizon, neglecting refraction, and one has 24 hours of perpetual daylight.

For the summertime, at the north pole, from March 21 to September 21, the sun *never* sets, while from September 21 to March 21, the sun never rises above the horizon. If any of these exercises are not clear, please repeat. Make sure you understand the definitions of all the items that we have covered here.

Repeat of Lab Experiment No. 1

A celestial globe will be provided. (If not, see references for suggested commercial source.**) Check coordinates as described in text.

Exercises

1. Change latitude and simulate: altitude of NCP = observer's latitude.
2. Trace position of sun along ecliptic over course of year.

---

*Sidereal time is such that 24 sidereal hours = 23 hours 56 minutes mean solar time.

**See any issue of *Sky and Telescope Magazine.*

3. Simulate sunrise and sunsets for March 21, September 21, June 21, and December 21. Note that on March 21 and September 21, the sun rises *exactly* in the esat and sets *exactly* in the west. Also, verify that length of day and night are equal to 12 hours each during these dates, independent of latitude.
4. Trace out R.A., declination, sidereal time for a star on the globe.
5. Place rubber marker on globe at arbitrary position and define its coordinates.

Questions and Exercises:

1. What is the sidereal time at high noon on September 21?
2. What is the declination of the sun on a. March 21? b. December 21? c. June 21?
3. On the North Pole, what fraction of sky is visible at any time?

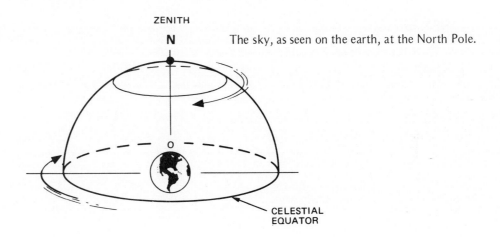

The sky, as seen on the earth, at the North Pole.

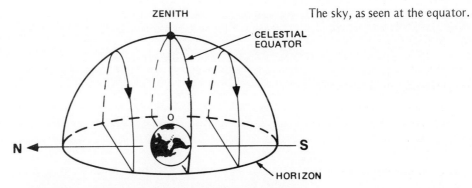

Figure Ex. 1.3. This shows the rotation of the celestial sphere as seen from the vantage point of the North Pole and from the vantage point of the equator. At the North Pole, circles are swept out by the stars which move in circles parallel to the horizon, whereas, at the equator stars rise and set vertically. with respect to the horizon.

EXERCISE NO. 2
DEMONSTRATE PRECESSION OF THE EQUINOXES

A commercial motor-driven gyroscope will be provided in the laboratory. Check on the following:

1. Provide a torque by placing various weights to the top of the arrow. Watch for the precession rates. Question: How is the precession *rate* effected by increasing the weight?

2. Repeat the same experiment by placing the weight to the tail of the arrow, i.e., a torque of opposite direction to the one previous is applied. Note the *direction* of precession and also the effects of increasing weight.

3. Now analyze your findings in relationship to the torque applied by the sun and moon on the *bulge* of the earth. Does the sun's attempt to *straighten up* the earth result in the expected precession as shown by the lab gyro?

EXERCISE NO. 3
THE 24 HOUR 50 MINUTE TIME BETWEEN TWO TIDES
(Repeated, to make sure it's clear)

The explanation for this particular time effect is very similar to the one that we discussed in relationship to the difference between a solar day and the sidereal day. If you recall, when the earth rotated on its axis to complete one complete rotation, it required 23 hours and 56 minutes, with respect to the stars. This was the sidereal day. The additional four minutes came about because of the earth's revolution around the sun (of ~1° per day). Examine Figures 1.12 and 1.20.

Note that the moon's motion is such that it appears to move 13° per day in the *easterly direction* with respect to the stars in its motion around the earth. The sky appears to move 15° per hour *westwards*. Hence, 13° corresponds to 50 minutes worth of time. Consequently, the interval between successive transits of the moon, with respect to the observer's celestial meridian, is 24 hours plus the additional 50 minutes arising from the moon's motion around the earth.

Examine Home Exercise No. 14 to be sure that you appreciate the fact that the moon's tidal effect on the oceans is twice as great as that of the sun.

QUESTION: Which exerts the greatest gravitational force on the earth, the sun, or the moon? Is it the sun, which is 180 times more powerful?

But if the sun is so much more powerful in its attracting force, why is the moon more effective with respect to the tides? The answer lies in the differential tidal effect. Even though the sun's mass is roughly 27 million times greater than that of the moon, the moon, being very much closer to the earth, has the advantage in the inverse cubed differential tidal effect force.

Explain in your own words.

EXERCISE NO. 5
DIRECT MEASUREMENT OF THE ACCELERATION OF GRAVITY

This experiment will be demonstrated by your instructor, who will suspend a weight held by means of a magnet on the ceiling, which can be released by turning off the magnetic field, while simultaneously turning on a clock. As soon as the weight, which in this case is a spherical ball, is released, a timer will be set in motion. The timer will automatically stop when the ball hits the ground and measure the amount of elapsed time while the sphere was travelling. The height from the ground to the ceiling will be measured very carefully and from a simple formula, which is $(S = 1/2 \, gt^2)$, the acceleration of gravity, g, can be determined, since S is the height that was measured and t is the elapsed time. This experiment will be repeated many times using various weights; that is, different size balls. Notice the differences in time involved for different weight balls.

Why do different size (or weight) balls travel at different speeds? (Hint: The bigger balls travel for a shorter time.)

Question: Does this hint help you? (Another hint: The distance between ceiling and floor is supposed to remain unchanged during the experiment. However, with successively larger diameter balls, the travel time decreases, since the bigger balls hit the ground sooner because of the shorter distance travelled.)

These physicists are clever, n'est pas?

Conclusion: Convince yourself that, when using larger balls, the distance s has to be shortened accordingly.

What value of g was obtained from this experiment? _____

It is possible that your instructor may substitute other experiments of this type for the measurement of g—stay alert.

EXERCISE NO. 6
KEPLER'S SECOND LAW
(See text Chapter 3)

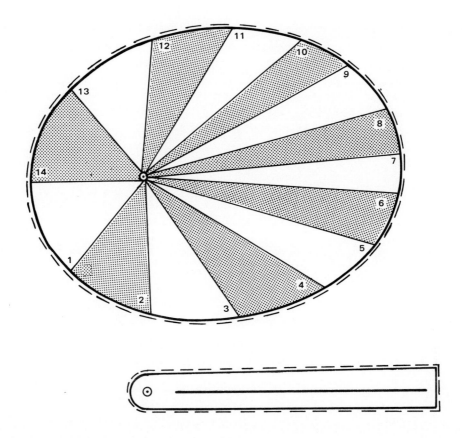

Figure Ex. 6. Cutout of ellipse and radius vector to be used to demonstrate Kepler's Second Law. Cut out radius as shown and cut slot where indicated. Then apply a pin to the center of the radius vector and the focus of the ellipse. The pin is used for indicating the position of the sun. Demonstrate to yourself that, by sweeping out equal areas in equal times, the speed by which one has to move the radius vector, say from one to two, is much faster than from six to seven. All areas, shaded and unshaded portions, of the ellipse are equal.

EXERCISE NO. 7
VERIFICATION OF KEPLER'S LAWS

Convince yourself of the validity of Kepler's third law, i.e., that P^2/a^3 is a constant. Use the values of P (sidereal period) of all planets and their corresponding mean distances as given in Table 2.3, page 30. Now construct the table as shown.

Name of Planet	P (years)	P^2	a (A.U.)	a^3	P^2/a^3
Mercury					
Venus					
Earth					
Mars					
Jupiter					
Saturn					
Uranus					
Neptune					
Pluto					

EXERCISE NO. 8
DEMONSTRATE ANGLE OF ELONGATION FOR MERCURY AND VENUS

Equipment required: about ten feet of string, two live people (aside from yourself).

Procedure: Let Mercury revolve around the sun and you (observer) be the earth. Note the angle that is *subtended* between the sun and planet (Mercury or Venus). Note the various angles that are possible as the planet revolves the sun. In particular, note that Mercury makes a maximum angle of 28° with respect to the sun and Venus 48°. Since Mercury and Venus "hug" the sun, either on its left or on its right side, convince yourself that Mercury and Venus can only be "seen" at the earth either shortly before sunrise or shortly after sunset.

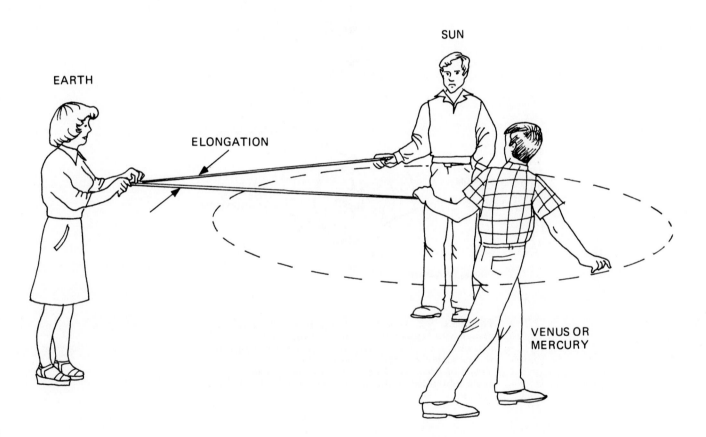

Figure Ex. 8.1. Demonstration of elongation.

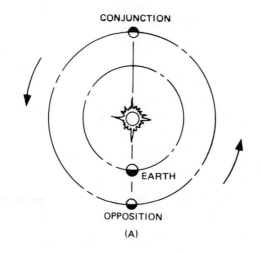

CONJUNCTION

EARTH

OPPOSITION

(A)

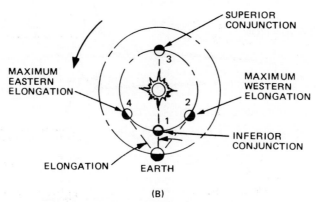

SUPERIOR
CONJUNCTION

MAXIMUM
EASTERN
ELONGATION

MAXIMUM
WESTERN
ELONGATION

INFERIOR
CONJUNCTION

ELONGATION

EARTH

(B)

Figure Ex. 8.2. This shows the position of a superior plasnet with respect to the sun and the earth and the definitions associated with these positions. Figure B shows a similar configuration for the inferior planets Venus or Mercury. Note the elongation angle is the angle subtended *at* the earth between the planet and the sun.

348

EXERCISE NO. 9
SPECTROSCOPY AND OPTICS

The purpose of this activity is first to get acquainted with the elementary optical principles of lenses, prisms, and diffraction gratings. These are the tools with which light can be manipulated and analyzed into its component colors or wavelengths.

Once you have mastered that, we shall proceed to a few applications: The spectroscope is the simplest device for analyzing the various colors from a source. You will be supplied with a variety of spectroscopes—study them. Then apply them to investigate the optical emission of different spectral sources. These sources consist of gases under low pressure whose atoms are excited upon application of 5,000 volts. If the method of excitation astounds you—remember, you too will jump when exposed to 5,000 volts (so please watch yourself and do not touch the high voltage leads of the discharge lamp).

Back to Spectroscopy

Study each of the sources set out at the lab tables and note the differences in the spectral lines. See whether you can get a visual impression of the totality of each spectra, as shown in Figure Ex. 9.

Note the most important conclusions:

1. Each atomic species, such as hydrogen or helium, emits its own characteristic spectrum (i.e., no two lines of different atoms are alike in wavelengths). Also note that brightness (or intensity) of the spectral lines differ from each other.

2. Study the difference between atomic spectra and molecular spectra. Molecular spectra normally are characterized by groups of lines bunched together, often terminating suddenly (in what is called a band head).

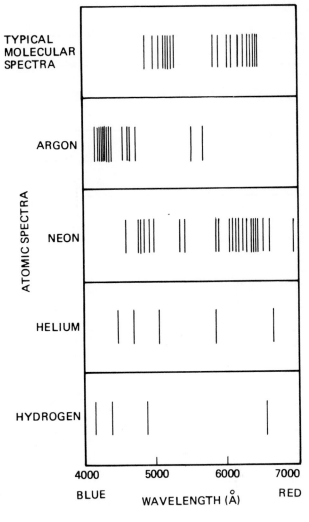

Figure Ex. 9. Typical spectral lines.

The aim of these exercises is to get a qualitative appreciation of the field. There is a lot more complication beyond this level if you wish to pursue it.

3. Study the laboratory setup demonstrating *absorption* and *emission* lines. The sodium spectrum is usually the most suited for this purpose. However, other samples may be supplied to illustrate this important principle.

4. Examine a hot source, such as tungsten filament and note the continuous color spectrum.

349

Question 1. Why do the tungsten atoms in the hot filament provide *all* the colors of the visible spectrum and not the sharp lines seen with, e.g., hydrogen and helium? Discuss this question. _____

_____

_____

_____

Question 2a. What do X-rays, UV, visible, infrared, and microwaves have in common? _____

_____

Question 2b. What is the difference between them? _____

_____

EXERCISES

The following assignments are designed to illustrate, illuminate, and reinforce concepts and ideas discussed in the book and in class. Other exercises are designed to supplement material covered only briefly in the book or barely touched on in class. The student is encouraged to perform these exercises (complete instructions are given) for practical experience.

EXERCISE NO. 10
STAR TRACKER OR MOON TRACKER

In order to better understand the coordinate system and its utility in locating and identifying stellar objects, it is decidedly worthwhile to construct a very simple direct viewing, lensless telescope. This so-called Tycho Brahe system does not need to have the precision of its namesake, nor does it have the slightest resemblance to Tycho's observatory. It will, nevertheless, be good enough to illustrate the diurnal motion of the heaven and the daily motion of the moon around the earth. For heaven's sake, don't panic concerning the construction of your own observatory.

Material needed:

wood or styrofoam blocks
straws
nails and hammer
a saw (let an experienced woodman cut the wood parts for you)

Cut out the parts shown on the next page and mount with glue on cardboard in order to provide stiffness.

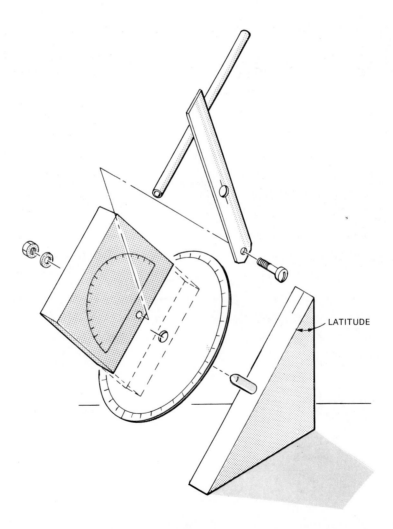

LATITUDE

Figure Ex. 10.1. Construction of a home-made Tycho Brahe precision telescope, without optical components. Cut out the figures as indicated. It is important that the wooden base be cut out such that one of the angles be equal to the observer's latitude, as shown in the drawing.

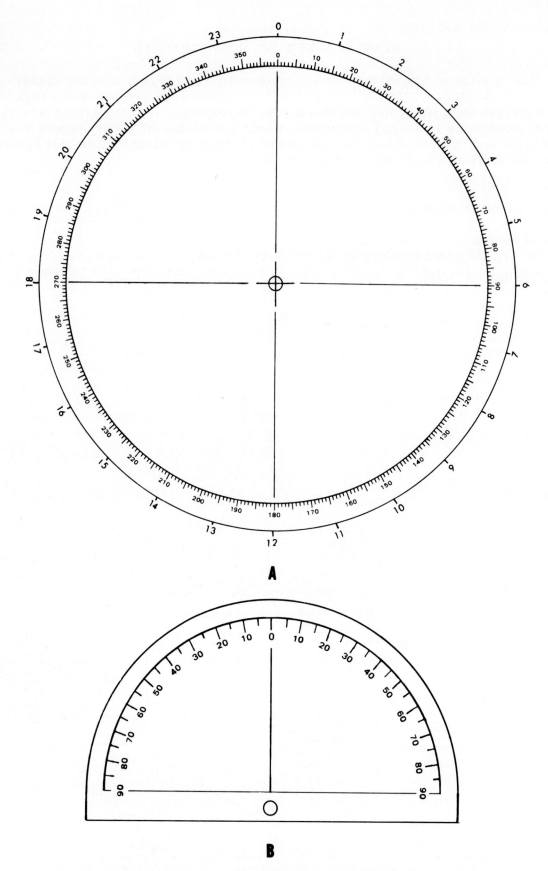

A

B

Figure Ex. 10.2.

Operation of Homemade Telescope

The first thing you want to check is the fact that the sky does make one complete diurnal rotation in 23 hours and 56 minutes. After you have constructed your telescope, orient it in such a manner that the plane of the 360° protractor lies in the sky's equatorial plane, i.e., the latter is supposed to be parallel to your telescope's equatorial plane. Then, proceed to locate a star that you recognize. Line it up through your telescope and note the time precisely. Come back the next night and watch to see whether this star will transit or pass through your telescope 23 hours and 56 minutes later. In the event that you should wish to do this experiment more rapidly, locate your star, note the time and also note the hour angle that the star makes on your protractor. Exactly one hour later, get your star back again through your telescope and note the angle by which you had to rotate in order to acquire the same star again. The rotation should correspond to 15°.

The next experiment involves locating the north celestial pole, which is about a half a degree from the star Polaris. Locate your telescope in such a way that you are pointing your telescope exactly at Polaris. Polaris should be describing a tiny circle as it moves around the north celestial pole. In the event that you are a photography buff, you may wish to duplicate the picture that is shown in Figure 1.2. I believe there is nothing like demonstrating observations yourself in order to believe it. This is generally known as the NIH phenomena, which stands for "not invented here." One, generally, does not believe anything unless you've either experienced it, seen it, or tried it yourself! I am a firm believer in experimentation. Who knows, you might be making new discoveries in the process. Remember, virtually all new comets are discovered by accident (i.e., when someone was taking pictures in the sky of some region and noticed an extra bit of light which wasn't there originally).

Figure Ex. 10.3 shows a more sophisticated homemade tracking system, especially designed to track balloons used for weather and wind determinations.

Those who are financially better suited than the average, might wish to purchase a commercial telescope. These can be obtained in all price ranges and in various qualities. I have no intention of recommending any one brand over another. However, those in the field know from experience which is adequate and which is superior; hence, I am not revealing any trade secrets if I were to discourage you from buying a cheap, shoddy telescope of the refracting variety, having a flimsy mount and no motor drive for automatic tracking. A motor drive is absolutely necessary in order to keep track of any celestial object, since you have now demonstrated to yourself that the sky is revolving (because of the earth's rotation, of course).

Since telescopes are hard to wear out, a secondhand or thirdhand purchase might be recommended for a beginner. There are two magazines that advertise these monthly, *Sky and Telescope* and *Astronomy*. A good reflecting telescope can be obtained in the $100 or $200 range. You will find new ones of superior quality in the $400 and $500 range. The top of the line, in both quality and compactness, is the Questar, a picture of which is shown in Figure Ex. 10.4.

Figure Ex. 10.3.

Figure Ex. 10.4.

EXERCISE NO. 11
THE MOON

Study the moon every day by *observation*. First convince yourself of the phases of the moon.

Tools needed: Two tennis balls and a light source.

Procedure: Darken room and illuminate with a bright light which is at table height level. Now, take a ball in each hand, making sure you designate one as earth and the other as moon.

Revolve the "moon" slowly around the "earth" as shown. Watch the changes in illumination of the moon as seen *from the earth*, it is the same process which accounts for the monthly variations in lunar illumination. It is really simple, once you demonstrate this phenomenon to yourself. However, unless you do it, the moon's phases could remain a mystery to you.

The time (29 1/2 days) between one new moon to the next new moon is called the synodic period of the moon. It is *not* its true period of revolution about the earth, which is 27 1/3 days and is called the sidereal period.

Question: Why is there a difference in time between synodic and sidereal period? Illustrate with a diagram.

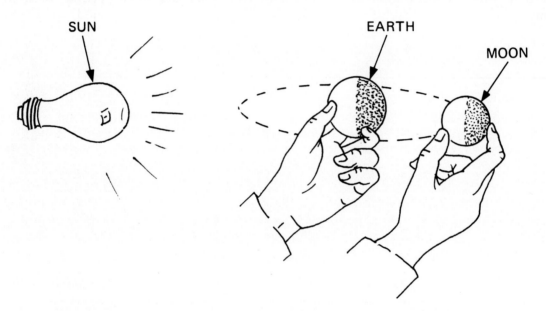

Figure Ex. 11. Demonstration of the moon orbiting the earth, phases of the moon and eclipses.

EXERCISE NO. 12
MOON'S ROTATION ON ITS AXIS

This moon exercise requires a partner.

Procedure: Pick a partner. One of you stays in the center and pretends to be the earth. The other person revolves counterclockwise around the earth, but, as this person revolves around the earth, be sure to always *face towards* the earth. Note: (1) the moon performs *one complete rotation* as it revolves once around the earth (2) as seen *from the earth*, one can never *see* the back part of the moon.

Question: In actual fact, astronomers see 59% instead of 50% of the moon during a complete lunar cycle around the earth. Why? Elaborate, there are two reasons for the extra 9%.

Since the advent of the NASA Apollo missions to the moon, we finally obtained pictures of the moon's rear side. They were quite spectacular!

EXERCISE NO. 13
THE MOTION OF THE MOON ON THE CELESTIAL SPHERE

This exercise is to measure the actual **angular distance** that the moon travels per day and to follow the changes of the moon's phase.

Equipment required: straws, protractor, hammer, nails, a little ingenuity, patience, powers of observation, determination, a clock or wristwatch (in working order)—Use Tycho Brahe telescope from Exercise No. 10.

Procedure: Align the straw with the moon, note time. Return on successive days at exactly the same time, and note in each case, the angle by which the moon has moved with respect to its previous position. Keep an exact log, and take measurements every day for at least 30 days.

Time	Angle Measured Since Previous Day	Draw Picture of Moon

Question: In order to get improved precision, should the daily observation of the moon be at intervals of 24 hours or 23 hours 56 minutes? Why?

EXERCISE NO. 14
TIDAL EFFECTS OF SUN AND MOON

A. Compare the relative effectiveness of the moon's differential tidal force on the earth, F_M with that of the sun's F_s. Newton's law of gravity states $F = \dfrac{GM_1 M_2}{d^2}$

therefore, *differential* tidal force $\Delta F = \dfrac{2G M_1 M_2}{d^3}$.

Note that the differential tidal force depends on the inverse *cubed* distance between the masses M_1 and M_2. Substitute values for the earth's mass M_E, moon's mass M_M, and the sun's mass M_s, using appropriate distances:

d_s (sun-earth) = 93,000,000 miles
d_m (earth-moon) = 240,000 miles

Now substitute numerical values in

$$\frac{(\Delta F)_M}{(\Delta F)_s} = \frac{2G M_E M_M}{d_m^3} \bigg/ \frac{2G M_E M_s}{d_s^3} = \frac{M_M d_s^3}{M_s d_m^3} =$$

B. Calculate the gravitational attractive forces of the sun on the earth and that of the moon on the earth. Compute their ratio and refer to Exercise No. 3.

a. Calculate center of mass of Sun-Jupiter system.

b. From this data, determine what the "wobble" of the sun would look like from the distance of Alpha Centauri (4 1/2 light years away). Determine "wobble" in seconds of arc. Is it measurable?

$$\text{Data: } \frac{\text{Mass of Sun}}{\text{Mass of Jupiter}} \approx \frac{1,000}{1}$$

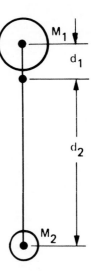

1 light year = 5.88×10^{12} miles
1 radian = 206,265"
Sidereal Period of Jupiter = 11.86 years

To obtain center of mass:

Hint: Use mathematical identity: if

$$\frac{m_1}{m_2} = \frac{d_2}{d_1}$$

then,

Example: if $1/2 = \frac{3}{6}$

$$\frac{m_1 + m_2}{m_2} = \frac{d_1 + d_2}{d_1}$$

$$\therefore \quad \frac{2 + 1}{2} = \frac{6 + 3}{6}$$

Figure Ex. 15.1.

a.

$$\frac{1,001}{1} = \frac{(5.2) \times 93,000,000}{d_1}$$

d_1 = 483,000 miles

i.e., Center of mass is just outside sun's surface (sun's radius is 430,000 miles).

b. Total angle subtended 4 1/2 light years away, due to 11.86 year wobble of sun around center of mass.

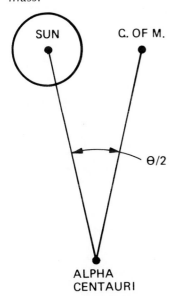

ALPHA
CENTAURI   **Figure Ex. 15.2.**

$$\theta = \frac{966,000 \text{ miles}}{4.5 \times 5.88 \times 10^{12} \text{ miles}} \text{ radians}$$

$$\theta = \frac{9.66 \times 10^5 \times 2.06 \times 10^5}{4.5 \times 5.88 \times 10^{12}} \text{ seconds of arc}$$

$$\theta = 0.75 \times 10^{-2} \text{ "seconds of arc}$$

Conclusion: With present earth based technology, the angle is measurable. Sun performs the wobble around center of mass in 11.86 years.

It is interesting to note that Van de Kamp discovered an invisible companion to Barnard's star, whose mass is only 50% larger than Jupiter's. Could this star have a whole entourage of planets? Only the most massive planet is so far detectable by this "wobble" technique, for nearby stars.

EXERCISE NO. 16

Determine the center of mass of the earth-moon system as measured from the earth's center. What effect does this have on the earth's motion in space? Would this motion be additional to: diurnal rotation, revolution around sun, and precession of equinoxes?

Hint: Study Ex. No. 15 for general technique of solution to such problems.

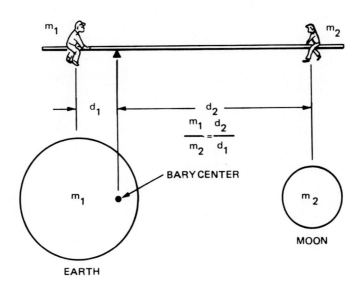

Figure Ex. 16.

EXERCISE NO. 17
CONSTRUCTION OF A SUNDIAL

This is an optional exercise which is highly recommended for those who are ingenious, handy, or if you wish to tell time on a remote island without clocks. You can use a sundial, see Figure Ex. 17.1. Note: It is essential for easy reading of a sundial to construct a circular ring around the wire which will cast a shadow on this ring. When the sun crosses the meridian, adjust the ring such that it reads 12:00 noon. It is highly instructive to use the sundial during the course of the year; you will make some very important discoveries. One of the things you will discover will be that the sun does not cross the celestial meridian at noon at different times of the year. Your mission will be to analyze this dilemma and to come up with plausible explanations. You are here! How do you account for it?

Hint: The difference between actual local solar time and mean solar time is given in Table A.

Question: How would you determine your latitude and longitude by measuring the latitude of the sun for about 40 minutes around noon time, given a sextant, see Figure Ex. 17.2, and a precise clock that measures *Greenwich* solar time? Examine Figure 1.15 and note that longitude is the angle between Greenwich and your local longitude circle. You also will have to know the declination of the sun for that date. The declination of the sun is easy (read it from globe), as long as one keeps track of the date.

The procedure that you are about to investigate was carried out routinely on ships everyday prior to modern radio triangulation fixes. In the unlikely event that you are stranded on a ship without modern radio equipment, the knowledge you are about to get may save your life. Is that relevant enough?

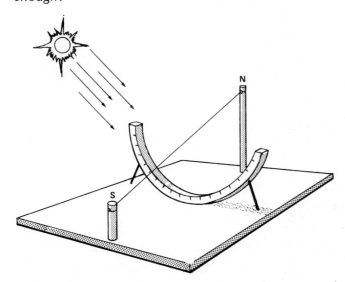

Figure Ex. 17.1. Construction of a sun dial. Note the semicircular hour circle.

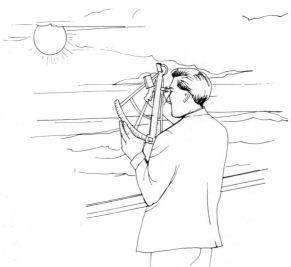

Figure Ex. 17.2. The use of a sextant in determining the altitude of the sun at high noon, thereby determining one's latitude and longitude.

Equation of Time

The difference in hour angle between the apparent sun and the mean sun is called the equation of time. It is the correction that must be added to or subtracted from clock time to equal sundial time (provided the dial is located on a standard meridian).

TABLE A
Equation of Time
(To the nearest half minute)
Apply these quantities to clock to get sun time.

Date	Min.	Date	Min.
Jan. 1	−3 1/2	July 1	−3 1/2
Jan. 16	−9 1/2	July 16	−6
Feb. 1	−13 1/2	Aug. 1	−6 1/2
Feb. 16	−14 1/2	Aug. 16	−4 1/2
Mar. 1	−12 1/2	Sept. 1	0
Mar. 16	−9	Sept. 16	+5
Apr. 1	−4	Oct. 1	+10
Apr. 16	0	Oct. 16	+14
May 1	+3	Nov. 1	+16 1/2
May 16	+4	Nov. 16	+15 1/2
June 1	+2 1/2	Dec. 1	+11
June 16	−1/2	Dec. 16	+4 1/2

EXERCISE NO. 18
THE SUN—APPLICATIONS IN THE USE OF SOLAR ENERGY

There are a number of important contributions which can and should be explored in the efficient use of the sun's energy. These two exercises or home projects are designed to permit you to demonstrate your creativity by making use of the sun's energy in two ways:

1. Design and operate a solar still. A schematic example is shown in Figure Ex. 18.1. The knowledge gained in its construction has distinct survival value. What is required is a bucket or cup at the bottom of a hole in the ground covered with transparent lucite or plastic or similar material. In order to make this still more effective it is advisable to place water-containing plants around the bottom of the hole. One can use leaves (anything green) or also brackish water. The distillation process can be visibly seen as the water droplets condense on the plastic sheet and drip into the bucket in the center. In order to collect efficiently the dripping water droplets, it is advisable to place a stone or some heavy object right in the center of the plastic sheet. Use your ingenuity to devise more elaborate devices or other clever schemes for water distillation. This basic principle can also be used to construct (on a small scale) a still for the production of alcoholic beverages. A demonstration of this solar principle on "interstellar" alcohol is presumably not illegal.

Another use of solar energy, of course, is for solar heating. Here I will not give any specific directions, other than to suggest that you use as inexpensive materials as possible to devise means of heating water to the temperature of at least 50 degrees centigrade. The Figure Ex. 18.2 shows a recent student project which was constructed very inexpensively.

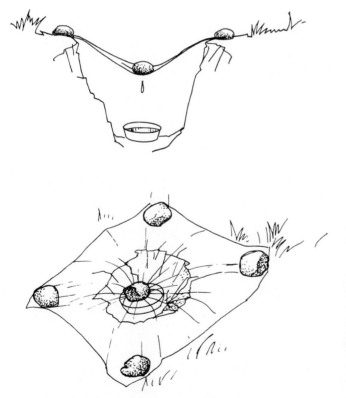

Figure Ex. 18.1. A schematic diagram of a suggested experimental arrangement for distillation of brackish water by means of solar heating.

Figure Ex. 18.2. Typical student project showing how a low cost solar heater may be constructed. In this example by Neil Bledsoe, a 1/2 gallon of water was heated by the sun in 1 hour from $60°F$ to $120°F$, while ambient temperature was $68°F$.

EXERCISE NO. 19

Compare the phases of Venus as seen by an observer on earth using:

a. Geocentric Theory   (Figure 18.8, page 253)
b. Heliocentric Theory (Figure 2.1, page 17)

What is the difference? Why was the information so vital to Galileo, who was the first to observe the phases of Venus? (See Fig. Ex. 19.)

Figure Ex. 19. The planet Venus. The phases of Venus were first seen by Galileo. Compare with moon. (Photo taken by 200-inch. Hale Observatories.)

EXERCISE NO. 20

Suggested term paper should include the following: Study the possible relationship of earthquakes and lunar tidal forces by:

1. Obtain data of exact times of past major quakes, include Richter scale.
2. Position of moon at the time of quake relative to earth.
3. Locate coordinates on earth of source of seismic activity causing earthquakes.
4. Determine phase of moon (counting days from new moon) at the time of earthquake.
5. Plot data and determine if there are any correlations.

EXERCISE NO. 21

Calculate the sun's temperature, given its luminosity and surface area (see Table TN 2, page 297).

Solution: Surface area of sun =

Luminosity of sun =

Hint: Use Stefan-Boltzmann law $E = \sigma T^4$ (ergs cm^{-2} sec^{-1})
and solve for T

EXERCISE NO. 22
THE ENERGY-FOOD-LABOR CYCLE

Study the closed ecosystem in India (*Reference*: Roger Revelle, Science *192*, 969 June 4, 1976). Elaborate on the food production, energy expanded by labor and overall efficiency of labor components within the system. Evaluate and criticize this paper on the basis of the limits of solar energy input and the hydrological cycle. Be as quantitative as possible.

EXERCISE NO. 23

This is a most difficult assignment. (To be attempted only if ambitious and adventuresome.)

Evaluate reasonable models which could simulate the large quasar z values by using the gravitational red shift. Take z = 2 as a working model.

Use formula:

$$z = \frac{\Delta\lambda}{\lambda} = \left(1 - \frac{2GM}{Rc^2}\right)^{-1/2} - 1$$

Here are some guidelines.

1. Note that any expression under a square root sign cannot be negative, or it will be imaginary.

   This implies that $\frac{2GM}{Rc^2} \leqslant 1$.

   Thus, by equating it to unity, one limiting value can be obtained for M/R.

2. Next, with z = 2, evaluate M/R. Then construct a table for both M and R and density ρ of sphere. Assume that objects have spherical shape and that emission arises from gas at surface of sphere.

3. You will immediately appreciate why it is important to examine the density of sphere, also, since there will be values of M and R, for which density exceeds 10^{14}, which is density of nuclear matter!

4. Here is one of the dilemmas: If the gravitational red shift causes the shift, then the emitting region ΔR has to be small compared to the size of the object, R. Why? Because the quasar lines are relatively narrow compared to the red shift. This implies that the ratio $\Delta R/R$ is equal to line width/λ. For Quasar 3C273, this is 0.07. Hence, we shall consider it.

5. One more restriction on a possible model came up: The amount of light obtained from the quasar hydrogen atoms could be measured. Once a certain size of emitting gas is isolated, its light output can, in principle, be computed, provided one is 100% certain of the excitation and emission mechanism. Greenstein and Schmidt, in 1964, examined this problem and could not come up with a reasonable model. Hence, they rejected the gravitational effect completely and relied on the Doppler effect only.

If you wish to take on·this challenge, seek another construction which will give you an appropriate red shift of z = 2, taking all the limitations into account. With some of the best astronomical minds working on this, you are now at the forefront of the battle lines. Welcome aboard.

M (gram)	R × 1/3 (cm)	Mass/Volume ρ	$\Delta R = 0.07R$ ΔR
2×10^{29}	10^2		
2×10^{31}	10^4		
2×10^{32}	10^5		
2×10^{33}	10^6		
2×10^{35}	10^8		
2×10^{37}	10^{10}		
2×10^{39}	10^{12}		
2×10^{44}	10^{17}		
2×10^{46}	10^{19}		

HEAVENLY FIGURES

EXERCISE NO. 24

Study the stars and constellations, with the instructor's guidance or by yourself.

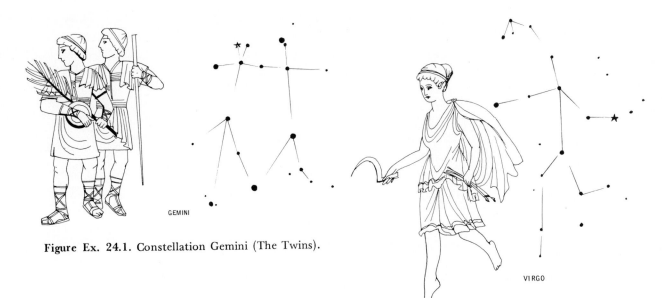

Figure Ex. 24.1. Constellation Gemini (The Twins).

Figure Ex. 24.2. Constellation Virgo (The Virgin):

This is a large constellation, consisting mainly of faint stars. The constellation is not ordinarily seen the way it is depicted here. The Virgin in the sky lies on her back. She lies outstretched along the ecliptic with her head beneath the tail of the lion. Her arms are reaching for the hair of Berenices, another constellation. She seems to be looking toward the constellation Herdsman, but he is turning his back on her. With all this activity in the sky, the brightest jewel of Virgo is situated in a rather peculiar spot in the constellation.

Since this constellation lies in the Zodiac, some of the wandering planets occasionally pass by the Virgin, as does the moon. Virgo gets a lot of attention.

Star charts pp. 385-407 courtesy of Griffith Observatory.

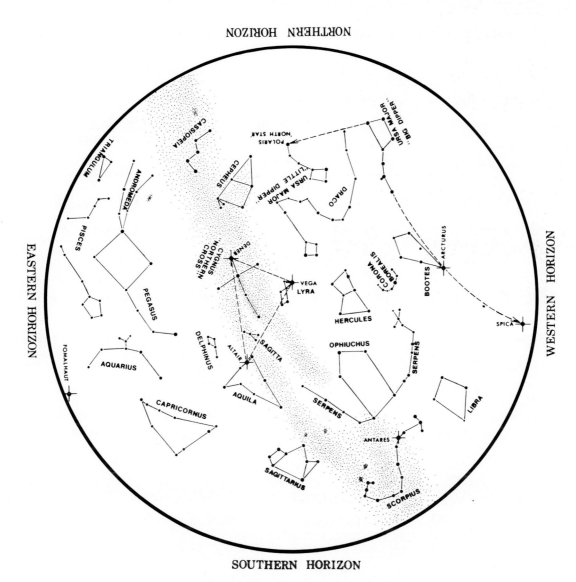

THE NIGHT SKY IN AUGUST

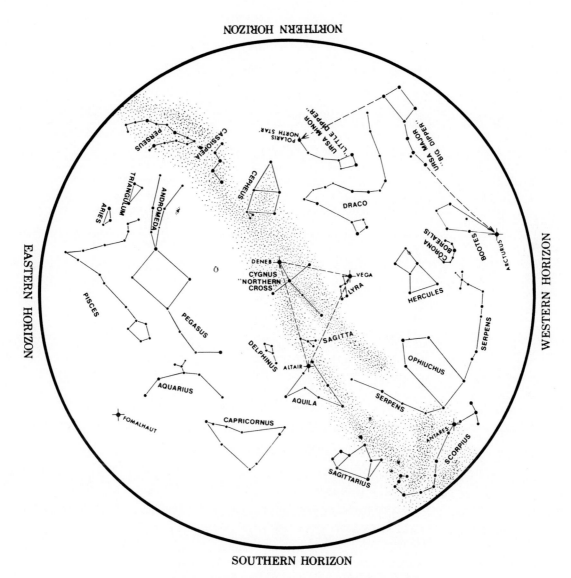

SOUTHERN HORIZON

THE NIGHT SKY IN SEPTEMBER

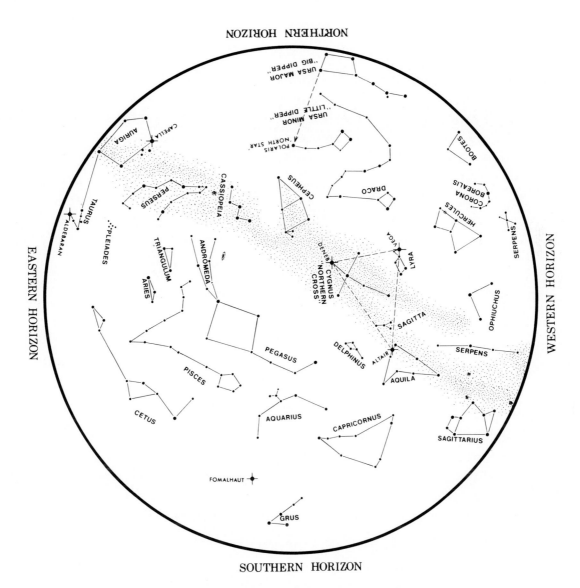

NORTHERN HORIZON

URSA MAJOR "BIG DIPPER"

URSA MINOR "LITTLE DIPPER"

POLARIS "NORTH STAR"

BOÖTES

CORONA BOREALIS

AURIGA
CAPELLA

DRACO

HERCULES

SERPENS

PERSEUS

CASSIOPEIA

CEPHEUS

VEGA

TAURUS

PLEIADES
ALDEBARAN

TRIANGULUM

ANDROMEDA

DENEB CYGNUS "NORTHERN CROSS"

LYRA

OPHIUCHUS

EASTERN HORIZON

WESTERN HORIZON

ARIES

SAGITTA

SERPENS

PEGASUS

DELPHINUS

ALTAIR

PISCES

AQUILA

CETUS

AQUARIUS

CAPRICORNUS

SAGITTARIUS

FOMALHAUT

GRUS

SOUTHERN HORIZON

THE NIGHT SKY IN OCTOBER

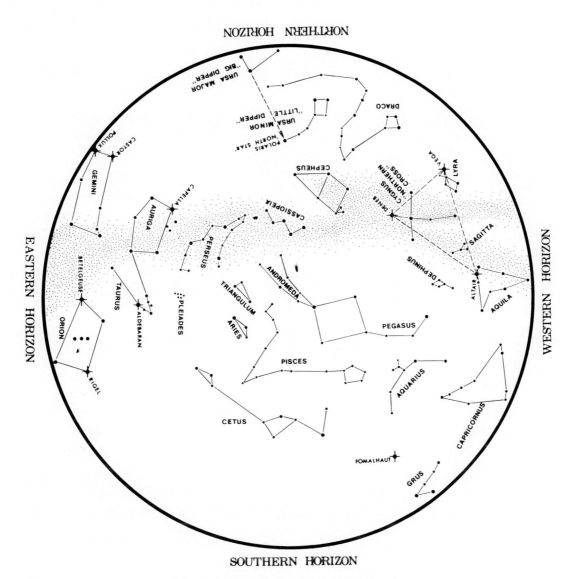

THE NIGHT SKY IN NOVEMBER

391

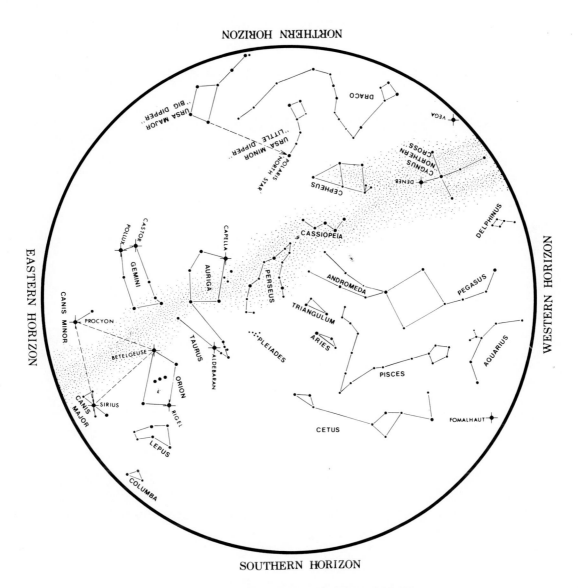

NORTHERN HORIZON

EASTERN HORIZON

WESTERN HORIZON

SOUTHERN HORIZON

THE NIGHT SKY IN DECEMBER

393

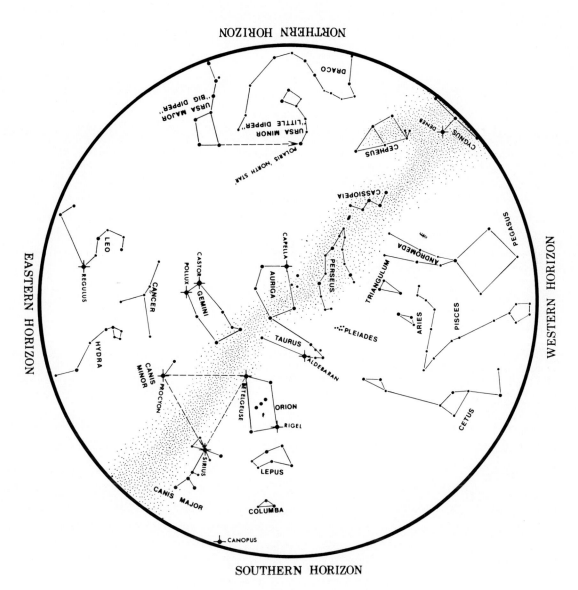

THE NIGHT SKY IN JANUARY

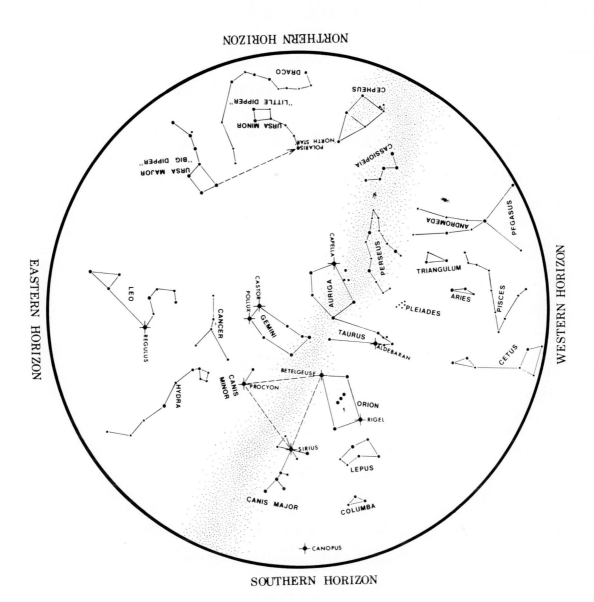

THE NIGHT SKY IN FEBRUARY

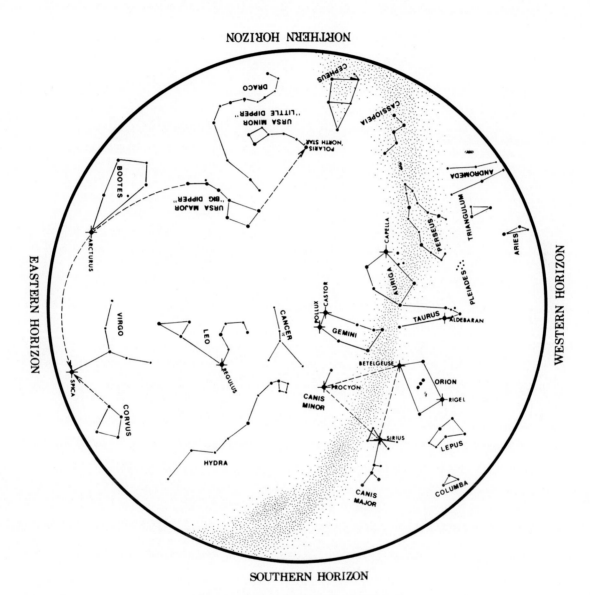

NORTHERN HORIZON

EASTERN HORIZON

WESTERN HORIZON

SOUTHERN HORIZON

THE NIGHT SKY IN MARCH

399

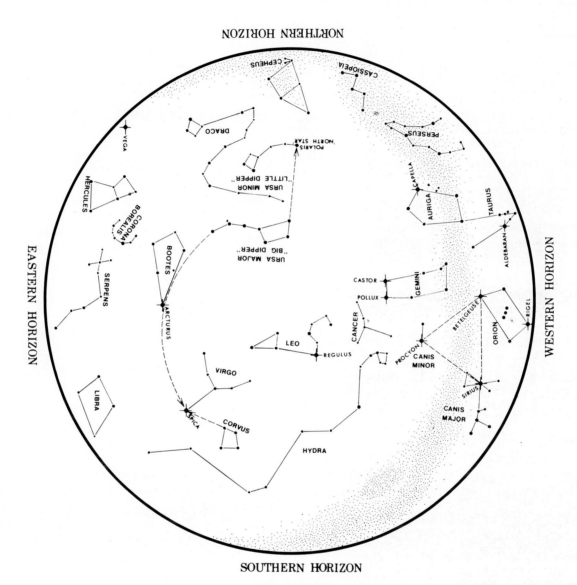

NORTHERN HORIZON

EASTERN HORIZON

WESTERN HORIZON

SOUTHERN HORIZON

THE NIGHT SKY IN APRIL

401

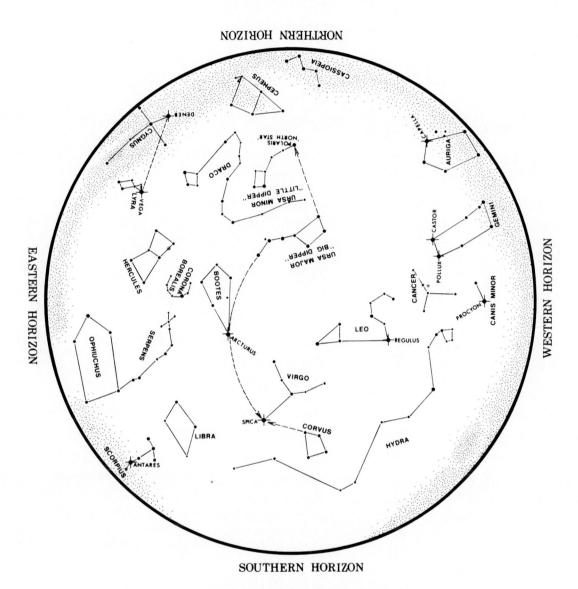

NORTHERN HORIZON

CASSIOPEIA

CEPHEUS

DENEB

CYGNUS

POLARIS "NORTH STAR"

DRACO

CAPELLA

AURIGA

VEGA

LYRA

URSA MINOR "LITTLE DIPPER"

GEMINI

HERCULES

CORONA BOREALIS

BOOTES

URSA MAJOR "BIG DIPPER"

CASTOR

POLLUX

CANIS MINOR

EASTERN HORIZON

WESTERN HORIZON

OPHIUCHUS

SERPENS

ARCTURUS

CANCER

PROCYON

LEO

REGULUS

VIRGO

LIBRA

SPICA

CORVUS

HYDRA

SCORPIUS

ANTARES

SOUTHERN HORIZON

THE NIGHT SKY IN MAY

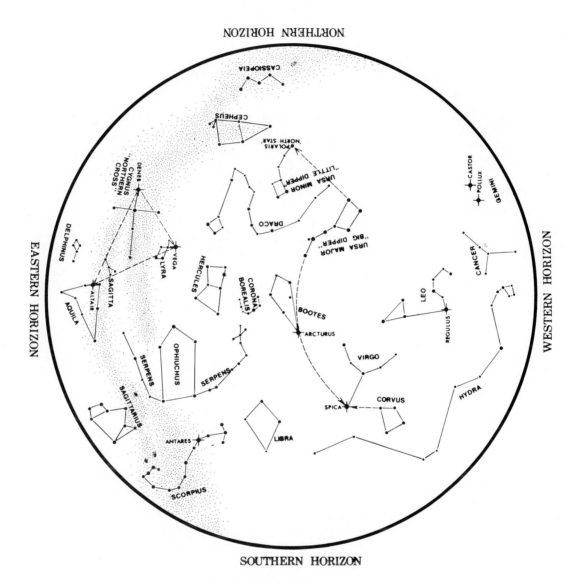

THE NIGHT SKY IN JUNE

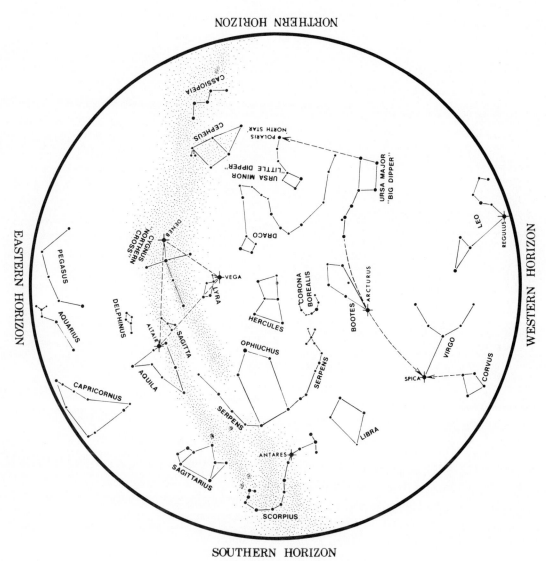

THE NIGHT SKY IN JULY

GLOSSARY OF TECHNICAL TERMS

Abcissa—Horizontal axis of a customary two-dimensional graphic display.

Absolute magnitude—The apparent magnitude a star would have at a distance of 10 pc.

Absorption spectrum—Dark lines superimposed on a continuous background resulting from the absorption of light by a cool, intervening gas.

Acceleration of gravity—The acceleration produced by the gravitational attraction on an object at the surface of a planet.

Alpha particle—The nucleus of a helium atom, consisting of two protons and two neutrons.

Altitude—Angular distance above or below the horizon, measured along a vertical circle, to an object in the sky.

Andromeda nebula—A close-by galaxy, roughly comparable in size to our galaxy.

Angular momentum = (mass) × (velocity) × (radius vector) An intrinsic quantity of a body resulting from its rotation about its axis or about an external point.

Angstrom (Å)—A unit of length equal to 10^{-8} cm.

Aphelion—Point in its orbit where a planet is farthest from the sun.

Apparent magnitude—A measure of the observed light intensity from an object in the sky.

Asteroid belt—Region between Mars and Jupiter, about 2.8 A.U. from sun, which is occupied by a large number of irregularly shaped bodies of varying sizes.

Astrology—The pseudoscience that deals with supposed influences of the stellar configurations and locations in the sky of the sun, moon, and planets on human destiny.

Astronomical unit (AU)—Mean distance of earth from Sun. About 93,000,000 miles.

Atom—Consists of a dense small nucleus surrounded by orbiting electrons.

Atomic number—The number of protons in each atom of a particular element.

Autumnal equinox—The intersection of the ecliptic and celestial equator where the sun crosses the equator from north to south.

Azimuth—The angle along the celestial horizon, measured westward from the south point, to the intersection of the horizon with the vertical circle passing through an object. (Modern navigation measures the *azimuth* from the north point.)

Balmer series—A series of electronic transitions in the hydrogen atom, arising from the second excited state and connecting with any of the higher lying states.

Barycenter—Center of mass of a body or of a group of bodies.

Be star—A spectral type B star with emission lines in its spectrum.

"Big bang" theory—A theory of cosmology in which the expansion of the universe is presumed to have begun with a primeval explosion.

Black body radiation—Describes an idealized distribution of electromagnetic energy from a black body.

Boltzmann's constant (k)—A physical constant in nature: k = 1.38 × 10^{-16} erg/deg.

Bode's law (1772)—A scheme by which a sequence of numbers can be obtained that give the approximate distances of the planets from the sun. Its significance was not appreciated until 1972. It implies conservation of angular momentum of each of the planets subsequent to their achieving orbital velocity at the protosun surface.

Bow shock—A disturbance of the solar wind plasma pattern as a result of planetary motion.

Calculus—A branch of mathematics that relates to an analysis of rates of change (*differential* calculus) or of the contribution of an infinite number of infinitesimal quantities (*integral* calculus).

Carbon cycle (earth)—The continuous recycling processes of carbon containing compounds driven by the sun's energy.

Carbon cycle (stellar)—A series of nuclear reactions involving carbon as a catalyst by which hydrogen is transformed to helium. Others elements involved in this energy generation mechanism are N and O nuclei.

Celestial equator—A great circle on the celestial sphere 90° from the celestial poles.

Celestial poles—Extension of the earth's axis to infinity; points about which the celestial sphere appears to rotate.

Celestial sphere—Imaginary sphere onto which all celestial objects are projected.

Center of gravity—See center of mass.

Center of mass—The mean position of the various mass elements of a body or system weighted according to their distances from that center of mass.

Centrifugal force—An apparent force experienced by a body in a reference frame which is rotating with respect to a stationary frame. For a body of mass m, moving in a circle of radius r with angular velocity w, this force is equal to mw^2r and its direction is outwards along the radius. It is, mathematically, an imaginary inertial force introduced to make valid the use of Newton's third law of motion in a moving frame of reference, and may be regarded as the reaction to the centripetal force.

Cepheid variable—A supergiant pulsating star whose light intensity varies in a periodic manner.

Circadian rhythm—Periodic changes (24 hours) in biological systems related to the light/day cycle (diurnal rotation). This word was coined by F. Halberg of U. of Minnesota (*circa*, about; di(em), day + an) = about one day.

Comet—A special body orbiting the sun. Structure of comet usually includes a head and a tail which becomes luminous as its distance to the sun is within a few Astronomical Units.

Conic section—The curve of intersection between a circular cone and a plane: curves can be an ellipse, a circle, a parabola, or a hyperbola.

Conservation of angular momentum—Important principle in physics which states that in the absence of external forces, the angular momentum of a system must remain unchanged for all time. Kepler's 2nd law is based on this theorem.

Conservation of energy—Kepler's 3rd law is an example of this principle applied to the planets, where the sum of potential plus kinetic energy of each planet remains unchanged.

Constellation—A configuration of stars, or the area of the sky assigned to a particular configuration.

Continental drift—Motion of the continental "plates" over the surface of the earth due to plate tectonics.

Continuous spectrum—A spectrum of light comprised of radiation of a continuous range of wavelengths.

Core (of earth)—The central part of the earth.

Coronagraph—An instrument used in the study of the top surface of the sun. Its main feature involves the blocking out of light from the central disc.

Cosmic rays—Highly energetic extraterrestrial ionizing radiation. Primary cosmic rays are usually composed of atomic nuclei with energies in the 10^6 to 10^{19} e.V range. (1 eV = 1.60×10^{-19} Joule.)

Cyclotrons—A device by which charged particles can be accelerated to high speeds using specially designed structures, magnetic fields and r.f. fields.

Deb (plural, Debs)—Acronym for developing bodies. These are bodies produced from the stellar core and ejected during their NOVA development phase. It is estimated that the sun in its 8 NOVA phases ejected over 10^{11} such Debs.

Declination—The angle measured along the hour circle from the celestial equator to the star.

Deimos—Satellite of Mars.

Density—The ratio of the mass of an object to its volume.

Depth perception—Ability to perceive depth of field by virtue of stereoscopic vision or artificial means.

Diatomic species—A molecule consisting of two atoms.

Dielectric—e.g., glass. Describes the electrical properties of a material having a high resistance to electrical conduction.

Diffraction grating—A grid pattern of closely spaced lines which causes light to be separated into various wavelengths upon transmission or reflection. It performs a similar function as a prism.

Diurnal rotation—Daily earth rotation.

Doppler shift—Change in wavelength, resulting from relative motion between emitter and receiver of radiation.

Duty cycle—Fraction of time a given phenomenon is operating. It refers usually to pulsed sources such as magnetrons, klystrons, or the like.

Dwarf (star)—A star whose diameter is comparable to that of the terrestial planets, but whose mass is comparable to that of normal stars on the main sequence.

Dyne—The metric unit of force: the force required to accelerate a mass of 1 gram in the amount 1 centimeter per second per second.

Eccentricity (e)—A measure of the shape of an ellipse. If e = 0, it is a circle; as e approaches unity, the shape of the ellipse becomes more elongated. At e = 1, it becomes a parabola.

Eclipse—The complete or partial blockage of light by one celestial body as it passes between another and our line of sight.

Eclipsing binary star system—A binary star system in which the plane of revolution of the two stars is practically edge on to our line of sight.

Ecliptic—Orbital path of earth around sun or apparent yearly path of sun projected on the celestial sphere.

Electromagnetic radiation—Radiation consisting of waves propagating via oscillating electric and magnetic fields; these include radio, infrared, light, ultraviolet, X rays, and gamma rays.

Electromagnetic spectrum—The panoramic display generated by spreading electromagnetic radiation into its constituent wavelengths.

Electron—A fundamental particle of matter having a

negative charge, finite spin and a finite mass. It is a basic constituent of all atoms.

Ellipse—A planar, mathematically generated curve whose shape resembles a uniformly stretched circle. It is one of the conic sections. Every ellipse has two foci and can be characterized by either the size of its major and minor axes, or the size of one of its axes and its eccentricity.

Elongation—The angle subtended at the earth between a planet and the sun.

Emission—Usually refers to emission of photons from an excited atom.

Emission line—A discrete bright spectral line.

Emission spectrum—A spectrum consisting of emission lines.

Energy conversion—Transformation of energy from one form to another.

Energy generation—Mechanism for the production of energy.

Epicycle—A fictitious circular orbit of a body in the Ptolemaic system, the center of which revolves about another circle (the deferent). These hypothetical circular motions of planets were proposed to explain their movements on the celestial sphere particularly their retrograde motion.

Equator—A great circle on the earth, 90° from its pole.

Equator system—A system of coordinates which is based on the celestial equator and the observer's meridian as reference frames. Its primary coordinates are hour angle, right ascension and declination.

Equinoxes—The intersections of the ecliptic and celestial equator.

Erg—The metric unit of energy; the work done by a force of one dyne moving through a distance of one centimeter.

Escape velocity—See Velocity of Escape.

Ether—A theoretical interstellar medium postulated to exist in the universe in the 19th century and disproved by the Michelson Morley experiment.

Extragalactic—Beyond the Galaxy.

Extraterrestrial—Outside the Earth, not pertaining to the Earth.

Faculae—An extended area of special activity on the sun's surface associated with sun spots.

Fiduciary mark—A special reference point.

Fission—The breakup of a heavy atomic nucleus (e.g., U^{235}) into two or more lighter ones.

Flare—A rapid brightening of a specific region on the sun's surface.

Fluorescence—The absorption of light at one wavelength and reemission at another wavelength.

Focal length—The distance from a lens or mirror to the point where light converged by it comes to a focus.

Foucault pendulum—A device used to demonstrate the earth's rotation by observing the rotation of the plane of oscillation of a simple pendulum.

Fraunhofer spectrum—The array of absorption lines in the spectrum of the sun.

Frequency—Number of cycles per second of a wave.

Fusion—The building of heavier atomic nuclei from lighter ones. (A process which requires extremely high temperatures and pressures, e.g., a fission-fussion bomb, or in the cores of certain stars.)

Fusion crust—The remelted and cooled outer layer of a meteorite caused by atmospheric frictional heating, mostly only a millimeter or so in thickness, usually black on fresh specimens.

Gabbro—An igneous rock composed chiefly of the minerals plagioclase (calcium-rich) and clinopyroxene; may also contain olivine, orthopyroxene, and lesser amounts of other minerals.

Galactic cluster—A group of stars located in the spiral arms or disk of the Galaxy.

Galaxy—An entity in the universe consisting of gas, a large number of stars (of the order of hundred billion) together with their possible retinue of planets, Debs (comets), "dust," and other parts.

Gamma rays—High frequency electromagnetic wave, usually emitted from radioactive nuclei.

Gaunt factor—An algebraic expression introduced in the discussion of the internal constitution of a typical star.

Gauss—A unit of magnetic flux density.

Geocentric theory—System which assumes the earth is at the center of the solar system and has all other bodies of the solar system revolve about the earth.

Giant (star)—A star whose diameter exceeds that of a ordinary star by one or two orders of magnitude.

Gibbous—A term used to describe a phase of a planet or moon in which more than half, but not all, of the illuminated disk can be viewed by the observer.

Glitches—A sudden change in the period of a pulsar.

Globular cluster—A group of about 10^4 to 10^5 stars constituting a close association. About 120 such star clusters form a system of clusters centered on the center of the Galaxy.

Gravitational constant, G—The constant of proportionality in Newton's law of gravitation; in metric units G has the value 6.668×10^{-8} dyne $\cdot$ cm^2/gm^2.

Gravitational red shift—The shift in wavelength of spectral lines arising from an intense gravitational field (always towards longer wavelengths).

Great circle—Circle on the surface of a sphere that is the curve of intersection of the sphere with a plane passing through its center.

Greenhouse effect—The effect of absorbing sun's energy by virtue of trapped reradiated radiation at longer wavelengths.

Gregorian calendar—Calendar which has a leap year every 4 years except century years not divisible by 400.

Granular cells—The visible temporary structures of cells on the sun's surface composed of bright interior and relatively cooler "walls."

Half-life—The time required for half of the radioactive atoms in a sample to disintegrate.

Halley's comet—An important periodic comet whose roughly 70 year recurrence has been recorded for the last 2500 years. It is named in honor of Halley, who first studied its motion and correctly predicted its return.

Heliocentric—Centered on the sun.

Heliocentric theory—Theory which is based on sun at center of planetary system.

Hertzsprung-Russell (H-R) diagram—A plot of absolute magnitude against temperature (or spectral class) for a group of stars.

Horizon (astronomical)—A great circle on the celestial sphere 90° from the zenith.

Horizon system—A system of celestial coordinates (altitude and azimuth) based on the astronomical horizon and the north point.

Hour angle—The angle measured westward along the celestial equator from the local meridian to the hour circle passing through an object.

Hour circle—A great circle on the celestial sphere passing through the celestial poles.

Hubble constant—Constant of proportionality in the relation between the velocities of remote galaxies and their distances. The Hubble constant is approximatley 50 km/s/10^6 pc.

Hydrological cycle—A continuous transfer of water from land and ocean and back again, driven by solar energy.

Hypothesis—A tentative (working) theory or supposition, which is subject to further tests and verification.

Igneous rock—Rock that has formed from the cooling of magma.

Inclination—The angle that the orbital plane of a secondary body or satellite makes with the orbital plane or equatorial rotational plane of the primary.

Inferior planet—A planet whose distance from the sun is less than that of the Earth.

Infrared (IR)—A portion of the electromagnetic spectrum having wavelengths longer than visible light but shorter than microwaves. Radiant heat energy is primarily composed of infrared radiation.

Interstellar dust—Microscopic solid grains of so far unknown chemical composition. Their physical properties are so far only indirectly inferred.

Interstellar lines—Absorption lines superimposed on stellar spectra, produced by interstellar atoms and molecules. (The background star serving as light source.)

Ion—An atom having a net positive or negative charge.

Ionization—The process by which an atom gains or loses electrons.

Ionosphere—The upper region of the earth's atmosphere in which many of the atoms are ionized.

Isotope—Any of two or more forms of the same element, whose atoms all have the same atomic number but different masses, e.g., $_{92}U^{235}$ and $_{92}U^{238}$.

Isotropic—The same in all directions.

Julian calendar—A calendar introduced by Julius Caesar in 45 B.C. It adds an additional day every 4 years (leap year).

Julian day—The number of the day in a running sequence beginning January 1, 4713 B.C.

Kappa (κ)—A Greek letter that is generally used to represent the *opacity* factor, i.e., the "resistance" for radiation to emerge from inside the star.

Kepler's laws—The three laws, discovered by Kepler, that describe the motions of the planets.

Kinetic energy—Energy associated with motion; the kinetic energy of a body is one-half the product of its mass and the square of its velocity.

Kinetic theory (of gases)—The science that treats the motions and bulk properties of molecules in gases.

Laser—An acronym for *light amplification by stimulated emission of radiation*; a device for amplifying a light signal at a particular wavelength into a coherent beam.

Latitude—A north-south coordinate on the surface of the earth; the angular distance north or south of the equator measured along a meridian passing through a place.

Law—A statement of order or relation between phenomena that, under given conditions, is presumed to be invariable.

Leap year—A calendar year with 366 days, intercalated approximately every four years to make the average length of the calendar year as nearly equal as possible to the tropical year.

Light—Electromagnetic radiation that is visible to the eye.

Light curve—A graph that displays the variation in light or magnitude of a variable or eclipsing binary star.

Light-year—The distance light travels in a vaccuum in one year; 1 LY = 9.46 $\times$ 10^{17} cm, or about 6 $\times$ 10^{12} mi.

Lithosphere—The upper layer of the earth.

Longitude—The angle measured along the earth's equator and subtended at the center of the earth between two great circles which originate and terminate at the North and South poles. These two great circles are drawn on the earth's surface such that one of them passes through Greenwich, England and the other through a point on earth whose longitude one wishes to determine.

Luminosity—The rate of radiation of electromagnetic energy into space by a star or other object.

Mach number—A factor which refers to the speed of an object in units of the velocity of sound.

Magellenic cloud—A nearby galaxy.

Magma—Molten or partially molten naturally occurring material from which igneous rocks crystallize as the temperature of the melt decreases; normally rich in silica and containing dissolved gases.

Magnesium-tetrabenzporphyrin (χ)—The largest organic molecule identified in the interstellar medium. Its discovery by F.M. Johnson was accomplished by laboratory matching of astronomical spectroscopic signatures.

Magnetometer—A geophysical instrument used to measure the intensity and/or direction of a planetary magnetic field or some portion or component thereof.

Mascon—Mass concentration.

Mass—A measure of the total amount of material in a body; defined either by the inertial properties of the body or by its gravitational influence on other bodies.

Mass-luminosity relation—An empirical relation between the masses and luminosities of objects in the universe.

Mass spectrometer—An analytical instrument that can be used to determine the amounts of various isotopes and molecular species present in a sample by separating them according to their mass to charge ratio as ions in motion in a strong magnetic field.

Megaparsec (Mpc)—One million (10^6) parsecs.

Meridian, celestial—The great circle on the celestial sphere that passes through an observer's zenith and the north celestial pole.

Metamorphism—A process, usually involving a change in temperature and/or pressure, whereby a rock or mineral is changed in texture or to a new mineral or assemblage of minerals that is stable under new physical/chemical conditions.

Meteor—Incoming meteorite. A large group of such particles may be referred to as a "Meteor shower."

Meteorite—The iron and/or stony portion of a meteoroid that survives atmospheric passage and reaches the surface of the Earth.

Mev range—Million electron volt range.

Microwave—Short-wave radio wavelengths.

Milky way (nonedible)—Galaxy, which contains our solar system. The band of light in the sky called by this name is our galaxy seen almost edge-on.

Mineral—A naturally occurring inorganic substance with a definite range of chemical composition and a specific atomic structure with long-range order.

Molecule—A combination of two or more atoms held together.

Momentum (linear)—A vector quantity defined by the product of mass and velocity of a body.

Moving frame—Refers to a moving set of coordinates—in contrast to another frame that is stationary.

Nautical mile—The mean length of one minute of arc on the earth's surface along a meridian.

Neap tide—High or low tides of less severity that occur during the moon's first and third quarter.

Neutrino—An elusive particle in nature that has no mass and no charge. It carries energy away in the course of certain nuclear transformations.

Neutron—A subatomic particle whose mass is approximately equal to that of the proton, but has no net charge.

Neutron star—A star of extremely high density composed almost entirely of neutrons.

Nucleus—The central, high density, positively charged core of an atom.

Newtonian focus—An optical arrangement in a reflecting telescope where the light is reflected by a flat mirror to a focus at the side of the telescope tube.

Newton's laws—The three laws of motion enunciated by Newton in the *Principia*. They form the basis of the study of Mechanics.

North celestial pole—A point on the celestial sphere produced by the extension to infinity of the earth's axis (in the northerly direction).

Nova—An exploding star.

Nucleosynthesis—The successive build-up of more complex nuclei via nuclear fusion and other nuclear reactions from smaller nuclear fragments, at the cores of stars.

Nutation—A small cyclical motion of the Earth's axis superimposed upon the precessional motion.

Obilesk—A tall narrow structure built in Egypt in ancient times.

Observer's celestial meridian—See Meridian, celestial.

Opacity—See Kappa.

Orbit—The path of a body that is in revolution about another body or point.

Orbital plane—The plane in which a body revolves.

Orthoclase—A potassium feldspar with composition close to $KAlSi_3O_8$, but commonly containing minor amounts of sodium and even less calcium. Differs from microcline in the symmetry of its crystal structure.

Oscillations—Vibrations about some point.

Parallax (general)—An apparent displacement of an object when observed from two different directions.

Parallax (astronomical)—The angle subtended at the star between the sun and the earth. It is measured in seconds of arc.

Parsec—A basic unit of distance in astronomy. It is equal to 3.26 light years.

Perihelion—The place in the orbit of an object revolving about the sun where it is closest to the center of the sun.

Periodic comet—A comet whose orbit has been determined to have an eccentricity of less than 1.0.

Period-luminosity relation—An empirical relation between the periods and luminosities of cepheid-variable stars.

Perovskite—A mineral with composition close to $CaTiO_3$.

Phobos—Satellite of Mars.

Photomultiplier—A device in which the electric current generated from incoming photons is greatly amplified by multiple stages within the tube.

Photon—A bundle of electromagnetic energy ($h\nu$), where ν is the frequency and h is Planck's constant.

Photosynthesis—The formation of carbohydrates in the chlorophyll-containing tissues of plants exposed to sunlight. In the process, oxygen is released to the atmosphere.

Plate tectonics—The study of the motion of plates on the earth's surface.

Polarized light—Light in which polarization is present: A fraction of the electromagnetic waves have their oscillations restricted to a certain plane, rather than oscillating in any direction, perpendicular to their direction of travel.

Porphyrin—A special class of molecules whose characteristic is a central ring structure composed of alternating single and double bonds. Chlorophyll and haem are in the category as well as MgTBP.

Positron—An "electron like fundamental particle" with a positive rather than a negative charge.

Precession—The motion of the axis of a rotating body about a cone when a torque is applied to it so as to tend to change the direction of the axis. The motion of the axis at any instant is at right angles to the direction of the torque.

Principle of relativity—The assumption basic to special relativity that the laws of physics are the same in all systems in uniform motion with respect to each other.

Propagation—Usually refers to the movement of a wave in a certain direction.

Proper motion—Small observed changes in nearby star's position due to its intrinsic motion in the sky with respect to the more distant background stars.

Proton—A subatomic particle that carries a positive charge, and one of the two principal constituents of the atomic nucleus.

Proton-proton chain—A chain of thermonuclear reactions by which nuclei of hydrogen are built up into nuclei of helium.

Protostar—An early stage in the development of a star. According to the Johnson hypothesis, the sun in this phase was a far more massive star and extended in size to the orbit of Mercury.

Pulsar—A rotating neutron star and associated revolving elements whose presence is detected by highly repetitive electromagnetic signals.

Pulsar frequencies—The repetition rate of pulsed pulsar radiation.

Quasars—A highly compact evolving object, presumably a galaxy in its early stages. It is characterized by its blue color, large red shifts, small size, and often erratic changes in its light output.

Quasi-stellar source (QSS)—A stellar-appearing object of very large redshift that is a strong source of radio waves; presumed to be extra-galactic and highly luminous (see Quasar).

Quantum electrodynamics—A highly specialized field of physics dealing with the properties of electromagnetic fields and their interactions.

Quantum mechanics—A branch of physics dealing with the physical (fundamental) properties of particles and their intersection.

Radar—A technique for sending and observing the reflection of radio waves from an object.

Radio-astronomy—The subdiscipline of astronomy concerned with the observation and study of electromagnetic radiation from the galaxy or extra-galactic sources in the radio regime.

Rayleigh scattering—Scattering of light by molecules of a gas.

Recurrent nova—A star that undergoes explosive phenomena repeatedly.

Red dwarfs—A dimutive star of relatively cool surface temperature.

Redshift—A shift to longer wavelengths of the light from remote galaxies; presumed to be produced in part by a Doppler shift.

Reddening (interstellar)—The reddening of starlight passing through interstellar dust, caused by the dust scattering blue light more effectively than red.

Reflecting telescope—Primarily refers to an optical "arrangement" where incoming light is collected and reflected by means of a (large) carefully ground mirror. Light from this reflector is focused and usually reflected further. The optical train used depending on application. The first reflecting telescope was constructed by Sir Isaac Newton.

Reflection—The return of light rays by an optical surface.

Regolith—A layer of fragmental and unlithified detritus that may overlie a planetary surface as in the case of the Moon.

Remanent magnetization—A component of the magnetization of a rock that is not related to recently applied or extant planetary magnetic fields of moderate strength; the component of rock magnetization "frozen in" to an igneous rock as its ferromagnetic mineral components were cooled through their Curie points.

Resonance effect—A phenomena whose effect is dramatically enhanced by repetitive impulses which are in phase or in resonance with the object's natural resonance frequency.

Retrograde motion (apparent)—An apparent westward motion of a planet on the celestial sphere with respect to the stars. This apparant backward motion of the planet occurs during that part of its orbital path when the earth overtakes the planet.

Retrograde (real)—Motion of a body in orbit that is counter to the general direction of motion of the Solar System; if the Solar System is viewed from the north, the motions of the planets are counterclockwise. Some satellites move in orbits that are clockwise about their primaries when viewed in the same orientation. Such motion is termed retrograde.

Revolution (astronomical)—Term associated or used to describe orbital motion of a body.

Right ascension—A coordinate for measuring the positions of celestial objects; the angle measured eastward along the celestial equator from the vernal equinox to the hour circle passing through object.

Roche limit—The distance from the surface of a larger primary planetary body to a smaller body at which the tidal stress across the smaller body exceeds its tensile strength.

Rotation—Turning of a body about an axis running through it.

S-wave—A seismic shear wave.

Sarsen circle—A special circle of stones at Stonehenge.

Seismology—The study of a planet's internal or surface motions by means of accoustic sensors.

Sidereal period—Interval between successive returns of an object measured with respect to a distant star, e.g., true period of revolution of a planet or satellite about the central object.

Sidereal year—Interval between successive transits of the Earth about sun with respect to distant background stars.

Sigma point (Σ)—The intersection of the observer's celestial meridian and the celestial equator.

Solar constant—Mean amount of solar radiation received per unit time, by a unit area, just outside the earth's atmosphere, and perpendicular to the direction of the sun's rays. The numerical value is about 130 watts per sq. foot.

Solar day-24 hours—Mean time interval between successive transits of the sun with the observer's meridian.

Solar system—The system of the sun and the planets, their satellites, the minor planets, comets, meteoroids, and other objects revolving around the sun.

Solar wind—The charged particle emission from the sun.

Spectral class—A subgroup of stars whose spectra are similar. This classification is based on the detailed analysis of stellar spectral lines.

Spectrogram—A photograph of a spectrum.

Spectroheliogram—A photograph of the sun obtained with a spectroheliograph.

Spectroheliograph—An instrument for photographing the sun, or part of the sun, in the monochromatic light of a particular spectral line.

Spectrometer—(a) An instrument which is used to isolate, observe or record the separate wavelengths of a source. It incorporates either a prism or diffraction grating, entrance and exit slits and mirrors. It usually has a motor drive to turn the grating and isolate one line at the time.

Spectroscope—(b) An instrument for directly viewing the spectrum of a light source (using the eye as detector).

Spectrograph—(c) Denotes an instrument which records a whole range of wavelengths simultaneously on a photographic plate.

Spectrophotometry—The measurement of the intensity of light from a star or other source at different wavelengths.

Spectroscopic binary star—A binary star in which the components are not resolved optically, but whose binary nature is indicated by periodic variations in radial velocity, indicating orbital motion.

Spectroscopic parallax—A parallax (or distance) of a star that is derived by comparing the apparent magnitude of the star with its absolute magnitude as deduced from its spectral characteristics.

Spectroscopy—Branch of physics dealing with the emission of light from atoms, its detection, analysis and interpretation.

Spectrum—The array of colors or wavelengths obtained when light from a source is dispersed by passing it through a prism or grating.

Spectrum analysis—The study and analysis of spectra, especially stellar spectra.

Spherical symmetry—Refers to the uniform properties of an object about its center such that this property depends on its distance from the center only.

Spiral galaxy—A galaxy with characteristic spiral arms.

Spring tides—The unusually severe high and low tides that occur during new and full moon.

Star—A celestial self-luminous body, generally expected to have a mass, size and luminosity within a given range of values.

Stefan-Boltzmann law—A formula from which the rate at which a black body radiates energy can be computed; the total rate of energy emission from a unit area of a black body is proportional to the fourth power of its absolute temperature.

Stellar fusion processes—Energy generated within stars by means of CNO or p-p cycles.

Stonehenge—Ancient astronomical observatory in England. Composed of regularly spaced stones in circular patterns.

Summer solstice—A particular point in space and time (about June 21) when the earth's position in its orbit about the sun is such, that the sun achieves maximum declination on the celestial sphere. The sun has maximum altitude at high noon for northern latitudes above 23 1/2°.

Sun—The star about which the earth and other planets revolve.

Sunspot—A particular configuration or structure in the solar photosphere that appears dark by contrast against the surrounding hotter photosphere. It revolves on the surface of the sun for 1 or 2 rotations and has a magnetic field associated with it.

Sunspot cycle (about 11 years)—Periodic changes in the sun's visible activity, particularly the total number of sunspots.

Supergiant (star)—An enormously large diameter star, whose radius could be as large as 10 A.U.

Super-nova—The largest known explosive event associated with a star. It is manifest by energy release comparable in magnitude to the normal energy output of a typical galaxy.

Synchrotron radiation—Electromagnetic radiation resulting from the acceleration of electric charges moving in magnetic fields.

Synodic period—The interval between successive occurrences of a particular configuration of a planet or satellite; for example, between successive oppositions or the time from full moon to full moon.

Tektites—Peculiar, rounded glassy bodies that are suspected to be of meteoritic origin.

Thermodynamics—A branch of physics dealing in general with physical and theoretical properties of matter, mainly in the gaseous state.

Triatomic species—A molecule consisting of three atoms bound chemically.

Ultra-violet radiation—The part of the E-M spectrum of shorter wavelength than the blue region of light. The human eye is no longer sensitive to such radiation.

Vector—A quantity that has both a magnitude and a direction, e.g., force, velocity or angular momentum.

Vega—A prominent star in the constellation Lyra.

Velocity—The rate of change of distance with time—in a particular direction.

Velocity of escape—The minimum speed with which an object must move in order to enter a parabolic orbit about another body (such as the earth), and hence move permanently away from the vicinity of that body.

Vernal equinox—The point on the celestial sphere where the sun crosses the celestial equator, passing from south to north.

Wave-particle duality—Every fundamental particle of nature acts both as a particle and a wave: There is a relationship between the particle's momentum and its associated wavelength. $\lambda \times p = h$: where λ = wavelength, p = momentum, and h = Planck's constant.

Wavelength—Distance between crests of a wave.

White dwarf—A dwarf star having a high surface temperature.

Widmanstätten figure—(Also Widmanstätten structure or pattern.) The pattern of intergrowth of nickel-rich and nickel-poor mineral phases observed on a fresh surface of most iron meteorites if polished and etched with dilute nitric acid.

Wien's law—A relationship between the wavelength (λ_m), at which maximum intensity of black body radiation occurs and the temperature T, such that $\lambda_m \times T$ = constant.

Winter solstice—The position of the sun in its orbit along the celestial ecliptic where its declination is $-23\ 1/2°$.

Wolf-Rayet star—One of a class of very hot stars that eject shells of gas at very high velocity.

X-rays—Photons of wavelengths of the order of Angstroms.

Zenith (observer's)—A point on the celestial sphere generated by extending the top of a plumb line to infinity upwards.

Zodiac—The group of constellations clustered about the ecliptic and arranged into zones.

Index